Theoretical Mechanics
for Sixth Forms

VOLUME ONE

Theoretical Mechanics
for Sixth Forms

VOLUME ONE

C. PLUMPTON
Queen Mary College, London

W. A. TOMKYS
Belle Vue Boys' Grammar School
Bradford

PERGAMON PRESS

OXFORD · LONDON · NEW YORK · PARIS

1964

PERGAMON PRESS LTD.
Headington Hill Hall, Oxford
4 & 5 Fitzroy Square London W. 1.

PERGAMON PRESS INC.
122 East 55th Street, New York 22, N. Y.

GAUTHIER-VILLARS ED.
55 Quai des Grands-Augustins, Paris 6ᵉ

PERGAMON PRESS G.m.b.H.
Kaiserstrasse 75, Frankfurt am Main

Distributed in the Western Hemisphere by
THE MACMILLAN COMPANY · NEW YORK
pursuant to a special arrangement with
Pergamon Press Limited

Library of Congress Catalog Card No. 63-11361

Set in 9 point Extended
Made in Great Britain

CONTENTS

v

CHAPTER XI

CHAPTER XII

CHAPTER XIII

PREFACE

THIS volume aims at providing a first-year course in theoretical mechanics for sixth-form pupils taking mathematics as a double subject and a two-year course for pupils taking mathematics as a single subject. No previous knowledge of theoretical mechanics is assumed.

Throughout the book, calculus has been used whenever it was appropriate to do so. Elementary ideas of vectors are introduced as early as possible in the course and the pupil is encouraged to use vector methods and vector notation. The development of the book is integrated as closely as possible with the development of the authors' *Sixth Form Pure Mathematics*, the worked examples and exercises are graded and increase in difficulty as the book progresses, and the miscellaneous exercises at the end of each chapter are chosen to give continual reminders of the work of earlier chapters.

After examining the nature of theoretical mechanics we first discuss the statics of a particle in illustration of the techniques of handling vector quantities, techniques which are developed in successive chapters concerning the kinematics of a particle moving along a straight line, projectiles and relative velocity. We then discuss the principle of moments, parallel forces and centres of gravity. The next group of chapters is concerned with the application of Newton's second law to the dynamics of a particle and the ideas of work and energy, impulse and momentum, and power. The chapter on friction, which interrupts this sequence, was delayed in order to allow a more rapid development of fundamental principles; when friction is introduced the opportunity is taken to coordinate the work of the preceding chapters by means of worked examples and exercises involving friction. This volume concludes with a chapter concerning motion in a circle. Some sections of the book, and some exercises, are marked with an asterisk. It is recommended that these should be omitted in the first reading.

We wish to thank the authorities of the University of London, the Cambridge Syndicate, the Oxford and Cambridge Joint Board and the Northern Universities Joint Board for permission to include questions (marked L., C., O.C., and N. respectively) from papers set by them. We also thank Mr. P. S. W. MacIlwaine and Mr. J. A. Croft who read the proofs and made valuable suggestions.

C. PLUMPTON
W. A. TOMKYS

ix

CHAPTER I

INTRODUCTION. THE FUNDAMENTAL CONCEPTS OF THEORETICAL MECHANICS

1.1. The Nature of Theoretical Mechanics

The work of Newton in the seventeenth century forms the basis of the hypotheses upon which we develop this work on elementary theoretical mechanics. The results of Newton's theories in so far as they concern quantities which are not very small, and in so far as they concern distances and speeds on a terrestrial rather than an astronomical scale, have been successfully *tested* by experience. In such a case experience and experiment, while they may disprove a hypothesis, cannot finally confirm its truth. If experimental results consistently agree with a hypothesis, however, *it is reasonable to accept the truth of the hypothesis within the physical range implied by the experiments*. Modern research, which involves very small quantities such as the interior of an atom and which makes investigations involving astronomical distances and speeds comparable with the speed of light, cannot make assumptions of absolute time and space which are necessary to Newtonian mechanics. Nevertheless, results which are derived from the Newtonian hypotheses discussed here are essential to the development of many technologies and a proper understanding of Newtonian mechanics is necessary before the wider problems involving the relative nature of time and space can be considered.

Our object in this subject of *theoretical mechanics* is to create a *mathematical model* of aspects of the physical world (limited as described above). In the first instance, we simplify the problems involved in this model by reducing the number of variable factors to as few as possible. In consequence in the early stages we find solutions to problems which refer to the ideal mathematical system postulated, but these problems have no precise parallel in any known physical situation. The application of the results of theoretical mechanics to real physical problems is a dependent development.

We begin by stating the hypotheses from which we develop the subject.

Time

The period of rotation of the earth relative to the fixed stars provides a unit of time which is as nearly constant as any other measure available to us. This period is defined as the unit of time and it is called the *sidereal day*.

The *mean solar second* is defined in terms of the earth's motion on a date near the beginning of this century.

Position

In order to describe the position of a point, it is necessary to have a frame of reference. Thus the position of a point on the Earth's surface can be described *with reference to the equator and the Greenwich meridian* by means of its latitude and longitude, but this description would be inadequate to describe the position of the point in relation, say, to the Sun's centre. Position, and therefore motion (change of position) are relative terms depending on the chosen frame of reference. The units of length, or *difference in position*, are arbitrary and refer to fixed physical standards. In one system of units the unit of length is *one foot*. In another system of units, the unit of length is *one centimetre*.

Velocity is defined as rate of change with respect to time of displacement from a fixed position.

Acceleration is defined as rate of change with respect to time of velocity.

1.2. Newton's Hypothetical Laws

The hypotheses which Newton formulated and which are the foundations of the subject of theoretical mechanics are known as Newton's Laws of Motion and they may be stated as follows.

1. *A body remains in a state of rest or of uniform motion in a straight line, unless it is acted upon by an external force.*
2. *The rate of change of the momentum of a body is proportional to the impressed force and takes place in the direction of that force.*
3. *To every action there is an equal and opposite reaction.*

Newton's first law provides us with the conception of *force* as that which tends to change the state of motion of a body.

Mass

Momentum, the quantity referred to in the second law quoted above, is the product of a quantitative property of the body which is called its *mass* and its velocity. It is this property which determines the response of a body to the action of a force, and which is sometimes called the *inertia* of that body. The mass of a body is here invariable since a given body under the action of a given force acquires the same acceleration wherever and whenever the action takes place.

A *particle* of matter is defined as a body whose geometrical dimensions are sufficiently small to be neglected in comparison with the finite distances with which we shall be concerned.

1.3. Unit of Mass and Absolute Unit of Force

We now assign *arbitrarily* to a particular mass the designation *unit mass*. This unit is called one *pound* (1 lb) in one system of units and one *gramme* (1 gm) in the metric system of units. We assume that the quantitative property *mass* is additive and therefore that a single body, which is composed of n bodies each of mass equal to the arbitrarily chosen unit of mass, has a mass of n units.

Units of Force

Newton's second law may be stated mathematically as

$$P \propto \frac{\mathrm{d}(m\,v)}{\mathrm{d}t},$$

where P is the force acting on a body of mass m and of velocity v at time t. (Note that the change in v is *in the direction of* P.)

Then, $$P \propto m\,\frac{\mathrm{d}v}{\mathrm{d}t}$$

or $$P \propto m f,$$

where f is the acceleration of the body at time t. This statement depends on the postulate which we have made above that the mass of a body is invariable. In problems in which the "body" itself changes and in which, therefore, there is a variation of mass with time, this variation must be taken into consideration. Such problems include the case of rocket flight.

From $P \propto m f$ we have $P = k m f$ where k is a constant. If now we define the unit of force as that force which gives to unit mass unit acceleration, then $k = 1$ and

$$P = m f, \tag{1.1}$$

where P acts in a straight line and f is in the direction of P. This is the fundamental equation of kinetics, that part of theoretical mechanics which deals with motion and the forces which produce or modify it.

With this fundamental equation

1 *poundal* is the force which gives to a body of mass 1 lb an acceleration of 1 ft/sec²;

1 *dyne* is the force which gives to a body of mass 1 gm an acceleration of 1 cm/sec².

Each of these is called an *absolute* unit of force.

1. 4. Gravitational Units of Force

Newton's Law of Universal Gravitation states that every particle of matter attracts every other particle of matter with a force which varies directly as the product of the masses of the particles and inversely as the square of the distance between them.

In the foot-pound-second (FPS) system of units, the force of attraction, P pdl, between two particles of mass m_1 lb and m_2 lb which are at a distance d ft apart is given by

$$P = \frac{G m_1 m_2}{d^2}, \qquad (1.2)$$

where G is a constant number.

If now we assume

(i) that the force exerted by the earth on a body outside it is equal to the force which would be exerted by a particle of mass equal to that of the earth situated at its centre, and,

(ii) that for a body whose size is small compared with the earth and which is near the earth's surface, a sufficient degree of accuracy can be obtained by taking d as constant and equal to the earth's radius (R), then

$$P = \frac{G M m}{R^2}, \qquad (1.3)$$

where M is the mass of the earth and m is the mass of the body which is near the earth's surface.

Thus, if g is the acceleration of the body of mass m, equations (1.1) and (1.3) give

$$P = m g = \frac{G M m}{R^2}.$$

$$\therefore \; g = \frac{G M}{R^2}. \qquad (1.4)$$

The force P which is the force exerted by the earth on the body is called the *weight* of the body and it is constant only within the degree of accuracy implied by the assumptions (i) and (ii) made above. *With these assumptions*, but not otherwise, the weight of the body is proportional to its mass. If these assumptions are not made the weight of a body changes with its position relative to the earth's centre.

Assumptions (i) and (ii) above require

(a) that the earth is spherical,

(b) that the earth is constituted of matter whose mass per unit volume (density) is a function of the distance from the centre only, i.e. the earth is made up of concentric shells which are homogeneous,

(c) that the effect of the motion of the earth may be neglected.

In the FPS system the number g is approximately equal to 32 and the quantity g ft/sec² is known as the acceleration due to gravity and can be taken as the acceleration with which all bodies near to the earth's surface fall towards the earth.

The unit of *weight* is the weight of unit mass and the weight of 1 lb mass is g pdl, where g is the number defined above.

This quantity g pdl is called 1 pound weight (1 lb wt.); it is sometimes used as an alternative unit of force and is called the *gravitational unit of force*.

The relationship between absolute and gravitational units of force in the FPS system is therefore expressed by

$$1 \text{ lb wt.} = g \text{ pdl},$$

where $g \doteqdot 32$.

In the metric, CGS, system of units

$$P = \frac{G m_1 m_2}{d^2},$$

where P dyn is the force between the particles of masses m_1 gm and m_2 gm which are at a distance of d cm apart. If g cm/sec² is the acceleration of a particle of mass m gm towards the earth, of mass M gm, and if the radius of the earth is R cm,

$$m g = \frac{G m M}{R^2}.$$

$$\therefore g = \frac{G M}{R^2}.$$

In this case, the number g is approximately equal to 980, the quantity g cm/sec² is the acceleration due to gravity, 1 gm wt. is the unit of weight and also the gravitational unit force and

$$1 \text{ gm wt.} = g \text{ dyn},$$

where $g \doteq 980$.

Physicists and engineers (particularly electrical engineers) frequently use the metre-kilogram-second (MKS) system of units in which the unit of force is the *newton*, which is that force which imparts an acceleration of 1 m/sec² to a mass of 1 kgm.

Since experiment shows that the acceleration due to gravity varies slightly from place to place over the surface of the earth, gravitational units are being superseded by *technical* units in which an acceleration of

$$g_n = 980 \cdot 665 \text{ cm/sec}^2$$

is called the *standard acceleration*. That force which imparts the standard acceleration g_n to a unit of mass is a *technical unit of force* and there is one such technical unit corresponding to each of the common units of mass.

In this book we mainly use the FPS absolute and gravitational systems.

Examples. (i) Calculate (a) in poundals, and (b) in lb wt., the force which gives to a mass of 3 cwt an acceleration of 8 ft/sec².

The required force in poundals $= 3 \times 112 \times 8$ pdl.

$$= 2688 \text{ pdl.}$$

The required force in lb wt. $\doteq \dfrac{2688}{32}$ lb wt.

$$= 84 \text{ lb wt.}$$

(ii) In 1797–8 Cavendish, in a classical experiment, found that two spheres, each of mass 1 gm, placed with their centres at a distance 1 cm apart, attract each other with a force of $6 \cdot 66 \times 10^{-8}$ dyn. Using the *experimental* result $g = 980$ and the value $6 \cdot 38 \times 10^8$ cm for the radius of the earth, calculate an approximate value for the mass of the earth.

From $$g = \frac{GM}{R^2}$$

$$980 \doteq \frac{6 \cdot 66 \times 10^{-8} \times M}{(6 \cdot 38 \times 10^8)^2}.$$

$$\therefore M \doteq \frac{980 \times (6 \cdot 38 \times 10^8)^2}{6 \cdot 66 \times 10^{-8}}$$

$$\doteq 6 \cdot 0 \times 10^{27}.$$

The mass of the earth is therefore approximately $6 \cdot 0 \times 10^{27}$ gm. This gives an approximate value of $5 \cdot 5$ gm/cm³ as the mean density of the earth.

(iii) Calculate in lb wt. an approximate value of the weight of a body of mass m lb near the surface of a nearly spherical planet of mass $\frac{1}{10} M$ lb and radius $\frac{1}{2} R$ ft, where M lb is the mass of the earth and R ft the radius of the earth.

Near the earth's surface

$$m g = \frac{G M m}{R^2},$$

where G is the constant of gravitation.

$$\therefore G = \frac{g R^2}{M}.$$

Near the planet's surface,

$$P = \frac{g R^2}{M} \cdot \frac{M}{10} \cdot m \left| \frac{R^2}{4} \right.,$$

where P pdl is the gravitational pull between the body and the planet. Hence $P = \frac{2}{5} m g$ and the weight of the body at the planet's surface is
$$\frac{2}{5} m g \text{ pdl} = 0 \cdot 4 \, m \text{ lb wt.}$$

Thus far we have used symbols to denote numbers only, giving appropriate units after each symbol, e. g. m lb, P pdl, d cm. It is, however, common practise to use a symbol alone to denote a quantity which has both magnitude and dimensions. With this convention the relation

$$P = G m_1 m_2 / d^2$$

involves P which has the dimensions of force in absolute units, m_1 and m_2 each having the dimensions of mass, and d which has the dimensions of distance. The dimensions of G are therefore the dimensions of

$$\frac{\text{force} \times (\text{distance})^2}{(\text{mass})^2} \quad \text{in absolute units, i. e.}$$

$$\frac{\text{lb ft}}{\text{sec}^2} \times \text{ft}^2 \times \frac{1}{\text{lb}^2} \quad \text{in the F. P. S. system.}$$

The dimensions of G thus reduce to $\dfrac{\text{ft}^3}{\text{lb sec}^2}$ in the F. P. S. system, and the corresponding dimensions in the C. G. S. system are $\dfrac{\text{cm}^3}{\text{gm sec}^2}$. The *numerical* value of P thus varies with the system of units used.

Throughout this book we use these systems side by side. In each case the context makes it clear which convention is being used.

MISCELLANEOUS EXERCISES. I

1. Calculate in dynes the force required to give to a mass of 10 kgm an acceleration of 1 m/sec².

2. Calculate the acceleration of a particle of mass 4 cwt which is acted upon by a force of 50 lb wt. Take $g = 32$ ft/sec².

3. A force of 10 lb wt. acts on a particle and produces in it an acceleration of 4 ft/sec². Calculate the mass of the particle.

4. A particle of mass m lb is falling vertically towards the earth with an acceleration of a ft/sec² against an air resistance of R lb wt. Find an expression for a in terms of R, m and g.

5. Two particles of mass 5 gm and 10 gm respectively are 10 cm apart. Taking $6\cdot66 \times 10^{-8}$ as G, the constant of gravitation, calculate in kgm wt. correct to 3 significant figures the force of attraction between the particles.

6. The accelerations of gravity at two places A and B on the earth's surface are g_1 and g_2 respectively in CGS units.

(a) Write down an expression in dynes for the difference in the weight of a particle of mass m gm at A and the weight of a particle of mass m gm at B.

(b) Assuming (i) that the earth is an approximate sphere whose equatorial diameter is d_1 miles and whose diameter from pole to pole is d_2 miles and (ii) that the attraction between the earth and the particle is inversely proportional to the square of the distance of the particle from the centre of the earth, write down an expression for the ratio of the weight of a particle at the pole to its weight at the equator.

7. A particle is taken to a point at height h miles above the earth's surface so that its weight is reduced in the ratio 99 : 100. Taking 3960 miles as the radius of the earth, calculate h.

8. Calculate the mass of a body whose weight at a distance $11R/10$ from the centre of the earth is W lb wt. (R is the radius of the earth.)

9. Calculate in lb wt. an approximate value for the moon-weight of a man on the moon if his weight on the earth is 12 stone. (Take, mass of moon $= 1/80$ mass of earth, radius of moon $= 1/4$ radius of earth.)

10. With the data of exercise 9, determine the distance from the centre of the earth of a point in the line between earth and moon at which the gravitational attraction of the earth is equal to the gravitational attraction of the moon and at which, therefore, a body would have no apparent weight. (Take the distance between the centres of the earth and the moon as 238,000 miles correct to three significant figures.)

CHAPTER II

SYSTEMS OF COPLANAR FORCES ACTING ON A PARTICLE

2.1. Vector Quantities

A quantity which is completely defined if it is defined in magnitude only is known as a *scalar* quantity. A quantity which is completely defined if it is defined in magnitude and direction is known as a *vector* quantity. If, in order to define a vector completely, it is necessary also to define its position, it is described as a *localized vector*. A vector which is not localized is called a *free vector*. The *displacement* of a particle, which involves "direction of displacement" and "distance displaced" is a vector quantity. Free vectors can be represented diagrammatically by segments of straight lines which also are completely described if they are described in magnitude and direction.

$\overrightarrow{AB}$ means "the vector AB", i.e. the displacement of the point A to the point B in the direction AB.

The Laws of Vector Addition

(a) $$\overrightarrow{AB} + \overrightarrow{BC} = \overrightarrow{AC}. \qquad (2.1)$$

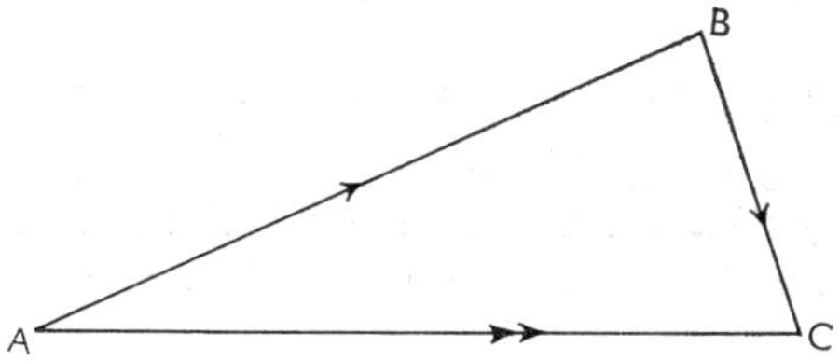

FIG. 1.

Each side of this equation represents a displacement from A to C (Fig. 1). This is known as the Triangle of Vectors.

(b) $$\overrightarrow{AB} + \overrightarrow{BC} + \overrightarrow{CD} + \cdots + \overrightarrow{PQ} = \overrightarrow{AQ}, \qquad (2.2)$$

where $ABCD \ldots PQ$ is a closed polygon (Fig. 2). Each side of this equation represents a displacement from A to Q. This is known as the Polygon of Vectors.

(c) If the vector $\overrightarrow{OP}$ makes an angle θ (anticlockwise) with the direction OX (Fig. 3) and if N is the foot of the perpendicular from P to OX,

$$\overrightarrow{OP} = \overrightarrow{ON} + \overrightarrow{NP},$$

i. e. $OP = OP \cos\theta$ in the direction OX and $OP \sin\theta$ in the direction which makes an angle of 90° anticlockwise with OX.

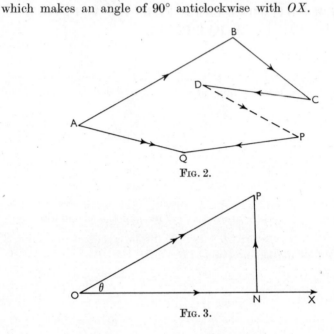

Fig. 2.

Fig. 3.

This process is known as the process of resolving the vector into two components at right angles to each other and it is analogous. to the process of *projection* discussed in *Sixth Form Pure Mathematics* (Chapter IV). Considering magnitudes only we note that

$$OP^2 = ON^2 + NP^2 \tag{2.3}$$

and that

$$\tan\theta = NP/ON. \tag{2.4}$$

2.2. Velocities and Accelerations as Vectors

Velocity is rate of change of displacement and is expressed as "displacement per unit time". It is a vector quantity and component velocities of a particle can be added by the "triangle of velocities" or by the "polygon of velocities". The velocity of a particle can be resolved into component velocities at right angles by the method of § 2.1(c).

Similarly, acceleration of a particle is a vector quantity, and accelerations can be added by the triangle of accelerations or by the polygon of accelerations and resolved into components by the method of § 2.1(c).

2.3. Force as a Vector

Newton's second law of motion states in effect that the force acting on a particle is in the direction of, and proportional to, the acceleration it produces. A single force is thus defined completely by the magnitude and direction of the acceleration it produces in a particle of given mass. Force is a vector quantity and a number of forces acting upon a particle may be added by the "triangle of forces" or by the "polygon of forces", the result of the addition, called the *resultant* of the forces, being given in magnitude and direction. *Force is a localized vector*, and the *position* of the resultant force will be through the particle upon which the component forces act.

2.4. The Parallelogram of Forces

Forces P and Q represented by the vectors $\overrightarrow{OA}$ and $\overrightarrow{OB}$ act on a particle at O (Fig. 4). If the parallelogram $OACB$ is completed, then

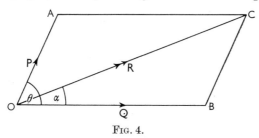

FIG. 4.

by the triangle of vectors $\overrightarrow{OB} + \overrightarrow{BC} = \overrightarrow{OC}$ and $\overrightarrow{BC} = \overrightarrow{OA}$. It follows that the resultant R of P and Q acting on the particle at O is represented by $\overrightarrow{OC}$.

This result is stated, in the law known as the *Parallelogram of Forces*, thus:

If two forces acting on a particle are represented by two adjacent sides of a parallelogram, their resultant is represented by the corresponding diagonal of the parallelogram.

From triangle OBC,

$$\text{Magnitude of } R = \sqrt{\{P^2 + Q^2 - 2PQ \cos(180 - \theta)\}}$$
$$= \sqrt{(P^2 + Q^2 + 2PQ \cos\theta)},$$

and, if θ is the angle between the directions of P and Q and α is the angle between the directions of R and Q, then, from triangle OBC, the direction of R is given by

$$\frac{P}{\sin\alpha} = \frac{R}{\sin(180 - \theta)},$$

i.e.
$$\sin\alpha = \frac{P\sin\theta}{R}.$$

Alternatively
$$\tan\alpha = \frac{P\sin\theta}{Q + P\cos\theta}.$$

2.5. Equilibrium of Forces

If the vector sum of a system of forces acting on a particle is zero, the forces produce no total acceleration in the particle which is said to be in *equilibrium*. It is convenient in such a case to refer to the system of forces as being a system of forces "in equilibrium". The single force, which, added to a given system of forces, produces a state of equilibrium is called the *equilibrant* of the system. From these definitions we deduce at once that,

(a) the equilibrant of a single force P acting on a particle is a force, acting on the particle, which is equal in magnitude and opposite in direction to P, and,

(b) the equilibrant of a system of forces acting on a particle is equal in magnitude and opposite in direction to the resultant of the system.

We state the following laws, which relate to the forces acting on a particle in equilibrium.

I. If three forces acting at a point are in equilibrium, the forces can be represented *in magnitude and direction* by the sides of a triangle taken in order round the triangle.

II. If a number of forces *acting at a point* are in equilibrium, the forces can be represented in magnitude and direction by the sides of a closed polygon taken in order round the polygon.

The converse of each of these laws, *related to forces acting at a point*, is true.

III. If three forces, acting at a point, can be represented in magnitude and direction by the sides of a triangle taken in order round the triangle, the forces are in equilibrium.

IV. If a number of forces acting at a point can be represented in magnitude and direction by the sides of a closed polygon taken in order round the polygon, the forces are in equilibrium.

2.6. Forces in the Physical World

Thus far the definition we have given of a force has been related solely to the acceleration it produces. Science cannot, as yet, precisely relate the nature of a force to the other known properties of matter. We now discuss briefly the more common forces in the physical world.

1. *Gravitational force* which arises from the mutual attractions of two particles of matter. This was discussed in Chapter I. The *weight* of a body arises from gravitational forces and is the measure of the force of attraction which the earth exerts on the body. It is the resultant of the forces of attraction which the earth exerts on the separate particles of the body. We shall be concerned in Chapter VII in considering the line of action of this force.

2. The *action and reaction* between two bodies in contact are connected by Newton's third law (Chapter I, § 1.2) which states that these forces are equal in magnitude and opposite in direction. In general, each of these forces can be resolved into two perpendicular components, one at right angles (normal) to the reacting surface which we call the *normal reaction* and one parallel to the reacting surface. The parallel component is called *Friction*, and friction is discussed in Chapter IX of this volume. Contact between two bodies is *defined* as *smooth* contact if the component of reaction parallel to the reacting surface is zero.

3. *Tensions in light inextensible strings.* In a string, the mass of which is small, which is stretched tight, and which is inextensible, any one part exerts on the other part a force which is called the *tension*

in the string. Figure 5 represents a tight string attached to two bodies at A and B. The string exerts a force T on one body at A and an equal and opposite force T on the other body at B. At the point C of the string the portion AC exerts on that part of the system to the right of C a force T along BC and the portion CB exerts on that part of the system to the left of C and equal and opposite force T along AC.

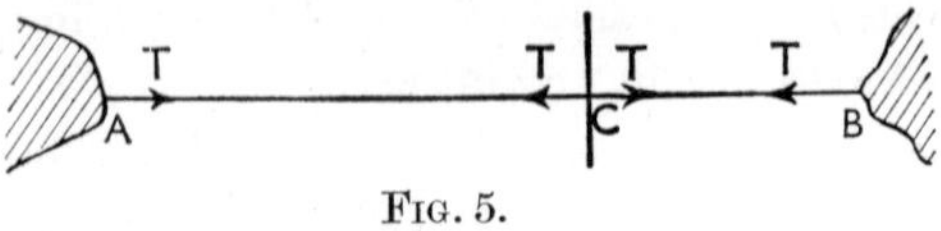

FIG. 5.

4. *Tensions in elastic strings.* A property of matter known as *elasticity* relates the tension to the extension in a string which is elastic. This is discussed in § 2.10.

5. *Electromagnetic force.* The relation between gravitational force and electromagnetic force is the subject of much modern research but it is not yet known. Electromagnetic forces are not discussed in this book.

Examples. (i) A thin smooth pole AB in contact with smooth horizontal ground is being pulled along the ground by two horizontal ropes BP and BQ at angles of 30° and $-45°$ respectively with the direction AB (Fig. 6). A force of 56 lb wt. is exerted by the rope BP and a sufficient force is exerted by the rope BQ to ensure that the resultant of the two forces acts in the line AB. Find (a) by drawing, (b) by calculation, the force exerted by the rope BQ.

(a) BP is drawn to a scale of 1 cm to 10 lb wt. to represent 56 lb wt. (Fig. 7).

BX is drawn so that $\angle PBX = 30°$, and
PY is drawn so that $\angle BPY = 105°$ to meet BX at T.
Then BT represents the resultant of forces represented in magnitude and direction by BP and PT.

By measurement $PT = 4.0$ cm.

Therefore when a force of 40 lb wt. (approximately) is exerted by the rope BQ, the resultant is in the direction AB.

(b) Again referring to Fig. 7, from the triangle BPT,

$$\frac{PT}{\sin 30°} = \frac{BP}{\sin 45°}.$$

$$\therefore PT = \frac{5.6 \sin 30°}{\sin 45°} = 3.96.$$

Therefore, when a force of 39·6 lb wt. is exerted by the rope BQ, the resultant is in the direction AB.

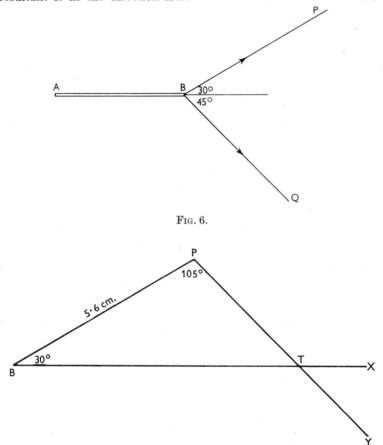

Fig. 6.

Fig. 7.

(ii) One end A of a light inextensible string AB is attached to a fixed point and to the other end B is attached a particle of weight m gm wt. The system is held in equilibrium with the string taut and displaced through an angle θ with the vertical by a force P gm wt. which acts on the particle, Find, in terms of θ, the smallest possible value of P and state the value of the tension in the string in this case [Fig. 8 (i)].

The particle is in equilibrium under the action of three forces.

1. The tension in the string, T gm wt.
2. The weight of the particle.
3. The force P gm wt.

These forces can therefore be represented by the sides of a triangle taken in order round the triangle [Fig. 8(ii)]. Since $\overrightarrow{QR}$, representing m gm wt. vertically, is fixed in magnitude and direction and $\overrightarrow{RS}$,

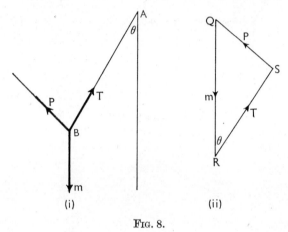

(i)   (ii)

Fig. 8.

representing the tension in the string, is fixed in direction, $\overrightarrow{SQ}$ representing the force P gm wt. is smallest when it is at right angles to RS. Then

$$P = m\sin\theta, \qquad T = m\cos\theta.$$

(iii) A light inextensible string of length 24 in. is fastened at its ends A and B to two pegs 20 in. apart in the same horizontal line. A mass of 9 lb is attached to the string at C, 5 in. along the string from A, and an equal mass is attached at D, 5 in. along the string from B. Find (a) the vertical depth of C below AB, and (b) the tensions in each of the three parts of the string.   (N.)

The system, which is shown in Fig. 9(i) is symmetrical about a vertical line through the mid-point of CD. Therefore CD is horizontal and the tension in DB is equal to the tension in CA.

$$AB = 20 \text{ in.}, \qquad CD = 14 \text{ in.}, \qquad AC = 5 \text{ in.}, \quad \therefore \cos\angle BAC = 3/5.$$

$$\therefore \ C \text{ is 4 in. below } AB.$$

Figure 9 (ii) represents the triangle of forces for the forces acting *on the 9 lb mass at C*.

$$\therefore \quad T_2 = 9 \cot\theta \text{ lb wt.} = 9 \cdot \tfrac{3}{4} \text{ lb wt.} = 6\tfrac{3}{4} \text{ lb wt.,}$$

$$T_1 = 9 \operatorname{cosec}\theta \text{ lb wt.} = 9 \cdot \tfrac{5}{4} \text{ lb wt.} = 11\tfrac{1}{4} \text{ lb wt.}$$

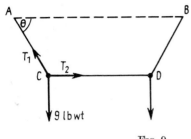 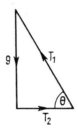

Fɪɢ. 9.

EXERCISES 2.6.

In Fig. 10, R represents the resultant of two forces P and Q, $\angle AOB = \theta$, $\angle COA = \alpha$. Exercises 1 to 10 refer to this figure.

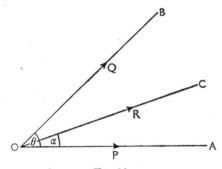

Fɪɢ. 10.

1. $P = 5$ lb wt., $Q = 4$ lb wt., $\theta = 60°$; calculate R, α.
2. $P = 5$ lb wt., $Q = 4$ lb wt., $\theta = 120°$; calculate R, α.
3. $P = 3$ gm wt., $Q = 5$ gm wt., $R = 4$ gm wt.; calculate α, θ.
4. $P = 10$ lb wt., $R = 12$ lb wt., $\alpha = 30°$; calculate Q, θ.
5. $R = 12$ lb wt., $\theta = 60°$, $\alpha = 30°$; calculate P, Q.
6. $R = 20$ lb wt., $\theta = 90°$, $\alpha = 60°$; calculate P, Q.
7. $R = 24$ lb wt., $\theta = 120°$, $\alpha = 90°$; calculate P, Q.
8. $Q = 2P$, $\theta = 60°$; calculate R in terms of P and calculate α.
9. $R = \tfrac{1}{2}(P + Q)$ and $\theta = 120°$. Prove $P = Q$.
10. $\theta = 2\alpha$ and $R = P\sqrt{2}$. Prove $\theta = 90°$.
11. A particle C of mass 10 lb is attached by two equal light strings AC and

BC, each 15 in. long, to two points A and B at the same horizontal level and 2 ft apart Calculate the tension in each of the strings.

12. A particle of mass 2 lb rests on a smooth plane inclined at 30° to the horizontal and it is supported there by a string lying along a line of greatest slope of the plane. Calculate the normal reaction between the particle and the plane and the tension in the string.

13. A boat is being towed along a canal by means of a horizontal rope fastened to a point of its bow which makes an angle of 5° in a horizontal plane with the direction of the boat's motion. The tension in the rope is 5 times as great in magnitude as the resultant thrust of the water on the boat. Assuming this resultant thrust to act through the point to which the rope is tied, calculate its direction.

14. A body of mass 3 cwt is supported by two chains which are attached to a small ring in the body and to a beam in the ceiling. If the inclinations of the chains to the vertical are 30° and 45° respectively, find, graphically or otherwise, the tension in each chain. (N.)

15. The resultant of two forces P, Q is equal to P in magnitude; and that of two forces $2P,Q$ (acting in the same directions as before) is also equal to P. Find the magnitude of Q and prove that the direction of Q makes an angle of 150° with that of P. (O.C.)

16. Two strings of lengths 6 ft and 8 ft are attached to a hook and to two points 10 ft apart at the same horizontal level. The hook carries a mass of 10 lb, which hangs in equilibrium. Find the tensions in the strings. (N.)

17. A pulley carries a mass of 30 lb and can slide freely up and down a smooth vertical groove. It is held up by a string passing round the pulley so that the two parts of the string make angles of 30° and 60° with the horizontal; show that the tension in the string is slightly under 22 lb wt. (O.C.)

18. A light string $ABCD$ is fastened at its ends A, D to fixed supports, and masses of X lb and 30 lb hang in equilibrium from B and C respectively. The strings AB, CD are inclined respectively at angles 30° and 60° to the horizontal and BC is horizontal. Find, graphically or by calculation, the tension in BC and the value of X. (N.)

19. A particle of mass 20 lb, is suspended from a fixed point by a string, and is in equilibrium with the string inclined at 20° to the vertical under the action of a force in a direction making an angle of 60° with the downward vertical. Find graphically, or otherwise, the magnitude of the force and the tension of the string.

Assuming that the force remains constant in magnitude but varies in direction, find the greatest possible inclination of the string to the vertical. (O.C.)

20. A bead A of mass 1 oz slides on a smooth circular wire which is fixed in a vertical plane. The bead is attached by a string AB to the highest point B of the wire and when the bead is in equilibrium AB makes an angle of 30° with the vertical. Calculate in oz wt.:

(i) the tension in the string AB,

(ii) the reaction of the wire on the bead. (L.)

21. $ABCD$ is a light inextensible string; the part AB is vertical, the angle $ABC = 120°$, CD is horizontal and the ends A and D are held fixed. Find the magnitude of the horizontal force at B required to keep the string in the above position when a load of 6 lb hangs from C. Find also the tension in AB. (L.)

2.7. The Resultant of Any Number of Forces Acting on a Particle

The resultant of more than two forces acting on a particle can be found by successive applications of the law of vector addition (2.1) or by the polygon of forces (2.2). In most cases the former method is long and can involve so much calculation that the probability of error is a high one. The polygon of forces provides a method by *drawing* which we shall use for a special purpose (in Volume 2) when we consider Frameworks. Direct use of the polygon of forces for the theoretical calculation of resultants and equilibrants generally involves difficult trigonometry.

The Law of the Resolved Parts (Fig. 11)

$\overrightarrow{OB}$, $\overrightarrow{BC}$, $\overrightarrow{CD}$, $\overrightarrow{DE}$ are vectors, B_1, C_1, D_1, E_1 are the projections of B, C, D, E respectively on the line Ox and B_2, C_2, D_2, E_2 are the

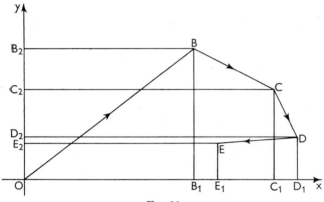

FIG. 11.

projections of B, C, D, E respectively on the line Oy, which is at right angles to Ox. Then

$$\overrightarrow{OB} + \overrightarrow{BC} + \overrightarrow{CD} + \overrightarrow{DE} = \overrightarrow{OE}$$

and, if the vectors are considered as free vectors,

$$\overrightarrow{OB} = \overrightarrow{OB_1} + \overrightarrow{OB_2},$$
$$\overrightarrow{BC} = \overrightarrow{B_1C_1} + \overrightarrow{B_2C_2}$$
$$\overrightarrow{CD} = \overrightarrow{C_1D_1} + \overrightarrow{C_2D_2},$$
$$\overrightarrow{DE} = \overrightarrow{D_1E_1} + \overrightarrow{D_2E_2}.$$

$$\therefore \ \overrightarrow{OB} + \overrightarrow{BC} + \overrightarrow{CD} + \overrightarrow{DE} = (\overrightarrow{OB_1} + \overrightarrow{B_1C_1} + \overrightarrow{C_1D_1} + \overrightarrow{D_1E_1}) +$$
$$+ (\overrightarrow{OB_2} + \overrightarrow{B_2C_2} + \overrightarrow{C_2D_2} + \overrightarrow{D_2E_2}) =$$
$$= \overrightarrow{OE_1} + \overrightarrow{OE_2}$$
$$= \overrightarrow{OE}.$$

Also $OB_1 = OB \cos BOx, \ \ OB_2 = OB \sin BOx$ etc.,
$$OE^2 = OE_1^2 + OE_2^2,$$
$$\tan EOx = OE_2/OE_1,$$

and these results in combination enable us to find the resultant (and therefore the equilibrant) of any number of forces acting on a particle.

Conditions of Equilibrium

Because $OE^2 = OE_1^2 + OE_2^2$, necessary and sufficient conditions for the resultant of the system to be zero are $OE_1 = 0$ and $OE_2 = 0$.

If a particle is acted upon by a system of coplanar forces and is in equilibrium, the sums of the resolved parts of the forces in any two directions at right angles are separately zero.

Note: It is not a necessary condition that the chosen directions should be at right angles. If P and Q are respectively the sums of the components in two directions making an angle θ, where $0° < \theta < 180°$, with one another and if R is the resultant of the system,

$$R^2 = P^2 + Q^2 + 2PQ \cos\theta = (P + Q \cos\theta)^2 + Q^2(1 - \cos^2\theta)$$

and since $-1 < \cos\theta < 1$, R can be zero only if P and Q are separately zero.

Examples. (i) Find the resultant of the forces shown in Fig. 12 (i). It is advantageous to have a systematic method of arrangement for exercises of this kind.

Force	Component in the direction of the 10 lb. wt. force (x)	Component in the direction perpendicular to the 10 lb. wt. force (y)	x	y
10 lb wt.	10	0	10	0
8 lb wt.	$8 \cos 60° = 8 \times 0{\cdot}5$	$8 \sin 60° = 8 \times 0{\cdot}8660$	4	6·9280
12 lb wt.	$-12 \cos 30° =$ $-12 \times 0{\cdot}8660$	$12 \sin 30° = 12 \times 0{\cdot}5$	$-10{\cdot}392$	6
16 lb wt.	0	-16	0	-16
Resultant			$+3{\cdot}608$	$-3{\cdot}072$

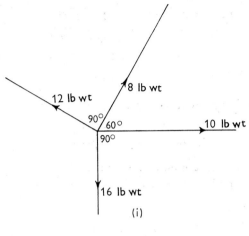

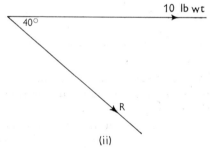

FIG. 12 (i), (ii).

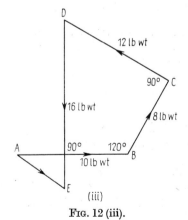

FIG. 12 (iii).

The resultant is $\sqrt{\{(3{\cdot}608)^2 + (3{\cdot}072)^2\}}$ lb wt. acting in the direction shown in Fig. 12 (ii) where $\tan\theta = \dfrac{3{\cdot}072}{3{\cdot}608}$, i.e. $4{\cdot}74$ lb wt. approximately in a direction making a clockwise angle of $40°$ approximately with the 10 lb wt. force.

Figure 12 (iii) is the polygon of forces for this system. The resultant is represented by $\overrightarrow{AE}$ in this figure.

(ii) A small smooth ring P of mass 10 gm is threaded on to a string of length 31 in. the ends of which are attached to two points A and B at the same horizontal level and 25 in. apart. Calculate the magnitude of the *horizontal* force acting on P which will hold P in the position in which $\angle APB = 90°$ and calculate the tension in the string in this position.

Figure 13 (i). The ring is in equilibrium under the action of three forces,

(1) its weight 10 gm,

(2) the horizontal force X,

(3) the reaction of the string on the ring which is equal in magnitude and opposite in direction to the action of the ring on the string and which is measured by the resultant of the *tensions* in the two parts of the string. *Because the ring is smooth*, these tensions are equal.

The system of forces acting on the ring is therefore shown as Fig. 13 (ii).

If $PB = x$ in., $AP = (31 - x)$ in., and from the right-angled triangle APB

$$x^2 + (31 - x)^2 = 25^2.$$

$$\therefore\ 2x^2 - 62x + 336 = 0,$$

i.e. $$2(x - 24)(x - 7) = 0.$$

Clearly $$PB < AP.$$

$$\therefore\ PB = 7 \text{ in.,} \quad AP = 24 \text{ in.,} \quad \sin\theta = 7/25, \quad \cos\theta = 24/25.$$

The ring is in equilibrium.

(a) The sum of the horizontal components of the forces is zero.

$$\therefore\ X + T\sin\theta - T\cos\theta = 0,$$

i.e. $$X + T\cdot\frac{7}{25} - T\cdot\frac{24}{25} = 0.$$

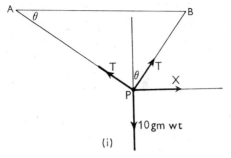

Fɪɢ. 13 (i).

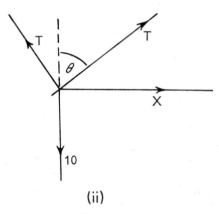

(ii)

Fɪɢ. 13 (ii).

(b) The sum of the vertical components of the forces is zero.

$$\therefore \ T\cos\theta + T\sin\theta - 10 = 0,$$

i.e.

$$T \cdot \frac{24}{25} + T \cdot \frac{7}{25} - 10 = 0.$$

$$\therefore \ T = \frac{250}{31} \doteqdot 8\cdot0, \quad X = \frac{17\,T}{25} \doteqdot 5\cdot5.$$

The horizontal force is 5·5 gm wt. and the tension in the string is 8·0 gm wt.

T.M.S.F.I. 3

EXERCISES 2.7.

In each of Exercises (i)–(vi) find, correct to two significant figures, the magnitude of the resultant of the forces shown in the figure (Fig. 14) and in each case calculate, correct to the nearest degree, the angle which the resultant makes with the largest force. In each case, also, obtain an approximation to the magnitude and direction of the resultant by drawing a polygon of forces.

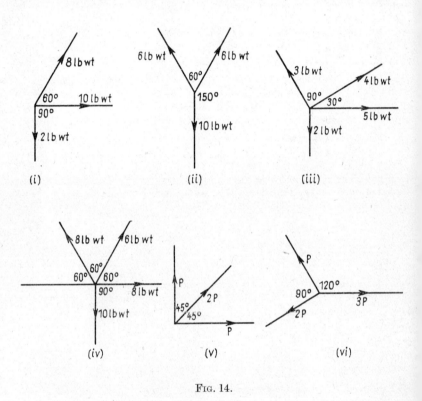

Fig. 14.

7. Three forces, acting at the same point, are 12 lb wt. due W., 5 lb wt. due S. and 10 lb wt. N. 30° E. Find by calculation the magnitude and direction of their resultant.   (N.)

8. Find *by calculation* the resultant in magnitude and direction of forces of 11 lb wt. due E., 9 lb wt. due N., and 11 lb wt. 40° S. of W., the three forces all acting at the same point.   (N.)

9. Find, graphically or otherwise, the magnitude and the direction of the resultant of the following forces acting at a point: 20 lb wt. E., 42 lb wt. NW., 60 lb wt. W. 30° S., 15 lb wt. S. (O.C.)

10. Four horizontal wires are attached to a telephone post and exert the following tensions on it: 20 lb wt. N., 30 lb wt. E., 40 lb wt. SW., and 50 lb wt. SE. Calculate the resultant pull on the post and find its direction. (O.C.)

11. ABC is a triangle in which $AB = 7$ in., $BC = 3$ in., $CA = 5$ in. Find (1) graphically,(2) analytically, the resultant of the following forces acting at a point: 3 lb wt. in the direction BC, 9 lb wt. in the direction AC, 9 lb wt. in the direction BA. (O.C.)

12. Three forces act at a point O. They are 7 lb wt. due N., 5 lb wt. due E., and 4 lb wt. SE.

Find their resultant in magnitude and direction. (N.)

13. OX is a fixed line in a plane. A force of 3 lb wt. acts on a particle at O along OX, and coplanar forces 4 lb wt. and 5 lb wt. act on the particle in directions making angles of 60° and 120°, measured in the same sense, with OX.

Find, graphically, or by calculation, the resultant of this system of forces. (L.)

14. A wheel has eight spokes equally spaced. Forces 8, 7, 6, 5, 4, 3, 2, 1 lb wt. act outwards along the spokes. Prove that the magnitude of the resultant is about 10·45 lb wt. and find its line of action. (O.C.)

In each of Exercises 15–18 calculate the forces and the angles named, given that the system shown in the corresponding figure is in equilibrium.

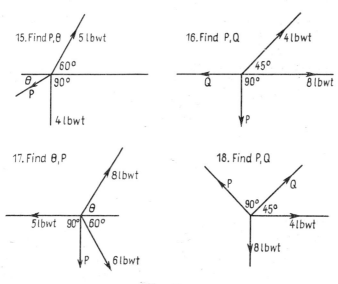

FIG. 15.

3*

19. Two small smooth pulleys A and B are at the same horizontal level. A particle P of mass 10 lb is attached to a point of a string which passes over the two pulleys and carries at one end a mass of 8 lb and at the other end a mass of 6 lb. P is between the pulleys. Find the magnitude and direction of the force acting on the particle which would maintain the system in equilibrium with $PA = PB$ and $\angle APB = 90°$.

20. $ABCD$ is a rectangle. A particle at A is acted upon by forces along BA, CA and DA which are represented in magnitude by kDA, kCA and kBA respectively. Prove that the line of action of the additional force required to keep the particle in equilibrium bisects the angle BAD and find the magnitude of the vector which represents the force in terms of k, AB and AD.

2.8. The Equilibrium of a Rigid Body acted upon by Three Forces only

Definition

A rigid body is an aggregate of particles in which the distance between any two marked points in the body is invariable (and so the angle between any two marked lines in the body is invariable). This definition is a mathematical ideal which provides a sufficiently close approximation to an accurate description of the bodies with which we shall be concerned.

The Weight of a Rigid Body

The resultant of the weights of all the particles of a rigid body is called the *weight of the body*. In Chapter VII we shall show that there is one point, fixed in relation to the body, through which this resultant force passes no matter what the position of the body. This point is called the *Centre of Gravity* of the body. In cases in which the body has a symmetrical shape and a uniform density the position of the centre of gravity is the centre of symmetry. Thus the centre of gravity of a uniform thin rod is at the mid-point of the rod; the centre of gravity of a uniform circular disc is at its geometrical centre, etc. We shall discuss the investigation of the position of the centre of gravity in more complicated cases in Chapter VII.

The Equilibrium of a Rigid Body under the Action of Three Non-parallel Coplanar Forces

If a rigid body is in equilibrium under the action of three forces which are not all parallel, the lines of action of at least two of them must meet at a point and these forces therefore have a resultant which acts through this point of intersection. This resultant can be in equilibrium with the third force only if these two forces are equal in magnitude, opposite in direction and act in the same straight line. The last condition is possible only if the third force passes through the point of intersection of the other two, i.e. if the three forces are concurrent.

We conclude that necessary and sufficient conditions for a rigid body to be in equilibrium under the action of three non-parallel forces only are:

1. The three forces must act through a point.

2. The vector sum of the three forces must be zero.

The second condition is expressible in three alternative ways,

either (a) the sum of the components of the forces in two different directions separately vanish,

or (b) the forces can be represented by the sides of a triangle taken in order round the triangle,

or (c) *Lami's Theorem.* If the three forces P, Q, R shown in Fig. 16 (i) are in equilibrium, they may be represented by the sides of the triangle shown in Fig. 16 (ii). Hence

$$\frac{P}{\sin(180 - \alpha)} = \frac{Q}{\sin(180 - \beta)} = \frac{R}{\sin(180 - \gamma)}.$$

$$\therefore \ \frac{P}{\sin \alpha} = \frac{Q}{\sin \beta} = \frac{R}{\sin \gamma}.$$

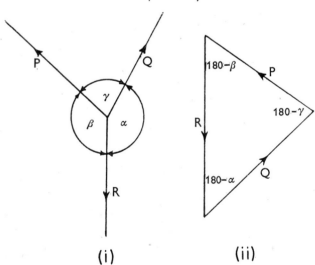

(i)　　　　　　(ii)

Fig. 16.

If three forces acting at a point are in equilibrium, each is proportional to the sine of the angle between the other two. This is Lami's theorem.

2.9. Two Useful Trigonometric Formulae

If P is the point which divides the side AB of the triangle ABC (Fig. 17) in the ratio $m:n$ and if $\angle ACP = \alpha$, $\angle PCB = \beta$, $\angle CPB = \theta$, then

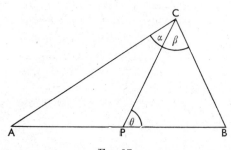

Fɪɢ. 17.

$$(m + n) \cot\theta = n \cot A - m \cot B, \qquad (2.5)$$

$$(m + n) \cot\theta = m \cot\alpha - n \cot\beta. \qquad (2.6)$$

For from $\triangle ACP$, $\dfrac{AP}{\sin(\theta - A)} = \dfrac{CP}{\sin A}$,

and from $\triangle BCP$, $\dfrac{PB}{\sin\{180 - (\theta + B)\}} = \dfrac{CP}{\sin B}$.

By division, $\dfrac{AP}{PB} \cdot \dfrac{\sin\{180 - (\theta + B)\}}{\sin(\theta - A)} = \dfrac{\sin B}{\sin A}$,

i.e. $\dfrac{m}{n} \cdot \dfrac{\sin(\theta + B)}{\sin(\theta - A)} = \dfrac{\sin B}{\sin A}$.

$\therefore \dfrac{m}{n} \cdot \dfrac{\sin\theta \cos B + \cos\theta \sin B}{\sin\theta \cos A - \cos\theta \sin A} = \dfrac{\sin B}{\sin A}$.

$\therefore m \sin\theta \cos B \sin A + m \cos\theta \sin B \sin A = n \sin\theta \cos A \sin B$

$$- n \cos\theta \sin A \sin B,$$

and, dividing through by $\sin\theta\sin B\sin A$,

$$m\cot B + m\cot\theta = n\cot A - n\cot\theta.$$
$$\therefore\ (m + n)\cot\theta = n\cot A - m\cot B.$$

Similarly,

$$\frac{AP}{\sin\alpha} = \frac{CP}{\sin(\theta - \alpha)},$$

and

$$\frac{PB}{\sin\beta} = \frac{CP}{\sin\{180 - (\theta + \beta)\}},$$

from which $\quad (m + n)\cot\theta = m\cot\alpha - n\cot\beta.$

Examples. (i) A thin uniform rod AB, of length $2l$ and weight W, is freely hinged to a vertical wall at A and is supported in a position inclined at $60°$ to the upward vertical by a string attached to the wall at a point C distance l above A and attached to the rod at P so that $AP = \frac{1}{2}l$. Find an expression for the tension in the string and expressions for the magnitude and direction of the reaction at the hinge.

A body is said to be *smoothly hinged* or *freely hinged* when the action of the hinge on the body is a single force through the centre of the hinge.

The rod is in equilibrium under the action of the three forces shown in Fig. 18 (i), viz.

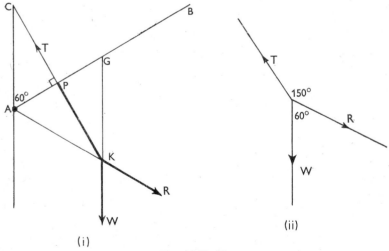

(i)

(ii)

FIG. 18 (i), (ii).

1. Its weight, W, acting vertically downwards through its mid-point G.

2. The tension, T, in the string PC.

3. The reaction, R, at the hinge which must pass through the inter-section, K, of W and T.

$$AP = \tfrac{1}{2}l, \quad AC = l \quad \text{and} \quad \angle CAP = 60°.$$

$$\therefore \ \angle CPA = 90°.$$

$$\therefore \ \varDelta APK \equiv \varDelta GPK.$$

$$\therefore \ \angle AKP = \angle GKP = 30°.$$

The forces are therefore as shown in Fig. 18 (ii) and by Lami's theorem,

$$\frac{T}{\sin 60°} = \frac{R}{\sin 150°} = \frac{W}{\sin 150°}.$$

$$\therefore \ R = W, \quad T = W \sqrt{3}.$$

(ii) A uniform rod, of weight W and length $2l$, rests in a smooth hemispherical bowl of radius a, with one end projecting beyond the edge of the bowl. If the axis of the bowl is vertical and the rod makes an angle θ with the horizontal, show that the reactions of the bowl on the rod at its two points of contact are $W \tan\theta$ and $W \cos 2\theta \sec\theta$ and that $2a \cos 2\theta = l \cos\theta$.

Figure 19 shows the rod in the bowl and the three forces which act on it. These are:

1. The reaction S at A which is normal to the reacting surface of the bowl and therefore passes through the centre O of the hemisphere.

2. The reaction at P. In this case the contact between the rod and the edge of the bowl is assumed to be tangential, and the normal reaction R at P is then at right angles to the rod, i. e. at right angles to the direction in which the point P of the rod would move if the rod slipped. The lines of action of these two forces will intersect at C which is an extremity of the diameter of the circle with centre O through A and P.

3. The weight of the rod. This must pass through C, and the mid-point M of the rod is therefore vertically below C.

The horizontal through A intersects the line representing W at Q on the circumference of the circle. Then

$$\angle OPA = \angle OAP = \angle PAQ = \theta.$$

$$\therefore \ \angle ACQ = 90 - 2\theta \quad \text{and} \quad \angle PCQ = \theta.$$

Applying Lami's theorem for the forces at C,

$$\frac{R}{\sin(90+2\theta)} = \frac{S}{\sin(180-\theta)} = \frac{W}{\sin(90-\theta)}.$$

$$\therefore \frac{R}{\cos 2\theta} = \frac{S}{\sin\theta} = \frac{W}{\cos\theta}.$$

$$\therefore R = W\cos 2\theta \sec\theta, \qquad S = W\tan\theta.$$

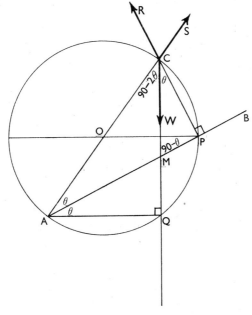

Fig. 19.

Also $AQ = AC\cos 2\theta = AM\cos\theta.$

$$\therefore 2a\cos 2\theta = l\cos\theta.$$

(iii) Two smooth uniform spheres, each of radius a, and of weights $2W$ and W respectively, are suspended from a fixed point by two light inextensible strings each of length a, the spheres resting in contact with one another. Show that the strings are inclined to the vertical at $19° 6'$ and $40° 54'$.

Find, in terms of W, the tensions in the strings.   (N.)

In this example we are concerned with the equilibrium of two bodies. In such a case we make an analysis of the forces acting on the bodies *separately* considering each of the possibilities: (a) weights, (b) normal actions and *reactions* at surfaces in contact, (c) tangential components of action and *reaction* at *rough* surfaces in contact, (d) tensions in tight strings, (e) external forces.

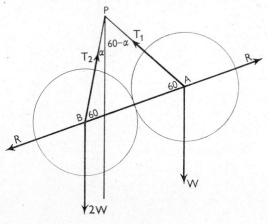

FIG. 20.

Figure 20, on which this analysis is made, shows that each sphere is acted on by three forces only

(1) the normal reaction R between the spheres,

(2) the tension in the supporting string,

(3) its weight.

For equilibrium in each case these forces must meet at a point; the line of action of the tension in each string must therefore pass through the centre of its respective sphere, and the equilibrium position of each sphere is thus decided.

PAB is an equilateral triangle.

Let PB make an angle α with the downward vertical. Then PA makes an angle $(60 - \alpha)$ with the downward vertical.

For the sphere of weight $2W$:

The angle between T_2 and $2W$ is $180 - \alpha$.

For the sphere of weight W:

The angle between T_1 and W is $120 + \alpha$.

But $\angle PBA = \angle PAB = 60°.$

Therefore for the sphere of weight $2W$,

$$\frac{R}{\sin(180 - \alpha)} = \frac{2W}{\sin 120},$$

and for the sphere of weight W,

$$\frac{R}{\sin(120 + \alpha)} = \frac{W}{\sin 120}.$$

Equating values of R we have

$$2\sin(180 - \alpha) = \sin(120 + \alpha).$$

$$\therefore \quad 2\sin\alpha = \sin 120 \cos\alpha + \cos 120 \sin\alpha.$$

$$\therefore \quad 2\sin\alpha = \tfrac{1}{2}\sqrt{3}\cos\alpha - \tfrac{1}{2}\sin\alpha.$$

$$\therefore \quad \tan\alpha = \sqrt{3}/5, \quad \alpha = 19° \, 06'.$$

The strings are inclined to the vertical at $19° \, 06'$ and $40° \, 54'$. Also

$$\frac{T_1}{\sin(120 - \alpha)} = \frac{W}{\sin 120}, \quad \frac{T_2}{\sin(60 + \alpha)} = \frac{2W}{\sin 120}.$$

$$\therefore \ T_1 = \frac{W \sin 79° \, 06'}{\sin 60°} = 1.13\,W, \quad T_2 = \frac{2W \sin 79° \, 06'}{\sin 60°} = 2.27\,W.$$

(iv) A non-uniform thin rod AB of length $3l$ has its centre of gravity at a point M of its length where $AM : MB = 2 : 1$. The rod is connected by two strings each of length $5l/2$ to a point O above AB and in the same vertical plane as the rod and the strings. Calculate the angle which the rod makes with the vertical in its position of equilibrium.

The rod is in equilibrium under the action of the three forces (Fig. 21),

(1) the tension in the string OA,
(2) the tension in the string OB,
(3) its weight, which must act vertically downward through O, the point of intersection of the two tensions.

Therefore OM is vertical, and if θ is the angle between AB and the vertical, by equation (2.5)

$$3 \cot \theta = 2 \cot A - \cot B.$$

$$\cos A = \cos B = \tfrac{3}{5}, \quad \therefore \cot A = \cot B = \tfrac{3}{4}.$$

$$\therefore \ 3 \cot \theta = \tfrac{3}{4}, \quad \cot \theta = \tfrac{1}{4}.$$

$$\therefore \qquad \theta = 75° \ 58'.$$

The rod makes an angle of $75° \ 58'$ with the vertical in the equilibrium position.

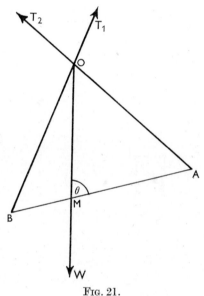

FIG. 21.

2.10. Elastic Strings

Modulus of Elasticity

Hooke's Law states that if a wire, or spring, or extensible string, is stretched in such a way that it will return to its natural length when released, the *tension* is proportional to the *extension*. (When a spring is compressed, it is in a state of thrust; the *thrust* is proportional to the compression.)

If an elastic string of natural length l is stretched to a length $l + x$, and if T is then the tension in the string, Hooke's Law states that

$$T = \frac{\lambda x}{l},$$

where λ is a constant called the *modulus of elasticity*. The quantity x/l is dimensionless and therefore the dimensions of λ are the same as the dimensions of T. *The modulus of elasticity, therefore, has the dimensions of force* [lb ft/sec²]. (*Note* that there is a convention in which Hooke's Law is stated as $T = kx$, where k is a constant having the dimensions of *force per unit length*.)

Example. A light elastic string of modulus $4/\sqrt{3}$ lb wt. and unstretched length 4 ft is attached at its ends to two points, A and B, 4 ft apart and in a horizontal line. Two particles, each of mass 1 lb,

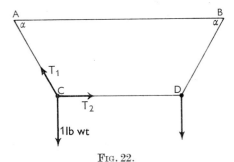

FIG. 22.

are attached to fixed points, C and D, of the string such that the unstretched lengths of AC and DB are each 1 ft. If in the equilibrium position the inclinations of AC and BD to the horizontal are each α, show that

$$\tan\alpha - \sin\alpha = \tfrac{1}{2}\sqrt{3}.$$

Verify that $\alpha = 60°$ is a solution of this equation and hence calculate the tensions in the several portions of the string in this position.   (N.)

The system is symmetrical about the perpendicular bisector of AB (Fig. 22) and it is sufficient to consider the equilibrium of the particle at C. This particle is in equilibrium under the action of

(1) the tension T_1 in the string CA,
(2) its weight,
(3) the tension T_2 in the string CD.

Let the stretched length of AC be $(1+x)$ ft and let the stretched length of CD be $(2+y)$ ft Then,

(a) the sum of the horizontal components of the forces vanishes so that

$$T_2 = T_1 \cos\alpha,$$

(b) the sum of the vertical components of the forces vanishes so that

$$T_1 \sin\alpha = 1.$$

Also by Hooke's Law

(c)
$$T_1 = \frac{4}{\sqrt{3}} \cdot \frac{x}{1},$$

(d)
$$T_2 = \frac{4}{\sqrt{3}} \cdot \frac{y}{2},$$

and from the geometry of the figure, projecting on the horizontal,

(e)
$$2(1+x)\cos\alpha + (2+y) = 4.$$

We note that we have obtained five equations for the five unknown quantities T_1, T_2, α, x and y. This check is a useful one at this stage.

From (b) and (c)
$$x = \frac{\sqrt{3}}{4\sin\alpha},$$

from (a), (b) and (d)
$$y = \frac{2\sqrt{3}}{4} \cdot \frac{\cos\alpha}{\sin\alpha}.$$

Therefore from (e)

$$2\left(1 + \frac{\sqrt{3}}{4\sin\alpha}\right)\cos\alpha + 2 + \frac{2\sqrt{3}}{4} \cdot \frac{\cos\alpha}{\sin\alpha} = 4.$$

$$\therefore \ 2\cos\alpha + \frac{\sqrt{3}}{\tan\alpha} = 2.$$

$$\therefore \ \tan\alpha - \sin\alpha = \tfrac{1}{2}\sqrt{3}.$$

But $\tan 60° = \sqrt{3}$ and $\sin 60° = \tfrac{1}{2}\sqrt{3}$, and therefore $\alpha = 60°$ is a solution of this equation.

$$\therefore \ T_1 = 1 \operatorname{cosec}\alpha = \tfrac{2}{3}\sqrt{3} \doteqdot 1.15; \quad T_2 = T_1 \cos\alpha \doteqdot 0.58.$$

The tensions in AC and BD are each 1·15 lb wt. and the tension in CD is 0·58 lb wt.

EXERCISES 2.10.

1. A uniform rod AB is 8 ft long and of mass 10 lb. The rod rests inclined at 30° to the horizontal with the upper end A against a smooth vertical wall. The lower end B is fastened to a string, the other end of which is attached to the wall at C, vertically above A. Find the tension in the string.   (N.)

2. A uniform beam 12 ft long is hinged at A to a wall and is of mass 40 lb. It is held at 40° with the upward vertical by means of a chain 8 ft long making an angle of 30° with the downward vertical, and attached to a point on the wall vertically above A.

Find the tension in the chain and the direction of the reaction at the hinge. (N.)

3. A uniform beam AD, 8 ft long and of mass 30 lb is kept at an angle of 60° with the horizontal by a strut BC, B being on the same level as A. AB is 8 ft and BC is at right angles to the beam.

Find the stress in the strut and the direction of the reaction at A. (N.)

4. A thin uniform rod AB is 4 ft long and is of mass 2 lb. It can rotate in a vertical plane about a smooth pin on the rod 1 ft from the lower end A. It is kept in equilibrium at an angle of 30° to the horizontal by a force P acting horizontally at B. Calculate the magnitude of P and the direction of the pressure on the pin. (N.)

5. A uniform plank 20 ft long is of mass 250 lb. It is hinged to a wall at its lower end A, and is held at 50° to the vertical by a chain attached to a point 15 ft vertically above A and fastened to the plank at 15 ft from A. Find the tension in the chain and the direction of the reaction at A. (N.)

6. A uniform rod AB, 6 ft long and of mass 3 lb, rests in a vertical plane at an angle of 60° with the downward vertical, A being in contact with a smooth vertical wall. The other end B of the rod is supported by a string attached at B and running to a point C on the wall vertically above A.

Find the tension in the string and the length of the string. (N.)

7. A heavy non-uniform bar AB, 3 ft long and of mass 3 lb, is held in a horizontal position by two strings attached at A and B and making angles of 30° and 50° with the horizontal. Find the tension in each string and also the point where the weight of the rod acts. (N.)

8. A uniform pole, of length 8 ft and mass 150 lb, rests in equilibrium with its lower end P in a socket. The pole is supported by a rope of length 5 ft joining a point R of the pole to a fixed hook S vertically above the socket; $PR = 6$ ft, $PS = 5$ ft. Show that the tension in the rope is 100 lb wt. and find, in magnitude and direction, the force exerted by the socket on the pole. (N.)

9. A smooth circular cylinder of radius 4 ft is fixed with its axis horizontal. A uniform rod ABC, of length 12 ft and mass 64 lb, rests against the curved surface of the cylinder at B. The end A is smoothly hinged to a fixed point on the same level as the axis of the cylinder. The rod is inclined at 30° to the horizontal and lies in a plane perpendicular to the axis of the cylinder. Find, in magnitude and direction, the forces exerted on the rod at A and B by the hinge and cylinder respectively. (N.)

10. A uniform beam LM of mass 36 lb rests with the end L on a rough horizontal plane and the end M against a smooth vertical wall. The beam makes an angle of 30° with the wall. Find, in magnitude and direction, the forces exerted on the beam by the wall and by the plane. (N.)

11. The end A of a uniform rod AB of weight W is smoothly hinged to a fixed point and the end B is supported by a string joining B to a point C at the same level as A. If $AB = BC$ and AB is inclined at 30° to the horizontal, find the tension in the string and the reaction at the hinge. (N.)

12. A uniform rod, of mass 20 lb, hangs from a ceiling by means of two strings attached to the ends of the rod, the distance between their points of attachment to the ceiling being greater than the length of the rod. In the position of equilibrium the strings are inclined to the vertical at angles of 30° and 60°. Find the tensions in the strings and the inclination of the rod to the vertical.   (N.)

13. A uniform rod AB, of weight W, is freely hinged to a wall at A and is in equilibrium under the action of a force of magnitude $2W/5$ in the vertical plane containing the rod, acting at B perpendicular to AB. Find the angle of inclination of the rod to the vertical and the magnitude and direction of the reaction at the hinge.   (N.)

14. A uniform straight rod AB of mass 12 lb is free to turn about the end A. The rod is kept in equilibrium by a light string attached to B and to a fixed point C at the same horizontal level as A, ABC being an equilateral triangle. Prove that the action at A makes an angle θ with the horizontal such that

$$\tan\theta = 3\sqrt3.\qquad\qquad (N.)$$

15. The upper end of a ladder, whose centre of gravity is at the middle, rests against a smooth vertical wall, and the lower end rests on a smooth plane which is inclined at an angle 30° to the horizontal. Prove that, if θ is the inclination of the ladder to the vertical, $\tan\theta = 2/\sqrt3$.   (N.)

16. A uniform sphere, whose mass is 8 lb and diameter 3 ft, is kept in equilibrium on a smooth plane, inclined at an angle of 30° to the horizontal, by means of a string, of length 1 ft, attached to a point in the plane and to a point on the surface of the sphere. Prove that the tension in the string is 5 lb wt.   (N.)

17. A gate of mass 60 lb is supported by two hinges A and B, the hinge A being uppermost and the line AB being vertical. The centre of gravity of the gate is 2 ft from the line AB, and $AB = 4$ ft. Assuming the reaction at A to be horizontal, calculate the magnitude of the reaction at B and its inclination to the vertical.   (N.)

18. A smooth plane is inclined at an angle α to the horizontal. A sphere of weight W and radius a is held in contact with the plane by a light thread of length a, one end of which is attached to the plane and the other to the surface of the sphere. Calculate the tension in the thread.   (C.)

*19. A horizontal square plate $ABCD$ lies on a smooth horizontal table and is kept in equilibrium by a force P parallel to CB through the point of intersection of the diagonals and in the direction from C to B, by a force Q along the edge CD in the direction from C to D, and by a horizontal force R at A. Find, in terms of P, the magnitudes of the forces Q and R.   (N.)

*20. A light rod AB, 25 in. long, is capable of revolving in a vertical plane about its end A which is fixed. A small smooth light ring slides on the rod and is attached, by a light inextensible string 24 in. long, to a fixed point C which is 26 in. vertically above A. If a mass W lb is hung from B and the system is in equilibrium, find the tension in the string and the magnitude of the reaction at A.

Show also that, if θ is the angle this reaction makes with the downward vertical,

$$191\tan\theta = 150.\qquad\qquad (N.)$$

*21. A light elastic string of modulus $3w$ and natural length a is tied at one end to the highest point of a fixed smooth sphere of radius a. A particle of weight w is attached to the other end of the string and is in contact with the sphere. If in the position of equilibrium the line joining the particle to the centre of the sphere makes an angle θ with the vertical, find an equation satisfied by θ; hence, with the aid of tables, find by trial an approximate value for θ.

If the particle of weight w is replaced by another particle of weight w' which is sufficiently heavy to hang in equilibrium away from the surface of the sphere, show that w' must be greater than about $1 \cdot 71\,w$.   (C.)

*22. A heavy particle is hung from two pegs, which are in a horizontal line and distance $2c$ apart, by two light elastic strings of natural lengths a, b and moduli λ, μ respectively. In the position of equilibrium the strings are inclined at equal angles α to the vertical. Show that

$$\sin\alpha = \frac{c\,(\lambda\,b - \mu\,a)}{a\,b\,(\lambda - \mu)} \,.$$ (N.)

*23. A plane lamina has two smooth rectilinear slots XO, OY cut in it, the angle XOY being a right angle. The lamina rests in equilibrium in a vertical plane upon two small fixed smooth parallel horizontal pegs, one of which is in each slot. The pegs are at the same level and distant c apart. If G is the centre of gravity of the lamina, angle $GOY = \alpha$, $OG = d$, and OG makes an angle θ with the vertical, show that in the case when O is above the pegs, and G and Y are on the same side of the vertical through O,

$$d \sin\theta + c \cos 2\,(\theta + \alpha) = 0 \,.$$ (N.)

*24. A light elastic string of natural length $2a$ is stretched with tension T between two points in the same vertical line distant $2c$ apart. A particle of weight w is then attached to the mid-point of the string, and, when this particle is in its equilibrium position, it is at a distance x below the original position of the mid-point. Prove that, if $w < 2T$,

$$x = \frac{w}{2\,T}\,(c - a) \,,$$

and find the value of x when $w > 2T$.   (N.)

2.11. Particles Suspended from a String

The example worked in this paragraph concerns a light string, fixed at each end, to which a series of particles are attached. In such a case, the equations of equilibrium, together with any equations which interpret the geometry of the configuration, are solved in the best way if use is made of *the constant horizontal component of the tension throughout the string*.

Example. Five points A, B, C, D, E in order upon a horizontal line are such that $AB = BC = CD = DE = 1$ ft. The ends of a light inextensible string are attached at A and E and masses of 1, 1 and 3 lb are attached to the string at points F, G and K so that

T.M.S.F.I.   4

in the position of equilibrium they are vertically below B, C and D respectively. If the point F is 2 ft below B, show that K is 3 ft below D and that the portion GK of the string is horizontal.

The forces acting on the particles are shown in Fig. 23. The sum of the horizontal components for each particle is zero. Therefore

(a) $T_1 \cos\theta_1 = T_2 \cos\theta_2 = T_3 \cos\theta_3 = T_4 \cos\theta_4 = H$ (say).

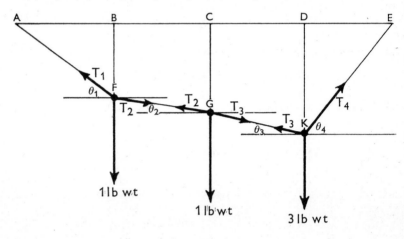

Fig. 23.

The sum of the vertical components for each particle is zero. Therefore

(b) $\qquad T_1 \sin\theta_1 - T_2 \sin\theta_2 = 1,$

(c) $\qquad T_2 \sin\theta_2 - T_3 \sin\theta_3 = 1,$

(d) $\qquad T_3 \sin\theta_3 + T_4 \sin\theta_4 = 3.$

Dividing equation (b) by H gives

$$\frac{T_1 \sin\theta_1}{T_1 \cos\theta_1} - \frac{T_2 \sin\theta_2}{T_2 \cos\theta_2} = \frac{1}{H}.$$

$$\therefore \ \tan\theta_1 - \tan\theta_2 = \frac{1}{H}.$$

Similarly $\qquad \tan\theta_2 - \tan\theta_3 = \dfrac{1}{H},$

and $\qquad \tan\theta_3 + \tan\theta_4 = \dfrac{3}{H}.$

Eliminating H from these equations gives

$$\tan\theta_1 - 2\tan\theta_2 + \tan\theta_3 = 0, \tag{1}$$

$$3\tan\theta_2 - 4\tan\theta_3 - \tan\theta_4 = 0. \tag{2}$$

But

$$\tan\theta_1 = 2, \tag{3}$$

and

$$DK = 2 + \tan\theta_2 + \tan\theta_3 = \tan\theta_4. \tag{4}$$

The solution of equations (1)–(4) is

$$\tan\theta_1 = 2, \ \tan\theta_2 = 1, \ \tan\theta_3 = 0, \ \tan\theta_4 = 3.$$

Therefore K is 3 ft below AD, and GK is horizontal.

MISCELLANEOUS EXERCISES. II

1. Forces P, $3P$, $5P$, and $2P$ act at a point in the directions E., N., NW., and SW. respectively. Find, *graphically*, the magnitude and the direction of their resultant.

O is any point in the plane of the parallelogram $ABCD$. Show that the system of forces, acting at O and represented in magnitude and direction by AO, OB, CO, OD, is in equilibrium. (C.)

2. Forces of magnitude 1, 2, 3 and 4 lb wt. act at a point in the directions N., W., SW., and SE. respectively. Find *graphically* the magnitude and the direction of their resultant. Use a scale of 1 inch to represent 1 lb wt. (N.)

3. A load of mass m lb is supported in equilibrium by two ropes attached to it. One rope is inclined at 30° to the vertical and the other at 60° to the vertical. If either rope breaks under a tension exceeding 500 lb wt., find, correct to three significant figures, the greatest possible value of m. (N.)

4. The diagonals of a square $ABCD$ of side 5 in. intersect at O and X is the mid-point of BC. Find the magnitude of the resultant of forces of 4, 1 and $3\sqrt{2}$ lb wt. acting along OA, OB and OX respectively.

If this resultant cuts CD at Y, find DY. (N.)

5. The triangle ABC is equilateral with D the mid-point of BC and AL the line through A parallel to BC. Forces of magnitudes 2, 3, x and y lb wt., acting along the lines AB, CA, AL and AD respectively, are in equilibrium. Find x and y.

If the force acting along CA is reversed in direction, what is the resultant of the new system? (N.)

6. The points A and B are at the same level, 26 in. apart. A load of mass 91 lb is suspended by two light strings AC and BC, where $AC = 10$ in., $BC = 24$ in. Find graphically or otherwise the tensions in the two strings. (N.)

4*

7. The sides of a regular hexagon $ABCDEF$ are each of length 2 in. Forces of 2 lb wt., 3 lb wt. and 4 lb wt. act along the lines AB, AD and AE respectively. Find

    (i) the magnitude of the resultant force,

    (ii) its inclination to AB,

    (iii) the distance of its line of action from F.   (N.)

8. A uniform thin rod of weight W rests with its upper end against a smooth vertical wall and its lower end on a smooth horizontal floor; the vertical plane through the rod is perpendicular to the wall. The rod is prevented from slipping by a light horizontal cord which joins the lowest point of the rod to the point of the junction of wall and floor vertically below the upper end of the rod. If the angle between the rod and the horizontal is α, find the tension in the cord. (N.)

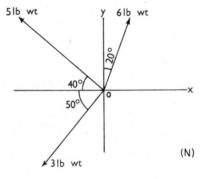

Fig. 24.

9. Rectangular axes Ox, Oy are taken, and forces 6, 5, 3 lb wt., coplanar with Ox, Oy, act as shown in Fig. 24. Calculate the magnitude of the resultant and the angle it makes with Ox.

Verify your result graphically.

10. A light rigid rod AB of length 5 in. is hung from a fixed point O by two light strings OA, OB of lengths 4, 3 in. respectively. A particle of mass 3 lb is attached to the rod at A, and a particle of mass 2 lb at B. Show that in the position of equilibrium the tensions in the strings OA, OB are $2\sqrt{5}$, $\sqrt{5}$ lb wt. respectively, and the stress in the rod AB is $\sqrt{5}$ lb wt.   (N.)

11. A particle of weight W is attached to two inextensible strings each of length 13 in. The other ends of the strings are attached to two points on the same horizontal level 2 ft apart. Find the tension in each of the strings in terms of W.

The strings are replaced by two elastic strings of equal modulus of elasticity and of natural length 13 in. attached in the same way. The particle now takes up a position of equilibrium 4 inches below its previous position.

Find (i) the modulus of elasticity in terms of W, (ii) the ratio of the tensions in the two cases.   (C.)

12. A light string $ABCD$ is attached to fixed points at its ends A and D so that D is vertically below A. Particles of weights w_1 and w_2 are attached to the string at B and C respectively and a horizontal force P is applied to the particle at B so that the string is in equilibrium in a vertical plane through AD. In the equilibrium position the angles BAD and ADC are each 45° and the angle ABC is 105°. Show that

$$P = w_1 + (2 + \sqrt{3})\, w_2.$$ (N.)

13. A small smooth ring C of mass 20 gm slides on an inextensible string whose ends are attached to two points A and B which are at the same horizontal level; AB is 17 cm. A force P parallel to AB is applied to the ring, and when there is equilibrium, with both parts of the string taut, CB is 8 cm and the angle ACB is a right angle. Find the tension in the string and the magnitude of the force P. (N.)

14. The ends of a uniform thin rod AB of mass 24 oz and length 14 in. are attached each by a light inextensible string of length 10 in. to a fixed peg O, so that AB is suspended freely in a horizontal position in the vertical plane OAB. The mid-points P, Q of the strings OA, OB are now joined by a light inextensible string of length 6 in. so that the system is in equilibrium with PQ and AB horizontal. Find the tensions in the portions AP, PO of the string and show that the tension in the string PQ is 7 oz wt. (N.)

15. (i) Forces P and Q act along $\overrightarrow{OA}$ and $\overrightarrow{OB}$ respectively, and $\angle AOB = \alpha$. Prove that, if the resultant R acts in a direction making an angle θ with $\overrightarrow{OA}$, then

$$R^2 = P^2 + Q^2 + 2PQ\cos\alpha,$$

and $$\tan\theta = \frac{Q\sin\alpha}{P + Q\cos\alpha}.$$

R is the resultant of two forces P and $2P$ acting at O, the angle between their lines of action being 60°; a third force S is greater than R and also acts at O. If the maximum and minimum magnitudes of the resultant of all three forces are 26 and 12 lb wt., find P in lb wt.

(ii) D, E and F are the mid-points of the sides BC, CA and AB of a triangle. Forces acting on a particle are represented in magnitude and direction by $\overrightarrow{DA}$, $\overrightarrow{EB}$ and $\overrightarrow{FC}$. Prove that the forces are in equilibrium. (O.C.)

16. A particle of mass 30 lb is tied to two light elastic strings, each of unstretched length 2 ft and modulus 100 lb wt., whose other ends are tied to points A, B at the same horizontal level and 4 ft apart. Prove that, if 2θ is the angle between the strings in the position of equilibrium

$$\cot\theta - \cos\theta = 0.15.$$

Verify that $\theta = 53° \, 8'$ is an approximate solution of this equation and hence calculate approximately the depth of the particle below AB in the position of equilibrium. (N.)

17. Figure 25 shows a fixed smooth semicircular wire, whose radius is a, and whose plane is vertical, on which a small ring P, of weight W, is threaded; Q is a small ring, of weight w, threaded on a fixed smooth vertical wire OA; the rings are joined by a light inextensible string of length $l(< a)$. The system is in equilibrium when OP and QP make angles θ and $\varphi(> \theta)$ with OA. Prove that

$$\tan\theta = \frac{w}{W + w}\,\tan\varphi.$$

Find also the tension in the string if $W = 3w$ and $l = \tfrac{1}{2}a$.　　　(O.C.)

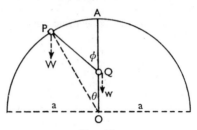

Fig. 25.

18. Three light elastic strings, AB, BC, CD, each of natural length a and modulus w, are fixed at A and D to points in a horizontal line and at a distance $2a$ apart. Two particles each of weight w are attached at B and C respectively. Show that in the position of equilibrium AB and CD are inclined to the vertical at an angle θ given by $3\tan\theta = 1 - 2\sin\theta$.　　　(N.)

*19. The ends of a string of length l are attached to two points A and B on a fixed horizontal beam at a distance a apart $(a < l)$. A smooth ring of weight W slides on the string and is in equilibrium under a horizontal force P when W is vertically below B. Prove that

$$P = aW/l$$

and find the tension in the string.

If now the horizontal force on the ring is Q, acting in the same direction as P, and the part of the string attached to B makes an angle $45°$ with AB produced when the ring is again in equilibrium, prove that

$$Q = \frac{W}{l}\,(l + a\sqrt{2}).$$

*20. Fixed points A and B are connected by a light string. Two particles, each of weight w, are attached at points X and Y of the string. The portions AX, BY of the string are at right angles, and are inclined to the horizontal at angles of $60°$ and $30°$ respectively. Calculate the inclination of the portion XY to the horizontal, and find, in terms of w, the tensions in AX, XY, BY.　　　(N.)

*21. Two masses W are attached to a light elastic string, one being at each point of trisection of the string when it is not under tension. The ends of the string are now fixed to two pegs in a horizontal line, the distance between the pegs being equal to the natural length of the string. In the position of equilibrium the parts of the string connecting each weight to a peg are inclined at an angle of $60°$ to the horizontal and the other part of the string is horizontal. Prove that the modulus of the string is $W\sqrt{3}$.　　　(N.)

*22. A light string $ABCD$ has a weight $2W$ attached to the point B and a weight W attached to C. The ends A and D are fixed to two points in a horizontal line. The portions AB, BC, CD are of such lengths that in the position of equilibrium B and C are vertically below the points of trisection of AD; AB is inclined at an angle of $45°$ to the vertical. Prove that the angles of inclination to the vertical of BC and CD are $\tan^{-1} 5$ and $\tan^{-1} (5/4)$ and find the tensions in AB, BC, and CD. (N.)

*23. Two smooth rings of weights P and Q are connected by a light straight rod and rest in equilibrium on the upper half of a smooth circular wire which is fixed in a vertical plane. The rod subtends an angle 2α at the centre of the circle and makes an acute angle β with the vertical. Prove that, if P is greater than Q,
$$\tan\beta = \frac{P+Q}{P-Q}\cot\alpha.$$
Find also the stress in the rod in terms of P, Q and α. (N.)

*24. A rod of weight W, whose centre of gravity divides its length in the ratio $2:1$, lies in equilibrium inside a smooth hollow sphere. If the rod subtends an angle of 2α at the centre of the sphere and makes an angle θ with the horizontal, prove that $\tan\theta = \frac{1}{3}\tan\alpha$.

Find the reactions at the ends of the rod in terms of W and α. (C.)

*25. The ends of an elastic string of natural length $2a$ are fixed in a horizontal line and at a distance $2a$ apart. A particle of mass m attached to the string at its middle point rests in equilibrium. If each half of the string is inclined to the vertical at an angle θ, find the modulus of the string. (L.)

*26. A particle of weight w is attached to the mid-point of a light elastic string of length $2l$ and modulus w. The ends of the string are attached to two fixed points on the same horizontal line and distant $2l$ apart. Prove that, when the system is in equilibrium with each part of the string making an angle θ with the horizontal, $\qquad \tan\theta - \sin\theta = \frac{1}{2}$.

By use of the tables find an approximate solution of this equation. (L.)

*27. Three smooth pegs A, B, C are fixed in a vertical wall. The triangle ABC is isosceles $(AB = AC)$, A is uppermost and BC is horizontal, the angle BAC being equal to α. A light inextensible string carrying equal weights W at its ends is hung over the pegs. Prove that the thrust of the string on the peg B is

$$2W\sin\frac{\alpha}{4},$$

and find the thrust on the peg A. (N.)

*28. A particle C of weight W is attached by light unequal inextensible strings to points A and B which are at the same horizontal level. When the particle is in equilibrium, prove that the tension in the string AC is

$$\frac{W\cos ABC}{\sin ACB}. \qquad\qquad \text{(N.)}$$

*29. Two forces acting at a point P are represented by PQ, PR in direction and magnitude. Prove that their resultant is represented in direction and magnitude by $2PS$, where S is the mid-point of QR.

The medians of the triangle ABC meet at G. At G there act three forces which are represented in direction and magnitude by GA, GB, GC. Prove that these forces are in equilibrium. (N.)

*30. The ends of a light inextensible string 24 in. long are tied to two points A and B at the same level and 8 in. apart. A small smooth ring C, of weight W, which can slide freely on the string, is acted upon by an applied force so that the ring rests in equilibrium vertically below A. If the applied force has the smallest possible magnitude, show, by using a triangle of forces or otherwise, that its direction must be perpendicular to the internal bisector of the angle ACB.

Find in terms of W the magnitude of the minimum applied force.   (N.)

*31. A circular hoop of weight W is free to turn in its own plane, which is vertical, about a fixed point A of its rim. A small ring of negligible weight is free to slide on the rim, which is smooth, and a string tied to the ring supports the hoop in equilibrium when the string is inclined at an angle α to the vertical, and the radius to A is inclined at an angle β to the vertical. Find the tension T in the string and the reaction R at the point A.

If α is constant and β of varies, find the minimum value of R in terms W and α.   (L.)

*32. Two uniform spheres, each of weight W and radius a, are suspended from a point O by strings of lengths a, $2a$, attached respectively to a point on the surface of each sphere. Prove that, in equilibrium, the point of contact of hee spheres is vertically below O and find the tensions in the strings and the traction between the spheres.   (L.)

CHAPTER III

THE KINEMATICS OF A PARTICLE MOVING IN A STRAIGHT LINE

3.1. Relationships Between Distance, Time, Velocity and Acceleration

Displacement, velocity, which is rate of change of displacement with respect to time, and acceleration, which is rate of change of velocity with respect to time, are all vector quantities. In this chapter we consider the relations between these quantities in the case of a particle moving in a straight line. The three quantities, are, in this case, *directed* quantities in so far as displacement from the origin in one direction is defined as positive and displacement from the origin in the opposite direction is defined as negative.

If s ft is the distance of the particle from the origin at time t sec and if, at this time, the velocity of the particle is v ft/sec and its acceleration is f ft/sec^2, then

$$v = \frac{\mathrm{d}s}{\mathrm{d}t}, \tag{3.1}$$

$$f = \frac{\mathrm{d}v}{\mathrm{d}t} = \frac{\mathrm{d}^2 s}{\mathrm{d}t^2}. \tag{3.2}$$

Also

$$f = \frac{\mathrm{d}s}{\mathrm{d}t} \cdot \frac{\mathrm{d}v}{\mathrm{d}s} = v \frac{\mathrm{d}v}{\mathrm{d}s}. \tag{3.3}$$

3.2. Graphical Relationships

The s, t Graph

The gradient of the s, t graph at the point $t = t_1$ gives the velocity at time t_1 sec. The *gradient* is measured in terms of the scale on the respective axes.

The v, t graph can be obtained from values of v given by the s, t graph.

Example. A particle is moving in a straight line. Values of its distance s ft from a fixed point in the line are tabulated below against corresponding values of the time t sec from the beginning of the motion. Draw an s, t graph for the motion and estimate the velocity of the particle at time $t = 40$.

t	0	10	20	30	40	42	45	46
s	0	15	56	150	300	350	450	550

The graph is shown in Fig. 26. The velocity at time $t = 40$ is represented by the gradient of the curve at P. Hence the required velocity is approximately

$$\frac{AB}{BC} \doteq \frac{430\,\text{ft}}{20\,\text{sec}} = 21 \cdot 5\,\text{ft/sec}.$$

Note on the Method of Drawing a Tangent to a Curve

When a plane mirror with a straight edge is placed along the *normal* to a curve, the curve and its reflection in the mirror appear unbroken at their common point. The tangent is the line at right angles to the normal from the point of contact with the curve.

The v, t Graph

(a) The gradient of the v, t graph at the point where $t = t_1$ gives the acceleration at time t_1 sec.

(b) Since $v = \dfrac{ds}{dt}$, the area enclosed by the v, t curve, the t-axis and the lines $t = t_1$, $t = t_2$ gives the change in the displacement of the particle from time t_1 to time t_2. For

$$\int_{t_1}^{t_2} v\,dt = \int_{t_1}^{t_2} \frac{ds}{dt}\,dt = s_2 - s_1,$$

where s_1 and s_2 are the displacements of the particle at times t_1 and t_2 respectively. The area is measured, as illustrated in the example below, in terms of the scales on the respective axes.

Computation of Area

The area can be computed approximately by one of the following methods.

(i) By counting squares.

(ii) By dividing the area into thin strips which are approximately trapeziums, and calculating the area of each trapezium with the formula:

Area of trapezium = $\frac{1}{2}$ sum of parallel sides × distance between the parallel sides.

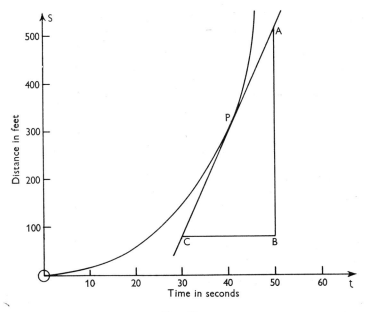

FIG. 26.

This method is the basis of the *trapezoidal rule* (discussed in full in *Sixth Form Pure Mathematics*, Vol. II, § 13.4). If $y_1, y_2, y_3, \ldots, y_n$ are ordinates of the curve which are at equal distances h apart, then the area bounded by y_1, y_n the x-axis and the curve is given by

$$A \doteqdot \tfrac{1}{2}h \{y_1 + y_n + 2(y_2 + \cdots + y_{n-1})\}.$$

(iii) By *Simpson's rule*. This rule is also discussed in full in the chapter of the book quoted above. If $y_1, y_2, y_3, \ldots, y_{2n+1}$ are an *odd* number of ordinates which are at equal distances h apart, then the area bounded by the curve, the x-axis, y_1 and y_{2n+1} is given by

$$A \doteqdot \tfrac{1}{3}h \{y_1 + y_{2n+1} + 2(y_3 + y_5 + \cdots + y_{2n-1})$$
$$+ 4(y_2 + y_4 + \cdots + y_{2n})\},$$

Example. The table gives corresponding values of the velocity ft/sec and the time t sec from the beginning of the motion of a particle moving along a straight line. The particle starts from a point O in the line.

(a) Draw a v, t graph of the motion and use your graph to estimate the acceleration of the particle at time $t = 30$.

(b) Construct a table of corresponding values of s and t where s ft is the distance of the particle from O at time t sec.

t	0	10	20	30	40	50	60	70	80	90
v	100	94	89	72	52	26	-8	-48	-88	-116

The graph is shown in Fig. 27. The acceleration at time $t = 30$ is represented by the gradient at P. This gradient, and therefore the acceleration, is negative. Therefore the acceleration at time $t = 30$ is approximately

$$-\frac{AB}{BC} \doteqdot \frac{-87 \text{ ft/sec}}{50 \text{ sec}} = -1.74 \text{ ft/sec}^2.$$

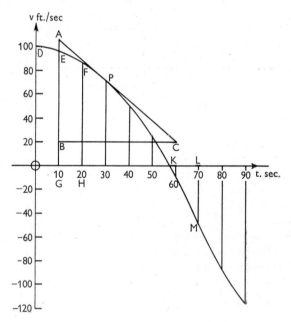

FIG. 27.

The displacement from O at time $t = 10$ is represented by the area $ODEG$, the displacement from O at time $t = 20$ is represented by the area $ODFH$, etc.

The displacement from O at time $t = 70$ is represented by:

$$\text{area } ODK - \text{area } KLM.$$

Hence, using the trapezium rule,

t	s	
10	$\frac{1}{2} \times 10(100 + 94)$	$= 970$
20	$\frac{1}{2} \times 10(100 + 188 + 89)$	$= 1885$
30	$\frac{1}{2} \times 10(100 + 188 + 178 + 72)$	$= 2690$
40	$2690 + 5(72 + 52)$	$= 3310$
50	$3310 + 5(52 + 26)$	$= 3700$
60	$3700 + 5(26 - 8)$	$= 3790$
70	$3790 - 5(8 + 48)$	$= 3510$
80	$3510 - 5(48 + 88)$	$= 2830$
90	$2830 - 5(88 + 116)$	$= 1810$

The f, t Graph

Since $f = \dfrac{dv}{dt}$, the area enclosed by the f, t curve, the axis of t, and the ordinates at $t = t_1$ and $t = t_2$ gives the *change* in the velocity from time $t = t_1$ to time $t = t_2$. For

$$\int_{t_1}^{t_2} f \, dt = \int_{t_1}^{t_2} \frac{dv}{dt} \, dt = v_2 - v_1,$$

where v_1, v_2 are the velocities at times $t = t_1$, $t = t_2$ respectively.

The v, t curve can be obtained from values of v given by the f, t curve and thus the change in the displacement from time $t = t_1$ to time $t = t_2$ can be found.

Example. Values of the acceleration f cm/sec^2 at time t sec from the start are given in the following table and shown in Fig. 28.

Estimate the values of the velocity v cm/sec for the given values of t, and estimate the displacement of the particle from the starting point at time $t = 60$.

t	0	10	20	30	40	50	60	70	80	90	100	110	120
f	4·00	3·92	3·70	3·20	2·50	1·52	0	−1·30	−2·16	−2·78	−3·08	−3·00	−1·90

From these values, using the trapezium rule, we find

t	0	10	20	30	40	50	60	70	80	90	100	110	120
v	0	39·6	77·7	112·2	140·7	160·8	168·4	161·9	144·6	119·9	90·6	60·2	35·7

and from these values, again using the trapezium rule, we find that the displacement from O at time $t = 60$ is approximately

$$\tfrac{1}{2} \times 10 \{0 + 168\cdot4 + 2(39\cdot6 + 77\cdot7 + 112\cdot2 + 140\cdot7 + 160\cdot8)\}$$
$$\doteqdot 6150 \text{ ft.}$$

We have been able to complete the estimation of the required values in this way, and without using Fig. 28, because the table

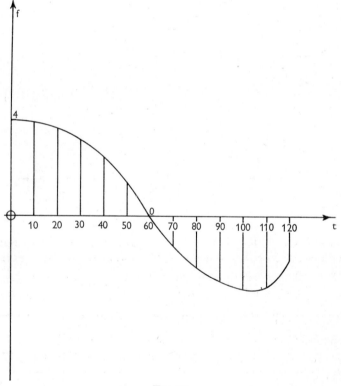

FIG. 28.

gave values of f at equal intervals of t and because these intervals were small enough to justify the approximation with the ordinates given.

The $\frac{1}{2}v^2$, s Graph

Since $\dfrac{d(\frac{1}{2}v^2)}{ds} = v\dfrac{dv}{ds}$ the gradient of the $\frac{1}{2}v^2$, s graph gives the acceleration.

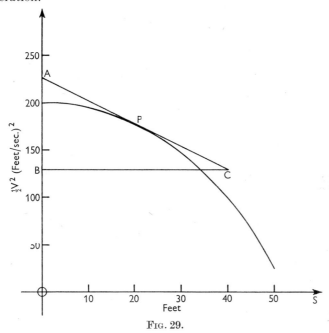

FIG. 29.

Figure 29 shows the $\frac{1}{2}v^2$, s graph for a particle moving in a straight line with velocity v ft/sec at distance s ft from the origin. The gradient at P is

$$-\frac{AB}{BC} \stackrel{.}{\cdot} -\frac{95 \text{ ft}^2/\text{sec}^2}{40 \text{ ft}} = -2 \cdot 4 \text{ ft/sec}^2 .$$

At distance 20 ft from the origin the acceleration is $-2 \cdot 4$ ft/sec².

Example. The scales of v and s for a v, s curve, $v = f(s)$, are chosen so that 1 ft/sec and 1 ft are represented by the same unit of length. Show that the *subnormal* of the curve at the point where $s = s_1$ represents the acceleration at displacement $s = s_1$.

In Fig. 30 the tangent at $P(s_1, v_1)$ to the v, s curve meets the s-axis at T, the perpendicular from P to the s-axis meets it at N, and the normal at P meets the s-axis at G. Then

$$\angle \ NPG = \angle \ PTN.$$

$$\therefore \ \frac{NG}{PN} = f'(s_1).$$

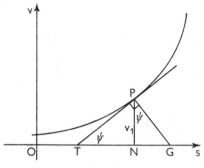

FIG. 30.

(This is a purely geometrical relationship which refers to the numerical value of $f'(s_1)$ and not to its dimensions. If the scales on the two axes were not as stated, the statement would not be true.)

$$\therefore \ NG = v_1 f'(s_1) = \left(v \frac{dv}{ds} \right)_1$$

numerically so that NG represents numerically the acceleration at displacement s_1.

The $\dfrac{1}{v}$, s Graph

Since $\dfrac{1}{v} = \dfrac{dt}{ds}$ the area enclosed by the $\dfrac{1}{v}$, s graph, the s-axis and the ordinates at $s = s_1$ and $s = s_2$ represents the time taken to change the displacement from s_1 to s_2.

The $\dfrac{1}{f}$, v Graph

Since $\dfrac{1}{f} = \dfrac{dt}{dv}$ the area enclosed by the $\dfrac{1}{f}$, v curve, the v-axis and the ordinates at $v = v_1$ and $v = v_2$ gives the time taken to change the velocity from $v = v_1$ to $v = v_2$.

Figure 31 shows the $\dfrac{1}{f}$, v graph for a particle moving in a straight line with velocity v ft/sec and acceleration f ft/sec² at time t sec. The time for the velocity to change from 0 to 40 ft/sec as the acceleration changes from 10 ft/sec² to 2 ft/sec² is represented by the area enclosed by the curve, the v-axis, the $\dfrac{1}{f}$-axis and the ordinate AB. The area $OPQR$ represents 1 sec. With this unit, area $OPAB \doteqdot 15\cdot4$,

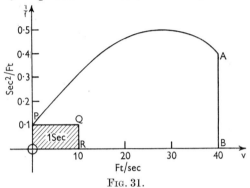

Fig. 31.

and the velocity therefore increases to 40 ft/sec in approximately 15 sec.

Notes

(a) With a continuous f, as $f \to 0$, $\dfrac{1}{f} \to \infty$ and the curve will have an asymptote parallel to the $\dfrac{1}{f}$-axis.

(b) For f negative, v *decreases*. The area below the v-axis representing the time taken for v to change from $v = v_1$ to $v = v_2$ where $v_1 > v_2$ represents, in this case, a *positive* period of time, because

$$\int_{v_1}^{v_2} \frac{1}{f}\,\mathrm{d}v = -\int_{v_2}^{v_1} \frac{1}{f}\,\mathrm{d}v.$$

The f, s Graph

Since $f = \dfrac{\mathrm{d}(\frac{1}{2}v^2)}{\mathrm{d}s}$, the area enclosed by the f, s graph, the s-axis and the ordinates at $s = s_1$ and $s = s_2$ gives the change in $\frac{1}{2}v^2$ from displacement s_1 to displacement s_2.

Figure 32 shows the f, s curve for a particle moving in a straight line with acceleration f ft/sec² and velocity v ft/sec at distance s ft from the origin. The increase in $\frac{1}{2}v^2$ as s increases from 0 to 50 is represented by:

Area OPQ enclosed by the curve from P to Q the f-axis and the s-axis *minus* the area enclosed by the curve from Q to R, the s-axis and the ordinate RA.

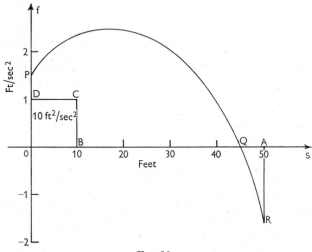

Fig. 32.

The area of the square $OBCD$ represents 10 ft²/sec². With this unit, and from the trapezium rule,

$$\text{Area } OPQ \fallingdotseq 85 \text{ units},$$

$$\text{Area } QRA \fallingdotseq 4 \text{ units}.$$

Therefore the increase in $\frac{1}{2}v^2$ as s increases from 0 to 50 is approximately $85 - 4 = 81$.

EXERCISES 3.2.

1. A ball falls vertically in a resisting medium and values of its depth (d ft) below the starting point at time t sec are given in the table below.

t	0	1	2	3	4	5	6	7	8	9	10
d	0	15	60	130	225	340	475	630	800	980	1170

Draw a graph of d against t and from your graph find an approximate value for the velocity of the ball
  (i) at time $t = 4$,
  (ii) at time $t = 7$.
— **2.** A tramcar starts from rest and covers s ft in t sec in accordance with the following table:

t	1	2	3	4	5	6	7	8
s	4	11	21	34	50	69	91	116

Plot the graph showing the relation between s and t and from your graph obtain the graph showing the relation between the speed v and t.
Deduce the acceleration of the tramcar when its speed is 20 ft/sec.   (N.)
3. The following table gives the speed in m.p.h. of a car at times, in sec, from the start of its motion.

time	0	10	20	30	40	50
speed	0	30	45	53	58	60

Find graphically the acceleration of the car, in ft/sec², 25 sec from the start of its motion.   (L.)
4. The speed of a train travelling between two stations is given in the following table.

Time from start (*minutes*)	0	1	2	3	4	5	6	$6\frac{1}{2}$
Speed (*m.p.h.*)	0	12	24	36	48	48	24	0

Assume that acceleration and retardation are both uniform and draw the speed–time graph using scales of 1 in. = 10 m.p.h. and 1 in. = 1 min.
  (a) Find from your graph
    (i) the time during which the train is running at full speed (48 m.p.h.);
    (ii) the distance in miles between the stations.
  (b) Find also the acceleration and retardation in ft/sec² giving your answers correct to two decimal places.   (L.)
5. The speed of a motor-car, starting from rest, is 11, 18, 23, 27, 30, 32, 34, $35\frac{1}{2}$, 37, 38 m.p.h. at the end of successive minutes. Estimate from a speed-time diagram (i) the total distance covered in the 10 minutes, and (ii) the acceleration after two minutes, expressing the acceleration in miles/min² and in ft/sec². Estimate when the acceleration is half that at the end of 2 minutes, and explain your procedure.   (O.C.)
6. A train is travelling at 45 m.p.h. when the driver, seeing a distant signal against him, applies the brakes, retarding the train uniformly to 5 m.p.h. in 1 min. He then travels at this speed for 2 min and, with the signals now in his favour, accelerates uniformly to 55 m.p.h. in 4 min. Draw the speed–time
5*

graph taking 1 in. to represent 1 min and 10 m.p.h. and, hence or otherwise, calculate

    (i) the total distance covered,

    (ii) the acceleration of the train in ft/sec^2,

    (iii) how many more seconds it would have taken him to stop had he continued to brake uniformly. (L.)

7. In the following table f ft/sec^2 is the acceleration of a car after t sec. Using 1 in. for a unit of acceleration and also for a unit of time draw the acceleration–time graph.

t	0	1	2	3	4	5	6	7	8
f	0	2·2	3·4	3·6	3·0	2·1	2·0	3·0	5·0

If the car starts from rest, draw on the same diagram the speed–time and the distance–time graphs with 1 in. for 5 ft/sec and 1 in. for 10 ft respectively. State the distance travelled by the car after 6·5 sec. (N.)

*8. The graph of $1/f$ as a function of v is drawn, where f is the acceleration and v the speed of a particle in rectilinear motion. By dividing the area into elements, or otherwise, show that the area intercepted between the graph, the two ordinates at v_1, v_2 and the v-axis represents the time required for the change in the speed from v_1 to v_2.

A car starts from rest with an acceleration defined by $f = 3 - \frac{1}{5}v$, where f, v are in foot-second units. By drawing the curve of $1/f$ against v and measuring the area required, or otherwise, find the time that elapses before the speed of the car is 14 ft/sec. (N.)

*9. The table gives values of the velocity v ft/sec of a particle moving in a straight line. The displacement of the particle from a fixed point O in the line is s ft at time t sec from the beginning of the motion.

s	0	1	2	3	4	5	6	7	8	9	10
v	3·6	3·7	4·0	4·5	5·2	6·1	7·2	8·5	10	11·7	13·6

Estimate the time taken by the particle to move from displacement $s = 0$ to displacement $s = 10$.

*10. With the data of question 9 draw an appropriate graph and from it deduce the acceleration of the particle at displacement $s = 6$.

3.3 Uniformly Accelerated Motion in a Straight Line

If the resultant force acting on a particle acts in the line of its motion and is constant in magnitude, the particle is accelerated uniformly. If the constant acceleration of the particle is a (say), then

$$\frac{dv}{dt} = a.$$

$$\therefore \quad v = u + at, \tag{3.4}$$

where u is a constant which is equal to the velocity of the particle at time $t = 0$. From equation (3.4)

$$\frac{ds}{dt} = u + at.$$

$$\therefore\ s = ut + \tfrac{1}{2}at^2 + C,$$

where C is constant. If $s = 0$ when $t = 0$, then $C = 0$ and

$$s = ut + \tfrac{1}{2}at^2. \tag{3.5}$$

Eliminating t between equations (3.4) and (3.5) gives

$$s = \frac{u(v-u)}{a} + \frac{1}{2}a\left(\frac{v-u}{a}\right)^2,$$

which reduces to

$$v^2 = u^2 + 2as. \tag{3.6}$$

Equation (3.6) is obtained directly from the relation

$$v\frac{dv}{ds} = a$$

by integration, thus:

$$\int v\frac{dv}{ds}\,ds = \int a\,ds.$$

$$\therefore\ \tfrac{1}{2}v^2 = as + A,$$

and if $v = u$ when $s = 0$, $A = \tfrac{1}{2}u^2$.

$$\therefore\ \tfrac{1}{2}v^2 = as + \tfrac{1}{2}u^2.$$

$$\therefore\ v^2 = u^2 + 2as.$$

Equation (3.4) shows the v, t curve of a uniformly accelerated motion to be a straight line; indeed this is implicit in the statement that the acceleration, which is the *gradient* of the v, t curve, is constant. The area enclosed by this straight line, the axis of t and the ordinates at $t = 0$ and $t - t_1$ gives the change of displacement in this time. Therefore if $s = 0$ when $t = 0$,

$$s = \tfrac{1}{2}(u + v)t. \tag{3.7}$$

This result can also be obtained by eliminating a between equations (3.4) and (3.5).

Examples. (i) A particle moves in a straight line with uniformly accelerated motion. At time 2 sec the particle is 10 ft from its starting point and at time 4 sec the particle is 40 ft from its starting point. Find

(1) the acceleration of the particle,

(2) the velocity of the particle at time 5 sec,

(3) the velocity of the particle when it is 160 ft from its starting point.

With the usual notation,

$$s = ut + \tfrac{1}{2}at^2,$$

and since $s = 10$ when $t = 2$, $10 = 2u + 2a$,

$s = 40$ when $t = 4$, $40 = 4u + 8a$.

Hence

(1) $a = 5$ so that the acceleration of the particle is 5 ft/sec²,

(2) from $v = u + at$, when $t = 5$, $v = 25$ so that the velocity of the particle at time 5 sec is 25 ft/sec.

(3) from $v^2 = u^2 + 2as$, when $s = 160$, $v^2 = 1600$, i.e. $v = \pm 40$. Since a is positive, v increases continuously from its value 0 at time $t = 0$ and therefore v cannot be negative for positive values of t so that the velocity of the particle at 160 ft from the starting point is 40 ft/sec.

(ii) Two points A and B are d ft apart. A particle starts from A and moves in the direction AB with initial velocity u and uniform acceleration a. A second particle starts at the same time from B and moves in the direction BA with initial velocity $2u$ and retardation a.

(a) Prove that the particles collide at time $d/3u$ from the beginning of the motion.

(b) Prove that, if the particles collide before the second particle returns to B, then $ad < 12u^2$.

If the displacement from A at time t_1 sec for the first particle is s_1 ft then the equation of motion for this particle is

$$s_1 = ut_1 + \tfrac{1}{2}at_1^2,$$

and the equation of motion for the second particle is

$$d - s_2 = 2ut_2 - \tfrac{1}{2}at_2^2,$$

where s_2 ft is the displacement of this particle from A at time t_2 sec.

At the instant of collision $t_1 = t_2 = t$ (say) and $s_1 = s_2 = s$ (say).

$$\therefore \quad s = ut + \tfrac{1}{2}at^2,$$

$$d - s = 2ut - \tfrac{1}{2}at^2.$$

$$\therefore \quad d = 3ut.$$

$$\therefore \quad t = \frac{d}{3u}.$$

From the equation for the displacement of the first particle, eliminating t,

$$s = \frac{ud}{3u} + \frac{1}{2}a\frac{d^2}{9u^2} = \frac{d}{3} + \frac{ad^2}{18u^2},$$

and, if the particles collide before the second particle returns to B, then

$$\frac{d}{3} + \frac{ad^2}{18u^2} < d,$$

i.e.

$$\frac{ad^2}{18u^2} < \frac{2d}{3},$$

i.e.

$$ad < 12u^2.$$

(iii) A particle moving with uniform acceleration a ft/sec^2 in a straight line moves x ft in the nth sec and y ft in the mth sec of its motion. Prove that

$$a = (y - x)/(m - n).$$

If u_1 ft/sec is the velocity at time $(n - 1)$ sec and u_2 ft/sec is the velocity at time $(m - 1)$ sec, from $s = ut + \tfrac{1}{2}at^2$,

$$x = u_1 + \tfrac{1}{2}a,$$

$$y = u_2 + \tfrac{1}{2}a.$$

From

$$v = u + at,$$

$$u_2 = u_1 + a(m - n).$$

$$\therefore u_2 - u_1 = y - x = a(m - n).$$

$$\therefore a = (y - x)/(m - n).$$

Otherwise

Because the acceleration is uniform the total displacement in the nth sec is
velocity at time $(n - \tfrac{1}{2})$ sec $\times$ 1 sec $= x$ ft.
Therefore the velocity at time $(n - \tfrac{1}{2})$ sec is x ft/sec.

Similarly the velocity at time $(m - \frac{1}{2})$ sec is y ft/sec.

$$\therefore\ y = x + a(m - n).$$

$$\therefore\ a = (y - x)/(m - n).$$

(iv) (a) A train takes a time T to perform a journey from rest to rest. It accelerates uniformly from rest for a time pT, and retards uniformly to rest at the end of the journey for a time qT; during the intermediate time it travels uniformly with speed v. Prove that the average speed for the journey is

$$\tfrac{1}{2}v(2 - p - q).$$

(b) In travelling a total distance S a train accelerates uniformly from rest through a distance pS, then travels with uniform speed V, and finally retards uniformly to rest through a distance qS. Find the average speed for the whole journey. (L.)

(a) The v, t graph of the motion is shown in Fig. 33 (i). If the total distance covered by the train is s, then s is represented by the area enclosed by the v, t graph and the t-axis

$$\therefore\ s = \left\{ \frac{T + (T - qT - pT)}{2} \right\} v$$

so that the average speed for the journey is

$$\frac{s}{T} = \frac{1}{2} v(2 - q - p).$$

(b) The v, t graph of the motion is shown in Fig. 33 (ii).
For the accelerated motion $pS = \frac{1}{2} V t_1$,
for the retarded motion $qS = \frac{1}{2} V(t_3 - t_2)$,
for the uniform motion $(1 - p - q) S = V(t_2 - t_1)$.

$$\therefore\ \frac{2qS}{V} + \frac{S(1 - p - q)}{V} + \frac{2pS}{V} = t_3 - t_2 + t_2 - t_1 + t_1 = t_3$$

so that the average speed for the journey is

$$\frac{S}{t_3} = \frac{V}{p + q + 1}.$$

(v) The greatest possible acceleration of a train is a_1 and the greatest possible retardation is a_2. Show that the least possible

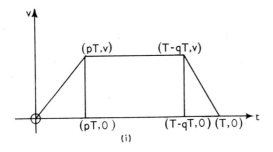

(i)

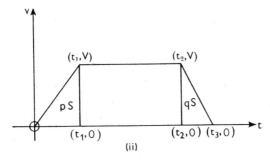

(ii)

FIG. 33 (i), (ii).

time T which the train can take to complete the journey of length s from rest to rest is

$$\sqrt{\left\{ \frac{2s(a_1 + a_2)}{a_1 a_2} \right\}}.$$

If V is the greatest velocity attained under the above conditions and if an additional condition is imposed that the velocity of the train shall not exceed V_1 where $V_1 < V$, show that the least time which the train may now take exceeds T by $s(V - V_1)^2/V_1 V^2$. (N.)

If the speed of the train at every instant is as large as possible, the train covers the distance s from rest to rest in the least possible time. But the greatest possible speed at time t_1 after starting is $a_1 t_1$ and the greatest possible speed at time t_2 before stopping is $a_2 t_2$. Therefore, if the train accelerates to speed V with acceleration a_1 in time V/a_1 and then immediately retards (with retardation a_2) to rest in time V/a_2, it takes the least possible time to complete the journey. In this case Fig. 34 (i) is a v, t diagram of the motion and A is $(T, 0)$ where

$$T = \frac{V}{a_1} + \frac{V}{a_2}.$$

$$\therefore V = \frac{a_1 a_2 T}{a_1 + a_2}.$$

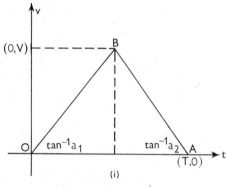

(i)

FIG. 34 (i).

Also, area $OBA = s$ so that

$$T = \frac{2s}{V}.$$

$$\therefore T = \frac{2s(a_1 + a_2)}{a_1 a_2 T}.$$

$$\therefore T = \sqrt{\left\{\frac{2s(a_1 + a_2)}{a_1 a_2}\right\}}.$$

If the velocity of the train cannot exceed V_1, where $V_1 < V$, then it follows by reasoning similar to that above, that when the train accelerates with acceleration a_1 to speed V_1, then travels with speed V_1 and finally comes to rest with retardation a_2, the train takes the least possible time for the journey. Figure 34 (ii) is a v, t diagram of the journey when the greatest speed is V_1 superimposed on a v, t diagram of the journey discussed above.

$$T_1 - T = AC$$

and, since the length of the journey is s in each case,

Area of triangle BSR = Area of parallelogram $ACQS$.

$$\text{But } \frac{\triangle BRS}{\triangle BOA} = \frac{(V - V_1)^2}{V^2}$$

$$\therefore s\left(\frac{V - V_1}{V}\right)^2 = (T_1 - T)V_1.$$

$$\therefore T_1 - T = \frac{s(V - V_1)^2}{V^2 V_1}.$$

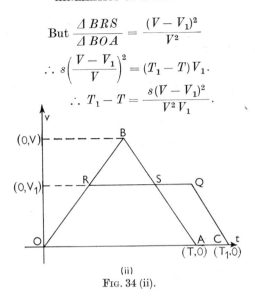

(ii)

FIG. 34 (ii).

EXERCISES 3.3.

In each of Exercises 1–15 a particle moves on a straight line with constant acceleration a ft/sec^2 so that the distance of the particle from the origin O at time t sec is s ft, the velocity of the particle at time t sec is v ft/sec and the initial velocity of the particle is u ft/sec.

1. $a = 2$, $v = 6$, $u = 5$; calculate t.

2. $a = -4$, $u = 17$, $v = 15$; calculate s.

3. $u = 4$, $t = 2$, $s = 20$; calculate v.

4. $u = 5$, $a = -2$, $t = 8$; calculate s.

5. $a = 6$, $t = 4$, $s = 96$; calculate u.

6. $v = -8$, $u = 2$, $t = 2$; calculate a.

7. $s = 114$, $u = 8$, $v = 1$; calculate t.

8. $v = 10$, $u = 8$, $s = 9$; calculate a.

9. $s = 80$, $u = 8$, $t = 2$; calculate a.

10. $s = -38$, $u = 17$, $a = -2$; calculate t.

11. $s = 48$, $u = 56$, $a = -8$; calculate the possible values of t.

12. $s = 4$ when $v = 5$; $s = 18$ when $t = 3$; calculate the possible values of u and a.

13. $s = 8$, $a = -2$, $v = \frac{1}{3}u$; calculate, u, v, t.

14. $v = nu$, $a = (1 + n)u^2$; calculate s.

15. $s = 7$ when $t = 2$; $s = 15$ when $t = 6$; calculate u, a.

16. A motor-car travels 176 ft while accelerating uniformly from 15 to 25 m.p.h. Find (i) the time taken in sec, (ii) the acceleration in ft/sec^2.   (N.)

17. Two particles A and B start to move along a straight line from a point O. A starts first, moving from rest with an acceleration of 3 ft/sec^2; 2 sec later B starts and keeps up a uniform velocity of 16 ft/sec.

Show that A and B will meet twice, and that the distance between the two points where they meet is $85\frac{1}{2}$ft. (N.)

18. A tube train covers 432 yd from rest to rest in 1 min. It first accelerates at 1 ft/sec², then goes uniformly and finally retards at 3 ft/sec². Find the time taken in each of the three stages of the journey. (N.)

19. A parachutist drops from a plane at 1750 ft, and falls vertically for a certain time with acceleration 2 ft/sec²; he then opens a subsidiary parachute and his acceleration changes to a retardation of 1 ft/sec² which lasts for the same length of time, when he reaches the ground. Find the total time of the drop and show that his velocity on reaching the ground is 18 m.p.h., approx. (N.)

20. Two cars H and K are moving in the same direction along parallel straight traffic lanes. Car H has a uniform acceleration of 8 ft/sec² and at the moment it passes a point A its speed is 2 ft/sec. Car K has a uniform speed of 42 ft/sec and passes the point A 2 sec after car H passed A. Find, in ft, the distances from A of the two points at which the cars are level. (N.)

21. A train is moving along a straight level track when the driver sees a signal set to danger 300 yd ahead. He shuts off steam and applies the brakes which produce a uniform retardation. In the first second after application of the brakes the train travels 109 ft and in the next second it travels 107 ft. Find the retardation in ft/sec² and show that the original speed of the train was 75 m.p.h. Find the time for the train to come to rest and the distance travelled during this time.

If the length of the train is 63 yd, find the time that elapses after first sighting the signal before the rear of the train passes the signal. (N.)

22. A car A, moving along a straight road with a uniform *acceleration* of 2 ft/sec², passes a point O when its velocity is 5 ft/sec. Find its velocity and position 8 sec after passing O. Find also its velocity when it is 36 ft from O.

Another car B travels along the same road in the same direction with a uniform *retardation* of 2 ft/sec². It passes O with a velocity of 25 ft/sec, 2 sec after A has passed O. Find the times at which the cars are level and the distance between the two points at which the cars pass one another. (N.)

23. A train takes $4\frac{1}{2}$ min to travel between two stations A and B, which are 4500 yd apart. It starts from A and finishes at rest at B. The train travels with uniform acceleration for the first 60 sec of the motion and with uniform retardation for the last 30 sec. The train's speed is constant during the remainder of the journey. Find this constant speed in ft/sec.

Show that the distance travelled whilst the speed is constant is 80 per cent of the total distance covered. Find the time at which the train is midway between A and B. (N.)

24. Two cars start simultaneously from rest at the same place and follow the same route. One accelerates uniformly at 0·5 ft/sec² until it reaches a speed of 60 ft/sec which it maintains steadily. The other accelerates uniformly at 0·4 ft/sec² until it reaches a speed of 80 ft/sec which it maintains steadily. Calculate

(i) how many seconds will elapse after the start before the cars are again level and each travelling at full speed,

(ii) the distance travelled by either car during this time. (L.)

25. A point, moving in a straight line, describes 16 ft in the 2nd sec of its motion, 28 ft in the 5th sec, 52 ft in the 11th sec. Prove that these distances are consistent with the supposition that the motion of the point is uniformly accelerated; also find the whole distance described in 10 sec from the beginning of motion. (O.C.)

26. A particle moving in a straight line with uniform retardation covers distances of $2s$ and s respectively in successive equal intervals of time. Show that, when the particle comes to rest, it will have covered a distance $\frac{1}{8}s$ after the end of the second interval.

If the velocity of the particle at the beginning of the first interval is u, find, in terms of s, how far the particle will have travelled when its velocity has been reduced to $\frac{1}{2}u$. (C.)

27. Particles P and Q are moving in the same direction along neighbouring parallel straight lines with constant accelerations of 3 and 2 ft/sec². At a certain instant P has a velocity of 3 ft/sec and Q is 30 ft behind P with a velocity of 11·5 ft/sec. Prove that P and Q will twice be abreast. Find the velocity of P when this happens first, and find also the maximum distance which Q gets ahead of P. (O.C.)

28. A motor-car, X, uniformly accelerated at 2 ft/sec², passes a point P on a straight road at 6 ft/sec; 2 sec later a motor-car, Y, uniformly accelerated at $1\frac{1}{2}$ ft/sec² and moving in the same direction as X, passes P at 15 ft/sec. Prove that Y overtakes X at a point Q on the road 6 sec after X passes P, and that X overtakes Y at a point R 12 sec later still.

Prove also that $QR = 360$ ft and that the maximum distance separating X and Y between Q and R is 9 ft. (O.C.)

29. A train covers the distance between two stations A and B which is $13\frac{1}{2}$ miles, in 24 min. It accelerates uniformly from rest at A, then travels at constant speed v for 12 min, finally retarding uniformly to stop at B. Determine the value of v in m.p.h.

If the retardation is in magnitude equal to twice the acceleration, obtain their values. (L.)

30. A train accelerates uniformly from rest and travels 600 yd in the 3rd minute after the start. At the end of the 5th minute, the acceleration ceases and the train runs uniformly for 10 minutes. The train is then brought to rest by a retardation of magnitude twice that of the acceleration. Find the total distance travelled and the time taken. (L.)

3.4. Free Motion Under Gravity

When a particle is projected vertically upwards, its downward acceleration due to gravity is g, and if the effect of air resistance is neglected, the equations of motion of the particle are:

$$v = u - gt, \tag{3.8}$$

$$s = ut - \tfrac{1}{2}gt^2, \tag{3.9}$$

$$v^2 = u^2 - 2gs, \tag{3.10}$$

$$s = \tfrac{1}{2}(u + v)t, \tag{3.11}$$

the upward direction being taken as the positive direction.

When a particle is projected vertically downwards, if the effect of air resistance is neglected and if the downward direction is taken as positive, the equations of motion of the particle are

$$v = u + gt, \tag{3.12}$$

$$s = ut + \tfrac{1}{2}gt^2, \tag{3.13}$$

$$v^2 = u^2 + 2gs, \tag{3.14}$$

$$s = \tfrac{1}{2}(u + v)t. \tag{3.15}$$

Examples. (i) A particle is projected vertically upwards with velocity u ft/sec. Find

(a) the greatest height reached,

(b) the time taken to reach the greatest height,

(c) the time of flight, i.e. the time taken by the particle to return to the starting point,

(d) the time which elapses between the particle reaching a height h ft on the upward flight and returning to a height of h ft on the downward flight.

(a) From $v^2 = u^2 - 2gs$, when $v = 0$, $s = u^2/2g$ so that the greatest height reached is $u^2/2g$ ft.

(b) From $v = u - gt$, when $v = 0$, $t = u/g$ so that the time taken to reach the greatest height is u/g sec.

(c) From $s = ut - \tfrac{1}{2}gt^2$, when $s = 0$, $t = 0$ or $t = 2u/g$ so that the time of flight is $2u/g$ sec.

(d) From $s = ut - \tfrac{1}{2}gt^2$, when $s = h$,

$$gt^2 - 2ut + 2h = 0.$$

If t_1 and t_2 are the roots of this equation,

$$t_1 = \frac{u + \sqrt{(u^2 - 2gh)}}{g}, \quad t_2 = \frac{u - \sqrt{(u^2 - 2gh)}}{g}.$$

$$\therefore t_1 - t_2 = \frac{2\sqrt{(u^2 - 2gh)}}{g}.$$

Hence the time which elapses between reaching the height h ft on the upward and downward journeys is

$$\frac{2\sqrt{(u^2 - 2gh)}}{g}.$$

(ii) A particle A is projected upwards from a point O with velocity 64 ft/sec and at the same instant a particle B is allowed to fall from P a point vertically above O. The particles collide at the instant when the upward velocity of A is equal to the downward velocity of B. Calculate the height h ft of P above O.

If s_1 ft is the distance of the particle A from O at t_1 sec from the start of the motion, and s_2 ft is the distance of the particle B from O at t_2 sec from the start of motion, then:

the equation of motion for particle A is

$$s_1 = 64t_1 - \tfrac{1}{2}gt_1^2$$

and the equation of motion for particle B is

$$h - s_2 = \tfrac{1}{2}gt_2^2.$$

At the instant of collision t sec after the start of the motion and at height s ft above O,
$$s = 64t - \tfrac{1}{2}gt^2,$$

$$h - s = \tfrac{1}{2}gt^2.$$

$$\therefore h = 64t.$$

Because the upward velocity of A is equal to the downward velocity of B at this point, $\qquad 64 - gt = gt.$

$$\therefore t = \frac{32}{g} = 1.$$
$$\therefore h = 64 \,(\text{taking } g = 32).$$

(iii) A particle is projected upwards with velocity u from a point at a height $4u^2/g$ above a horizontal plane. Find the time that elapses from the instant of projection to the instant of striking the plane, and find the velocity of the particle then.

With the usual notation, when the particle strikes the plane,
$$s = -4u^2/g.$$
From
$$s = ut - \tfrac{1}{2}gt^2,$$
$$-\frac{4u^2}{g} = ut - \frac{1}{2}gt^2.$$
$$\therefore g^2 t^2 - 2ugt - 8u^2 = 0.$$
$$\therefore (gt - 4u)(gt + 2u) = 0.$$
$$\therefore t = \frac{4u}{g} \qquad (\text{since } t \text{ is positive}).$$

The velocity at this time is v ft/sec where v is *negative* and

$$v^2 = u^2 - 2g\left(-\frac{4u^2}{g}\right).$$

$$\therefore v = -3u,$$

i.e. the velocity is $3u$ downwards.

EXERCISES 3.4.

1. A particle is projected vertically upwards with a velocity of 80 ft/sec. Calculate

(i) the greatest height of the particle,

(ii) the time which elapses from the beginning of the motion before the particle returns to the point of projection.

2. A particle is projected vertically upwards with a velocity of 20 ft/sec from a point 50 ft above a horizontal plane. Calculate

(i) the velocity of the particle when it strikes the plane,

(ii) the time which elapses from the beginning of the motion before the particle strikes the plane.

3. A particle is projected vertically downwards and it describes 100 m in the 10th sec of its motion. Calculate the velocity of projection. [Take g as 10 m/sec^2.]

4. A particle is projected vertically upwards with velocity 80 ft/sec. Calculate the time that elapses from the time the particle reaches a height of 19 ft going up to the time the particle reaches a height of 36 ft going down.

5. A ball, thrown vertically upwards from the ground, passes a point 20 ft above ground level when it is moving upwards and $\frac{1}{4}$ sec later passes the same point when it is moving downwards. Calculate the initial velocity of the ball.

6. Prove that, if a particle is projected vertically upwards with velocity u ft/sec and if the particle passes a point h ft above the point of projection in t_1 sec going up and in t_2 sec going down, then

$$gt_1t_2 = 2h.$$

7. A ball is thrown vertically upwards with initial velocity u ft/sec and 2 sec later a second ball is thrown vertically upwards from the same place with a velocity of $3u$ ft/sec. Find an expression for the time which elapses after the first ball is thrown up to the time when the two balls meet and show that the two balls meet when the first ball is instantaneously at rest if $u = (1 + \sqrt{2})g$.

8. A particle which had fallen from rest was observed to fall $\frac{5}{4}$ times as far in one second as it had fallen in the previous second. For how long had it been falling before the beginning of the first of these two seconds?

9. Two particles are projected simultaneously vertically upwards from the same horizontal plane, the first at u ft/sec and the second at $3u/2$ ft/sec. Find the rate of change of the vertical separation between them.

10. A particle projected vertically upwards passes a point 64 ft above the point of projection on its way up and 2 sec later passes a point 96 ft above the level of projection. Show that on the second occasion the particle is falling down and calculate the speed of projection.

MISCELLANEOUS EXERCISES. III

1. A body moving in a straight line traverses distances AB, BC, CD of 153 ft, 215 ft and 217 ft respectively in successive intervals of 3, 5, and 7 sec. Show that these facts indicate a uniform retardation, and find the time and the distance traversed when the body comes to rest.   (O.C.)

2. A particle is thrown vertically upwards with a velocity of 80 ft/sec. After what *times* will it be at a height of 64 ft, and what will its velocities be then? (N.)

3. A vertical wall is 6 ft high. A ball is thrown vertically upwards from a point on ground level close to the wall with an initial speed of 30 ft/sec. Find for how long it will be above the wall.

When the ball is on the way up and has reached a height of 4 ft above the ground, a second ball is thrown vertically upwards from a point on ground level close to the wall with an initial speed of 20 ft/sec. Find when and where the two balls pass one another.   (C.)

4. A ball is thrown vertically upwards with a velocity of 56 ft/sec; find its height when it is moving at the rate of 40 ft/sec and find the time between the instants at which it is at this height.   (O.C.)

5. A stone is thrown vertically upwards with a velocity of 80 ft/sec from a point 96 ft above ground level. Find the greatest height above the ground reached by the stone. Find also the time that elapses before the stone hits the ground.   (N.)

6. Four points A, B, C, D lie in this order on a straight line so that $AB = 500$ ft, $BC = 700$ ft and $CD = 900$ ft. A particle travelling along the line is observed to cover each interval AB, BC and CD in 10 sec. Show tha these conditions are consistent with the motion being uniformly acceleratedt and, assuming uniformly accelerated motion, find the speed of the particle ;at A. (N.)

7. A train runs from rest at one station to rest at another 5 miles distant in 10 min. If it gets up full speed uniformly in the first $\frac{1}{4}$ mile and slows down uniformly to rest in the last $\frac{1}{8}$ mile, what is the maximum speed in m.p.h.? (O.C.)

8. A particle P is thrown vertically upwards from O with velocity V; prove that, neglecting air-resistance, the maximum height H reached above O is given by
$$V^2 = 2gH$$
and that P returns to O after a time $2V/g$.

When P reaches a point A, at a vertical height h above O, on its upward flight, a second particle Q is projected vertically upwards from O with velocity V and later collides with P at A. Prove that
$$h = \tfrac{8}{9}H.$$ (O.C.)

9. Fig. 35 shows the speed-time graph for a train which starts from rest at one station and comes to rest at another. The time is measured along OX in min and the speed along OY in m.p.h. Find:
   (i) the distance in miles between the two stations,
   (ii) the acceleration of the train in ft/sec²,
   (iii) the time taken to travel the first half of the distance between the stations.   (L.)

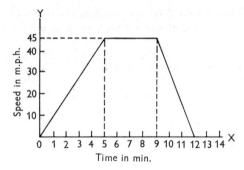

FIG. 35.

10. Two stations A and B are 5 miles apart on a straight track, and a train starts from A and comes to rest at B. For three-quarters of the distance the train is uniformly accelerated, and for the remainder uniformly retarded. If it takes 10 min over the whole journey, find its acceleration, its retardation, and the maximum speed it attains.   (N.)

11. A train travelling at a uniform speed of 50 m.p.h. passes a station A, and 6 min later the brakes are applied, so that the train comes to rest, under a uniform retardation, at a station B which is $5\frac{5}{8}$ miles from A. From the speed–time curve, or otherwise, find (i) the time taken by the train to travel from A to B, (ii) the retardation, in ft/sec², produced by the brakes.   (N.)

12. (a) A particle starts from rest and moves with uniform acceleration in a straight line. It covers 24 ft in the 5th sec of its motion. Find the acceleration.

(b) A train sets out at noon from A and travels towards B, which is 10 miles from A. The train starts from rest under a constant acceleration, which it maintains until it is travelling at 40 m.p.h., when it runs with constant speed. A second train passes B at noon travelling towards A at a constant speed of 30 m.p.h. The two trains meet half-way between A and B. Find the acceleration, in mile-hour units, of the first train and verify that this train ceases to accelerate before it meets the second train.   (O.C.)

13. A train, starting from rest at O with uniform acceleration f, attains a speed of 60 m.p.h. at a point A 2 miles from O. The brakes are then applied so as to produce uniform retardation numerically equal to $\frac{2}{5}f$, and at B the speed is 30 m.p.h. Find
     (i) the distance of B from O, and
     (ii) the time taken between O and B.   (O.C.)

14. A train starts from A with uniform acceleration $\frac{1}{2}$ ft/sec². After 2 min the train attains full speed and moves uniformly for 11 min. It is then brought to rest at B by the brakes producing a constant retardation of 5 ft/sec². Find the distance AB.   (O.C.)

15. A motor-car A travelling along a straight road, with uniform velocity u, passes at X a car B travelling, with uniform acceleration f, in the same direction, the velocity of B at X being $u_1(< u)$; B overtakes A at Y, thereafter travelling with uniform velocity. Find (i) the maximum distance between the cars between X and Y, and (ii) the uniform acceleration to be given to A at Y if A overtakes B at Z, where $YZ = XY$. (O.C.)

16. A particle is projected vertically upwards and at the same instant another is let fall to meet it. Show that, if the particles have equal velocities when they impinge, one of them has travelled three times as far as the other. (O.C.)

17. The driver of a train, travelling at 45 m.p.h. on a straight level track, sees a signal against him at a distance of 440 yd and, putting on the brakes, comes to rest at the signal. He stops for 1 min and then he resumes the journey, attaining the original speed of 45 m.p.h. in a distance of 660 yd. Assuming that retardation and acceleration are uniform, find how much time has been lost owing to the stoppage. (O.C.)

18. A car starts from rest at A and travels with a uniform acceleration of $\frac{1}{2}$ ft/sec². The car attains full speed in 2 min and then moves uniformly for 9 min. It is brought to rest at B by the brakes producing a uniform retardation of 4 ft/sec². Find the greatest speed of the car in ft/sec and the time taken to travel from A to B. Find also the distance AB.

Two minutes after the first car leaves A a second car, travelling with a uniform speed of 90 ft/sec, passes A. The second car overtakes the first at C. Find AC. (N.)

19. At a certain instant a cyclist travelling on a straight road with constant speed u sees at a distance d ahead a car starting to move away from him with constant acceleration f. Derive an expression for the distance between cyclist and car at time t later.

If $u^2 < 2\,df$, show that the cyclist will not overtake the car. In this case find how near he gets to the car. (N.)

20. A car with velocity u accelerates uniformly over a distance $2s$, which it covers in time t_1: it is then stopped by being slowed down uniformly over a distance s, which it covers in time t_2. Prove that

$$\frac{u}{2s} = \frac{2}{t_1} - \frac{1}{t_2}.$$ (O.C.)

21. A train completes a journey of 5 miles between two stations, A and B, in 10 min. It starts from rest at A and travels with uniform acceleration f until it reaches a speed of 40 m.p.h. This speed is then maintained for a suitable time, after which the brakes are applied to give it a uniform retardation $3f$ and bring it to rest at B. Determine the value of f and the time spent in retardation. (L.)

22. A train starts from rest and moves with uniform acceleration for 6 min. It then moves with constant speed for 20 min and is finally brought to rest by a uniform retardation of magnitude three times that of the initial acceleration. *During* the 4th min of the journey the train travels 840 yd. Show that the acceleration of the train is $\frac{1}{5}$ ft/sec². Find the greatest speed. Find also the distance travelled before the train reaches a speed of 30 m.p.h.

Draw a velocity–time diagram for the motion and find the time for the whole journey. (N.)

6*

23. Tho following table shows the acceleration f ft/sec^2 of a moving particle after t sec. Using 1 in. to represent a unit of acceleration and also to represent a unit of time, plot the acceleration–time curve.

t	0	1	2	3	4	5	6	7	8
f	3·3	3·2	3·0	2·7	2·4	2·0	1·5	1·2	1·0

If the particle starts from rest, use this curve to plot on the same diagram the speed–time and the space–time curves with 1 in. to represent 10 ft/sec and 1 in. to represent 50 ft. From the graph find the speed, and the distance the particle has moved at the end of 5·5 sec. (N.)

24. A train moves from rest at one station to rest at another station 2 miles away in 6 min. The motion is at first uniformly accelerated, so that the velocity reaches 30 m.p.h. in 90 sec. The velocity then remains constant for a time and finally the train is uniformly retarded till it comes to rest. Find (i) the time during which the velocity is constant, (ii) the magnitude of the final retardation in ft/sec^2. (C.)

25. A lift ascends 760 ft in 2 min travelling from rest to rest. For the first 30 sec it travels with uniform acceleration, for the last 20 sec with uniform retardation, and for the rest of the time it travels with uniform speed. Draw the speed–time graph and hence or otherwise calculate

(i) the uniform speed in ft/sec,
(ii) the uniform acceleration in ft/sec^2, and
(iii) the time taken by the lift to ascend the first 400 ft. (L.)

26. The velocity–time diagram consists of two straight lines AB, BC where the coordinates of A, B, C are (0, 10), (10, 10), (20, 25), the first coordinate in each case being the time in seconds and the second coordinate the velocity in ft/sec. Describe the motion of the particle, and find the total distance covered. (O.C.)

27. The time required by an express train, moving with constant acceleration, to travel between two bridges A and B is 6 min. Its average speed over the distance AB is 45 m.p.h. and during the 6th min it travels 1 mile. Find the speed at A (in m.p.h.) and the value of the acceleration in foot-second units. (O.C.)

28. A train takes time T to perform a journey; it travels for time T/n with uniform acceleration, then for time $(n-2)T/n$ with uniform speed V, and finally for time T/n with constant retardation. Prove that its average speed is

$$\frac{n-1}{n}\,V.$$

If the length of this journey is 40 miles, the time taken on the journey is 50 min, and the uniform speed is 60 m.p.h., find the time which is occupied in travelling at this speed. (O.C.)

29. A train whose motion is uniformly accelerated passes through a station A at 9 a.m. At 9.2 a.m. its distance from A is $1\frac{1}{8}$ miles and at 9.4 a.m. its distance from A is $2\frac{1}{2}$ miles. Find its speeds at 9 a.m. and at 9.6 a.m.

At 9.6 a.m. the brakes are applied so as to bring the train to rest at 9.7 a.m. at a station B, the retardation being uniform. Find the distance of B from A. (O.C.)

30. A particle traverses a distance of 300 yd in a straight line at an average speed of 12 ft/sec, starting from rest and finishing at rest. It moves with a uniform acceleration for the first 10 sec and is brought to rest by a uniform retardation in the last 20 sec of its motion and moves at a uniform speed during the rest of its motion. Find the acceleration and retardation. (O.C.)

31. A train accelerates uniformly from rest at a station A until its speed is 36 m.p.h.. It travels for a time at this speed and is then uniformly retarded to rest at a station B, the magnitude of the retardation being twice that of the acceleration. The distance from A to B is $6\frac{9}{20}$ miles and the time taken is $11\frac{1}{2}$ minutes. Sketch a speed–time graph and hence, or otherwise, find the distance in miles travelled at uniform speed, and the acceleration in m.p.h./min. (L.)

32. A train runs in 20 min from rest at one station to rest at another station 13 miles distant. For the first 2/5 mile it has a constant acceleration f and for the next mile it has a constant acceleration $\frac{1}{2}f$ then attaining its maximum speed. For the last 2 miles it has a constant retardation. Sketch the velocity–time diagram and show that the accelerations f, $\frac{1}{2}f$ are maintained for equal times. Find the maximum speed in m.p.h. (L.)

33. A train travels from one station to another 3 miles distant. It is first accelerated uniformly from rest reaching a speed of 45 m.p.h. in 70 sec. This speed is maintained until the train is 330 yd from its destination when the brakes are applied and the train brought to rest with uniform retardation. Calculate
   (i) the distance travelled whilst accelerating,
   (ii) the time taken whilst retarding,
   (iii) the time taken for the whole journey. (L.)

34. A particle starts from rest and travels 20 ft with uniform acceleration. It then maintains its speed for a time after which it is uniformly retarded to rest, the magnitude of the retardation being twice that of the acceleration. The total distance travelled is 90 ft and the total time taken is 6 sec. Find the greatest speed and the distance travelled at this speed. (C.)

CHAPTER IV

PROJECTILES

4.1. The Resolution of Uniplanar Motion into Components at Right Angles

Let the position, at any instant, of a particle in a plane be (x, y) referred to arbitrarily chosen rectangular axes Ox and Oy and let the components parallel to these axes of the resultant force acting on the particle at this instant be X and Y. Then

$$X = m f_x, \quad Y = m f_y, \tag{4.1}$$

where f_x and f_y are the components of acceleration of the particle parallel to the x- and y-axes respectively and m is the mass of the particle.

Example. A particle of mass m lb moves in a plane under the action of a force P pdl. At time t sec from the start of the motion, the components of P in directions parallel to two fixed rectangular axes Ox, Oy in the plane are $5m$ pdl and $5m(1 + t)$ pdl respectively. If the particle was initially at rest at O, calculate its distance from O at time $t = 1$.

In the Ox direction, from Newton's second law,

$$\frac{d^2 x}{d t^2} = 5 .$$

$$\therefore \frac{d x}{d t} = 5t + c, \quad \text{where } c \text{ is constant.}$$

But $\qquad \dfrac{d x}{d t} = 0 \quad$ when $\quad t = 0; \quad$ therefore $\quad c = 0$.

$$\therefore \frac{d x}{d t} = 5t .$$

$$\therefore x = \frac{5t^2}{2} + k, \quad \text{where } k \text{ is constant,}$$

76

and $x = 0$ when $t = 0$; therefore $k = 0$.

$$\therefore x = \frac{5t^2}{2}.$$

Also $\quad \dfrac{\mathrm{d}^2 y}{\mathrm{d}t^2} = 5 + 5t \quad$ and $\quad \dfrac{\mathrm{d}y}{\mathrm{d}t} = 0, \quad y = 0 \quad$ when $\quad t = 0$.

$$\therefore y = \frac{5t^2}{2} + \frac{5t^3}{6}.$$

When $\qquad t = 1, \quad x = \tfrac{5}{2}, \quad y = \tfrac{10}{3}.$

Hence the distance of the particle from O when $t = 1$ is

$$\sqrt{(x^2 + y^2)} = \sqrt{(\tfrac{25}{4} + \tfrac{100}{9})} = 4\tfrac{1}{6}.$$

EXERCISES 4.1.

1. At time t sec after the start of its motion the position of a particle, with reference to rectangular coordinates in the plane of motion, is given by $(2t, \frac{1}{2}t^2)$. Find the components of its velocity parallel to the axes at this time and prove that the particle is moving with constant acceleration. Calculate the magnitude and direction of this acceleration.

2. The position of a particle, moving in a plane, is related to coordinate axes Ox and Oy. The particle moves in the plane, starting at the origin, and at time t sec after the start of its motion, the components of its velocity are 4 units parallel to the x-axis and $6t + 1$ units parallel to the y-axis. Find

(i) the distance of the particle from the origin at time 1 sec,

(ii) the equation of the path of the particle.

4.2. The Free Motion of a Projectile

Throughout this chapter we assume that the resistance of the medium in which projection takes place is so small as to be negligible compared with the force of gravity.

A particle projected under gravity in such a medium, with initial velocity u at an angle α above the horizontal, has (Fig. 36)

(i) initial horizontal component of velocity $u \cos\alpha$ and initial vertical component of velocity $u \sin\alpha$,

(ii) no horizontal acceleration and uniform upward vertical acceleration $-g$.

If, therefore, at time t from the instant of projection the vertical displacement of the particle is s_1 and the vertical component of its velocity is v_1,

$$v_1 = u \sin\alpha - gt, \tag{4.2}$$

$$s_1 = ut \sin\alpha - \tfrac{1}{2}gt^2, \tag{4.3}$$

$$v_1^2 = u^2 \sin^2\alpha - 2gs_1. \tag{4.4}$$

If at this time the horizontal displacement of the particle is s_2 and the horizontal component of its velocity is v_2,

$$v_2 = u \cos \alpha,$$ (4.5)

$$s_2 = u t \cos \alpha.$$ (4.6)

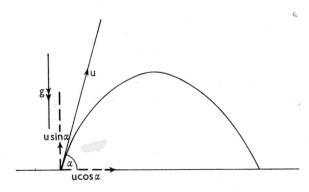

FIG. 36

The Time to Reach the Greatest Height

At the greatest height the vertical component of the velocity is zero and, if t_1 is the time taken to reach this height, from equation (4.2), $0 = u \sin\alpha - g t_1$ so that

the time to reach the greatest height is $\dfrac{u \sin \alpha}{g}$.   (4.7)

The Greatest Height

From equation (4.4), if h is the greatest height, $0 = u^2 \sin^2\alpha - 2gh$ so that

the greatest height reached is $\dfrac{u^2 \sin^2 \alpha}{2g}$.   (4.8)

The Time of Flight

The *vertical* displacement of the particle from its starting point, when the particle strikes the horizontal plane through that point, is zero. Therefore from equation (4.3), if T is the time at which the particle strikes the plane, T is the non-zero root of the equation

$$0 = u t \sin \alpha - \tfrac{1}{2} g t^2,$$

(the zero root represents the condition $s_1 = 0$ when $t = 0$). Therefore

$$\text{the time of flight is } \frac{2u\sin\alpha}{g}. \tag{4.9}$$

The Range on the Horizontal Plane

During the time of flight $(2u\sin\alpha)/g$ the particle has been moving with uniform *horizontal* component of velocity $u\cos\alpha$. Therefore the *horizontal* displacement of the particle when it strikes the plane again is

$$u\cos\alpha \times \frac{2u\sin\alpha}{g} = \frac{2u^2\sin\alpha\cos\alpha}{g} = \frac{u^2\sin 2\alpha}{g}.$$

$$\therefore R = \frac{u^2\sin 2\alpha}{g}, \tag{4.10}$$

where R is the range on the horizontal plane through the point of projection.

The Greatest Range

The expression for R in equation (4.10) has its greatest value, as α varies, when $\sin 2\alpha = 1$, i.e. when $\alpha = 45°$. Then $R = u^2/g$ so that

the greatest range on a horizontal plane through the point of projection is u^2/g. (4.11)

The Velocity at a Given Time

At time t from the beginning of the motion the horizontal component of the velocity of the particle is $u\cos\alpha$ and the vertical component is $u\sin\alpha - gt$. Therefore the resultant velocity of the particle at time t is

$$\sqrt{\{(u\cos\alpha)^2 + (u\sin\alpha - gt)^2\}}$$

in a direction making an angle with the positive horizontal direction whose tangent is

$$\frac{u\sin\alpha - gt}{u\cos\alpha}. \tag{4.12}$$

The Velocity at a Given Point of the Path

When the vertical displacement of the particle from its initial position is h, the horizontal component of its velocity is $u\cos\alpha$ and the vertical component of its velocity is $\pm\sqrt{(u^2\sin^2\alpha - 2gh)}$.

Therefore the magnitude of the resultant velocity of the particle when its vertical displacement is h is

$$\sqrt{(u^2 \cos^2 \alpha + u^2 \sin^2 \alpha - 2gh)} = \sqrt{(u^2 - 2gh)}.$$

Hence (Fig. 37) the resultant velocity of the particle when its vertical displacement is h is either

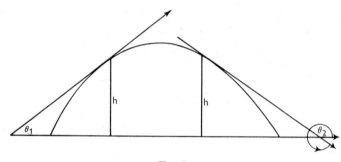

FIG. 37

(a) $\sqrt{(u^2 - 2gh)}$ in a direction making an angle θ_1 whose tangent is

$$\frac{+ \sqrt{(u^2 \sin^2 \alpha - 2gh)}}{u \cos \alpha} \qquad (4.13)$$

with the positive horizontal direction, or

(b) $\sqrt{(u^2 - 2gh)}$ in a direction making an angle θ_2 whose tangent is

$$\frac{- \sqrt{(u^2 \sin^2 \alpha - 2gh)}}{u \cos \alpha} \qquad (4.13\,\text{a})$$

with the positive horizontal direction.

Examples. (i) A shot, fired upwards from the top of a cliff with a velocity of 192 ft/sec at an angle of 30° with the horizontal, strikes the ground 256 ft vertically below the point of projection. Calculate

(a) the horizontal distance from the point of projection at which the shot strikes the ground,

(b) the direction of motion of the shot at the instant of striking the ground.

(a) *From the vertical component of the motion* and equation (4.3) we have

$$-256 = 192\, t_1 \sin 30° - 16 t_1^2,$$

where t_1 sec is the time after the instant of projection at which the shot strikes the ground.

$$\therefore \ 16t^2 - 96t_1 - 256 = 0 \, .$$

$$\therefore \ t_1^2 - 6t_1 - 16 = 0 \, .$$

$$\therefore \ t_1 = 8 \text{ since } t_1 \text{ must be positive.}$$

From the horizontal component of the motion and equation (4.6) we have $\quad$ horizontal range $= 192 \cos 30° \times 8$ ft $= 768 \sqrt{3}$ ft.

(b) If the shot strikes the ground with velocity V ft/sec at an angle θ with the horizontal, then, from equations (4.2) and (4.5),

$$V \sin\theta = 96 - 8 \times 32 = -160,$$

$$V \cos\theta = 96 \sqrt{3} \, .$$

Therefore the shot strikes the ground with a velocity of $\sqrt{\{(-160)^2 + (96 \sqrt{3})^2\}}$ ft/sec at an angle with the horizontal whose tangent is $-160/96 \sqrt{3}$, i.e. with a velocity of approximately 231 ft/sec at approximately 44° below the positive horizontal direction.

(ii) A particle is projected above a horizontal plane. During the 2nd sec of its motion its vertical displacement is increased by 16 ft and its horizontal displacement is increased by 24 ft. Calculate the initial velocity of the particle.

Let the velocity of the particle at time 1 sec from the instant of projection be v ft/sec inclined at $\theta°$ to the horizontal. From the vertical component of the motion in the 2nd sec and equation (4.3),

$$16 = v \sin\theta - \tfrac{1}{2}g,$$

$$\therefore \ v \sin\theta = 32 \, .$$

Therefore the initial vertical component of velocity is $u \sin\alpha$, where

$$32 = u \sin\alpha - g \, .$$

$$\therefore \ u \sin\alpha = 64 \, .$$

From the horizontal component of the motion in the 2nd sec $v \cos\theta = 24$. Therefore the initial horizontal component of velocity is

$$u \cos\alpha - v \cos\theta = 24 \, .$$

$$\therefore \ \tan\alpha = 64/24 = 8/3 \, .$$

$$\therefore \ \sin\alpha = 8/\sqrt{73} \, .$$

$$\therefore \ u = 8\sqrt{73} \, .$$

Hence the initial velocity of the particle is $8\sqrt{73}$ ft/sec at an angle with the horizontal whose tangent is 8/3.

(iii) Find the maximum range of a projectile fired over a horizontal plane with initial velocity u at an angle α with the horizontal if the greatest permitted height that the projectile may reach is $u^2/8g$.

From equation (4.8),
$$\frac{u^2 \sin^2 \alpha}{2g} \leqq \frac{u^2}{8g},$$
$$\therefore \sin^2 \alpha \leqq \tfrac{1}{4}.$$
$$\therefore \sin \alpha \leqq \tfrac{1}{2}.$$

But α is acute; therefore $\alpha \leqq 30°$.

From equation (4.10)
$$\text{Range} = \frac{u^2 \sin 2\alpha}{g}.$$

Therefore, since $\sin 2\alpha$ increases with α for $\alpha \leqq 30°$, the greatest range is
$$\frac{u^2 \sin 60°}{g} = \frac{u^2 \sqrt{3}}{2g}.$$

(iv) A particle is projected from a given point O with velocity V inclined at an angle α to the horizontal. After a time less than $(V \sin \alpha)/g$, the angle of elevation of the particle measured from O is φ and the angle which the direction of the velocity of the particle makes with the horizontal is ψ. Prove that
$$2 \tan \varphi = \tan \psi + \tan \alpha.$$

The range of a projectile on a horizontal plane through the point of projection O is 100 ft and the angle of elevation of the highest point measured from O is 45°. Find the velocity of projection.   (N.)

P is the point in the path of the particle reached at time t (Fig. 38).
$$\therefore \tan \varphi = \frac{V t \sin \alpha - \tfrac{1}{2} g t^2}{V t \cos \alpha} = \frac{V \sin \alpha - \tfrac{1}{2} g t}{V \cos \alpha}.$$

Also from (4.12) $\tan \psi = \dfrac{V \sin \alpha - g t}{V \cos \alpha}.$

Hence $g t = 2 V \sin \alpha - 2 V \cos \alpha \tan \varphi,$

and $g t = V \sin \alpha - V \cos \alpha \tan \psi.$

$\therefore 2 V \sin \alpha - 2 V \cos \alpha \tan \varphi = V \sin \alpha - V \cos \alpha \tan \psi.$

$\therefore 2 V \cos \alpha \tan \varphi = V \sin \alpha + V \cos \alpha \tan \psi.$

$\therefore 2 \tan \varphi = \tan \alpha + \tan \psi.$

With this notation, at the highest point $\varphi = 45°$, $\psi = 0$.

$$\tan\alpha = 2.$$

$$\sin 2\alpha = \frac{2\tan\alpha}{1+\tan^2\alpha} = \frac{4}{5}.$$

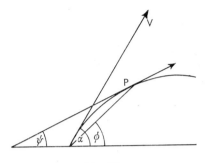

FIG. 38

But the range is $(V^2 \sin 2\alpha)/g$.

$$\therefore\ 100 = \frac{4V^2}{5g}.$$

$$\therefore\ V = 20\sqrt{10}\ \text{ft/sec.}$$

The velocity of projection is $20\sqrt{10}$ ft/sec at $63°\,26'$ above the horizontal.

(v) A projectile falls a ft short of the target when the angle of projection is α and goes b ft beyond it when the angle of projection is β. If θ is an angle of projection when the target would be hit, show that

$$(a + b)\sin 2\theta = a\sin 2\beta + b\sin 2\alpha. \qquad \text{(N.)}$$

Let the distance of the target from the point of projection be R ft and let the speed of projection be u ft/sec. From equation (4.10)

$$R - a = \frac{u^2\sin 2\alpha}{g}, \qquad (1)$$

$$R + b = \frac{u^2\sin 2\beta}{g}, \qquad (2)$$

$$R = \frac{u^2\sin 2\theta}{g}. \qquad (3)$$

Hence, from (1) and (2),

$$R(a+b) = \frac{u^2}{g}(a \sin 2\beta + b \sin 2\alpha) \qquad (4)$$

and from (3) and (4),

$$(a+b) \sin 2\theta = a \sin 2\beta + b \sin 2\alpha.$$

(vi) Two particles are projected from the same point with the same speed but at different elevations α and β. If both particles have the same horizontal range, prove that $\alpha + \beta = 90°$.

If the common speed of projection is 40 ft/sec, and the greatest height attained by one of the particles is 20 ft, find the greatest height attained by the other.   (N.)

From equation (4.10)

$$\frac{u^2 \sin 2\alpha}{g} = \frac{u^2 \sin 2\beta}{g},$$

where u is the speed of projection.

$$\therefore \ \sin 2\alpha = \sin 2\beta.$$

$$\therefore \ 2\alpha = 180° - 2\beta$$

(since both α and β are acute).

$$\therefore \ \alpha + \beta = 90°.$$

From equation (4.8) for the particle whose greatest height is 20 ft

$$\frac{40^2 \sin^2\alpha}{2g} = 20.$$

$$\therefore \ \sin^2\alpha = \frac{g}{40} = \frac{4}{5}.$$

For the second particle, since $\alpha + \beta = 90°$, therefore $\sin\alpha = \cos\beta$.

$$\therefore \ \sin^2\beta = \tfrac{1}{5}$$

so that the greatest height attained by the second particle is

$$\frac{40^2}{2g} \times \frac{1}{5} \text{ ft} = 5 \text{ ft}.$$

(vii) A particle is projected under gravity from a point O.

Prove that the horizontal distance between the two points on the path of the particle, which are at a vertical distance above O equal to $1/n$ of the greatest height is

$$R\sqrt{\left(1 - \frac{1}{n}\right)},$$

where R is the horizontal range. (N.)

If the velocity of projection is u, inclined at an angle α to the horizontal, from equation (4.10)

$$R = \frac{u^2 \sin 2\alpha}{g},$$

and, from equation (4.8), $\dfrac{1}{n}$ of the greatest height is $\dfrac{u^2 \sin^2 \alpha}{2gn}$. Therefore from the vertical component of the motion of the particle, if t is the time taken to reach the height $\dfrac{u^2 \sin^2 \alpha}{2gn}$,

$$\frac{u^2 \sin^2 \alpha}{2gn} = ut \sin\alpha - \tfrac{1}{2}gt^2,$$

i.e. $\qquad g^2 n t^2 - 2ugnt \sin\alpha + u^2 \sin^2\alpha = 0.$

This is a quadratic equation in t which has two roots t_1 and t_2 (say) which are

$$\frac{2ugn \sin\alpha \pm \sqrt{(4u^2g^2n^2 \sin^2\alpha - 4u^2g^2n \sin^2\alpha)}}{2g^2n}.$$

If $\qquad t_2 > t_1,\quad$ then $\quad t_2 - t_1 = \dfrac{2u \sin\alpha}{g}\sqrt{\left(1 - \dfrac{1}{n}\right)}.$

The times t_2 and t_1 are the times at which the particle is at a height R/n above the horizontal, and the horizontal distance covered in the time $t_2 - t_1$ is

$$u\cos\alpha \times \frac{2u \sin\alpha}{g}\sqrt{\left(1 - \frac{1}{n}\right)} = \frac{u^2 \sin 2\alpha}{g}\sqrt{\left(1 - \frac{1}{n}\right)} = R\sqrt{\left(1 - \frac{1}{n}\right)}.$$

EXERCISES 4.2.

1. A particle is projected with velocity 80 ft/sec at an inclination of 30° to the horizontal. Calculate the greatest height attained, and the magnitude and direction of the velocity when the particle is 24 ft below the point of projection. (N.)

2. A vertical tower on a horizontal plane is 84 ft high. A ball is thrown from the top of the tower, the components of the ball's velocity being 15 ft/sec horizontally and 20 ft/sec vertically upwards. Where will the ball be after 1 sec?

How long will the ball take to reach the plane and how far from the foot of the tower will it strike the plane? (N.)

3. A golfer strikes a golf ball so that its initial horizontal component of velocity is $2v$ ft/sec and its initial vertical component of velocity is v ft/sec. Find, in terms of v, the time of flight and the distance d ft to the first impact with the ground, which may be assumed to be horizontal. If $d = 450$ show that $v = 60$ and calculate the greatest height of the ball. (N.)

4. A particle is projected with a speed of 200 ft/sec at an angle of 30° to the horizontal. Find the greatest height attained above a horizontal plane through the point of projection. Find also, correct to the nearest yard, the range on this plane.

Calculate the time taken by the particle in passing from one to the other of the two points at which its height above the plane is 100 ft. (N.)

5. A ball is thrown with a velocity of 60 ft/sec at an angle of 30° with a horizontal plane through the point of projection. Find the height to which the ball will rise and the range on the plane.

A vertical wall of height 12 ft is at a horizontal distance of 60 ft from the point of projection. Find the distance of the ball from the top of the wall at the instant when it is vertically above the wall. (N.)

6. A golf ball is struck from a point T and pitches on a horizontal plane through T at a point R, where TR is 450 ft. The greatest height of the ball above the plane is $112\frac{1}{2}$ ft. Calculate, in magnitude and direction, the velocity with which the ball leaves T. Find also the time of flight. (N.)

7. A ball is thrown from the top of a tower 96 ft high with a velocity of 80 ft/sec at an angle of 60° with the upward vertical. Find, correct to the nearest foot, the distance of the ball from the top of the tower at the instant when the ball is moving horizontally. Find also the time taken for the ball to strike a horizontal plane through the base of the tower. (N.)

8. A wall 54 ft high stands on a horizontal plane. From a point O in this plane a ball is projected, in a plane at right angles to the wall, at an angle α with the horizontal, where $\tan \alpha = \frac{3}{4}$. The ball just clears the top of the wall. If O is 120 ft from the wall, find the time, in sec, taken to reach the wall and show that the speed of projection is 100 ft/sec.

Find also

(i) the greatest height, in ft, to which the ball will rise above the horizontal plane,

(ii) the range in ft, on this plane. (N.)

9. If two particles are projected with the same speed inclined at angles of 30° and 60° respectively to the horizontal, prove, without assuming formulae for range etc., that (a) their ranges on a horizontal plane through the point of projection are equal, (b) their times of flight are in the ratio 1 to $\sqrt{3}$, (c) their greatest heights are in the ratio 1 to 3. (N.)

10. If a particle is projected with speed V and elevation α, prove that the range on the horizontal plane through the point of projection is $(V^2 \sin 2\alpha)/g$ and that the greatest height attained is $(V^2 \sin^2\alpha)/2g$.

If the particle is projected at such an angle that the horizontal range is three times the greatest height, find the angle of projection. If with this angle the range is 400 yd, find the necessary speed of projection and the time of flight. (N.)

11. A particle is projected under gravity from a point of a horizontal plane. If the only force acting on the particle is that due to gravity, show that the time taken by the particle to attain the highest point of its path is one-half of the total time of flight.

If the vertical and horizontal components of the velocity are initially 64 and 50 ft/sec respectively, show that there are two instants at which the particle is 63 ft above the ground. Find also the horizontal distance described by the particle between these two instants. (N.)

12. A stone is projected at an angle of 60° with the horizontal, and with velocity 50 ft/sec, from a point on horizontal ground 25 ft from the foot of a wall 20 ft high. If the vertical plane of the motion is perpendicular to the wall, calculate the vertical height by which the stone clears the wall, and the speed of the stone when vertically over the wall. (N.)

13. A small stone is projected with a speed of 20 ft/sec at an elevation of 30° from a point on the horizontal edge of a vertical cliff 44 ft high and in a vertical plane at right angles to the edge. Find how far from the base of the cliff it will strike the level ground below the cliff.

A second small stone is thrown from the same point and in the same vertical plane as the first. If this second stone just clears, at the highest point of its flight, a mast whose top is $12\frac{1}{4}$ ft above the level of projection, find in what time after the instant of projection it reaches the ground below the cliff. (N.)

14. A particle is projected so as to have a range of 100 ft and to pass just over an obstacle 15 ft high at a distance of 25 ft from the point of projection. Prove that the particle is projected in a direction making an angle $\tan^{-1}\frac{4}{5}$ with the horizontal. (N.)

15. Prove that, if a particle is projected with velocity V at an angle of elevation α, the range R on a horizontal plane through the point of projection is given by $R = V^2 \sin 2\alpha / g$.

A particle is fired horizontally with a velocity of 120 ft/sec from a point A on the top of a vertical cliff so as to hit a boat B. If A is 400 ft above sea-level, find the horizontal distance of B from A.

Find the angle of elevation and the velocity of projection needed for a projectile fired from B to pass through A horizontally. (O.C.)

16. A particle is projected at an angle of elevation θ to the horizontal and moves freely under gravity. At a subsequent instant its horizontal and vertical displacements are equal and its direction of motion is then inclined at 45° to the downward vertical. Prove that $\tan \theta = 3$. (C.)

17. A shell fired at angle 45° with the horizontal from a point A strikes a point B above the level of A, the horizontal and vertical projections of AB being 2000 ft and 750 ft respectively. Find the initial velocity of the shell.

Find also the angle which the direction of motion of the shell makes with the horizontal when it reaches B, and draw a sketch of the path. (N.)

18. A particle is projected from a point A with a velocity whose horizontal and upward vertical components are u and v respectively $(v > 0)$. Show that when the particle is at its greatest height its angle of elevation as observed from A is $\tan^{-1}(v/2u)$.

A particle is projected from a point A on level ground at an angle $\tan^{-1}(4/3)$ with the horizontal. After time 2 sec it is observed to be at a point B and to be rising at an angle of $45°$ with the horizontal. Find the horizontal and vertical distances of B from A, and the time which elapses between the instant when the particle passes B and the instant when it reaches the ground again.   (N.)

19. A ball is thrown from a point on a horizontal plane with speed 40 ft/sec at an inclination of $60°$ to the horizontal. When the ball is moving horizontally its velocity is suddenly doubled. Find the distance from the point of projection at which it strikes the plane, and the direction and magnitude of the velocity with which it is moving at this instant.   (N.)

20. Show that the horizontal range of a projectile having initial velocity V at elevation θ is $(V^2 \sin 2\theta)/g$.

Show that there are two values of θ corresponding to a given horizontal range R less than V^2/g. If t_1, t_2 are the corresponding times of flight and h_1, h_2 are the corresponding greatest heights reached, show that

$$R = \tfrac{1}{2} g t_1 t_2 = 4\sqrt{(h_1 h_2)}.\qquad\text{(L.)}$$

21. A particle is projected from a point O with speed V and elevation α. At a certain point P on the trajectory the direction of motion of the particle and the line OP are inclined (in opposite senses) at equal angles β to the horizontal. Prove that the time taken to reach P from O is $(4V \sin\alpha)/3g$ and that

$$3 \tan\beta = \tan\alpha.\qquad\text{(L.)}$$

4.3. The Equation of the Path

If a particle is projected from a point O with velocity u inclined at an angle α to the horizontal and if (x, y) are the coordinates of the particle referred to horizontal and vertical axes Ox, Oy at time t after the instant of projection, then

$$x - ut \cos\alpha,$$

$$y = ut \sin\alpha - \tfrac{1}{2} g t^2.$$

From these equations, eliminating t,

$$y = u \sin\alpha \times \frac{x}{u \cos\alpha} - \frac{1}{2} g \frac{x^2}{u^2 \cos^2\alpha},$$

i.e.
$$y = x \tan\alpha - \frac{g x^2}{2 u^2 \cos^2\alpha}.\qquad(4.14)$$

This is the equation of the path of the particle referred to the stated axes. Alternative forms of the same equation which are frequently used are:

$$y = x \tan\alpha - \frac{g x^2 \sec^2\alpha}{2 u^2}$$

and
$$y = x \tan\alpha - \frac{gx^2}{2u^2}(1 + \tan^2\alpha).$$
(4.15)

From equation (4.15), if the particle passes through $P(x_1, y_1)$, (Fig. 39)

$$y_1 = x_1 \tan\alpha - \frac{gx_1^2}{2u^2}(1 + \tan^2\alpha),$$

i.e. $gx_1^2 \tan^2\alpha - 2u^2 x_1 \tan\alpha + 2u^2 y_1 + gx_1^2 = 0.$ (4.16)

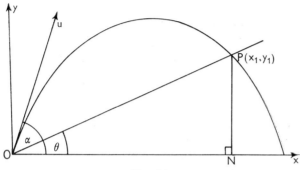

Fig. 39.

This is a quadratic equation in $\tan\alpha$ which has two (real) distinct roots, if

$$u^4 x_1^2 > 2u^2 g x_1^2 y_1 + g^2 x_1^4,$$

i.e. if $u^4 - 2gy_1 u^2 - g^2 x_1^2 > 0.$

In this case there are two possible directions of projection for which a particle projected with speed u from O passes through P. Equation (4.16) has coincident roots if

$$u^4 - 2gy_1 u^2 - g^2 x_1^2 = 0.$$

In this case there is only one direction of projection for which a particle projected with speed u from O passes through P.

Range up an Inclined Plane

If the particle reaches P, then its vertical component of velocity at O must be at least $\sqrt{(2gy_1)}$.

$$\therefore \quad u^2 \geqq 2gy_1.$$

But $u^4 - 2gy_1 u^2 - g^2 x_1^2 = (u^2 - gy_1)^2 - g^2(x_1^2 + y_1^2)$

$$= (u^2 - gPN)^2 - g^2 OP^2,$$

7*

where N is the foot of the perpendicular from P to the x-axis. Hence, there are two, one, or no possible trajectories from O to P according as u^2 exceeds, equals or is less than $g(OP + PN)$.

For the particle to reach P, $u^2 \geq g(OP + PN)$,

i.e. $$OP \leq \frac{u^2}{g(1 + \sin\theta)},$$

where θ is the inclination of OP to the horizontal. Hence, for a fixed θ, the greatest range up the plane OP is $u^2/\{g(1 + \sin\theta)\}$ and this corresponds to the case when equation (4.16) has equal roots. Equation (4.16) has no (real) roots if

$$u^4 - 2gy_1u^2 - g^2x_1^2 < 0.$$

In this case it is not possible to project a particle with speed u from O to pass through P.

Examples. (i) A projectile is fired with speed $\sqrt{(4gh/3)}$ from the top of a cliff of height h, and strikes the sea at a horizontal distance $2h$ from the gun. Find the two possible angles of elevation of the gun.   (N.)

The equation of the path of the particle, referred to horizontal and vertical axes Ox, Oy through the point of projection O is

$$y = x\tan\alpha - \frac{gx^2}{2u^2}(1 + \tan^2\alpha),$$

where $u = \sqrt{(4gh/3)}$ and α is the angle of projection with the horizontal. The point $(2h, -h)$ is on this curve.

$$\therefore \quad -h = 2h\tan\alpha - \frac{3h}{2}(1 + \tan^2\alpha).$$

$$\therefore \quad 3\tan^2\alpha - 4\tan\alpha + 1 = 0.$$

$$\therefore \quad \tan\alpha = 1 \quad \text{or} \quad \tan\alpha = \frac{1}{3},$$

so the two possible angles of elevation of the gun are $45°$ and $18° 26'$.

(ii) A particle is projected from a point A, with a velocity $\sqrt{(2gc)}$ at an elevation θ, in order to pass through a point P at a horizontal distance b from A and a vertical distance h above A. Prove that θ satisfies the equation

$$b^2\tan^2\theta - 4bc\tan\theta + b^2 + 4ch = 0.$$

Deduce that the particle cannot pass through P if $b^2 > 4c(c - h)$.

If α and β are the two possible angles of projection when $b^2 < 4c(c-h)$, prove that $\tan(\alpha+\beta) = -b/h$. (C.)

From equation (4.15), the equation of the path of the particle referred to horizontal and vertical axes Ax and Ay is

$$y = x\tan\theta - \frac{gx^2}{4gc}(1 + \tan^2\theta),$$

i.e. $\qquad x^2\tan^2\theta - 4cx\tan\theta + 4cy + x^2 = 0.$

The path passes through (b, h) if

$$b^2\tan^2\theta - 4bc\tan\theta + b^2 + 4ch = 0.$$

This equation in $\tan\theta$ has no real roots if

$$(4bc)^2 < 4b^2(b^2 + 4ch),$$

i.e. if $\qquad 16b^2c^2 < 4b^4 + 16b^2ch,$

i.e. if $\qquad b^2 > 4c(c-h).$

The particle cannot, therefore, pass through P if $b^2 > 4c(c-h)$.

If α and β are the two possible angles of projection when $b^2 < 4c(c-h)$, $\tan\alpha$ and $\tan\beta$ are the roots of the equation in $\tan\theta$ obtained above.

$$\therefore \tan\alpha + \tan\beta = 4c/b, \quad \tan\alpha\tan\beta = (b^2 + 4ch)/b^2.$$

$$\therefore \tan(\alpha+\beta) = \frac{\tan\alpha + \tan\beta}{1 - \tan\alpha\tan\beta} = \frac{4c/b}{1 - (b^2 + 4ch)/b^2} = -\frac{b}{h}.$$

(iii) A particle is projected under gravity from a point O with speed u at an acute angle α above the horizontal through O. Prove that the distance of the particle from O first increases and then, if $9\sin^2\alpha > 8$, decreases for a time

$$(u/g)\sqrt{(9\sin^2\alpha - 8)}.$$

Prove also that, if P is the position of the particle at time t, the tangent to the path at P meets the vertical through O in a point which moves with constant acceleration. (L.)

At time t from the instant of projection, referred to horizontal and vertical axes Ox and Oy, the coordinates of the particle are

$$x = ut\cos\alpha, \qquad (1)$$

$$y = ut\sin\alpha - \tfrac{1}{2}gt^2. \qquad (2)$$

Therefore the distance s of the particle from O at time t is given by

$$s^2 = u^2t^2\cos^2\alpha + u^2t^2\sin^2\alpha - gut^3\sin\alpha + \tfrac{1}{4}g^2t^4$$

$$= u^2t^2 - gut^3\sin\alpha + \tfrac{1}{4}g^2t^4.$$

$$\frac{d(s^2)}{dt} = 2u^2t - 3ugt^2\sin\alpha + g^2t^3$$

$$= t(g^2t^2 - 3ugt\sin\alpha + 2u^2).$$

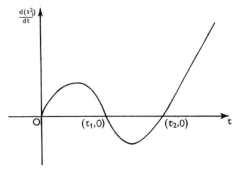

FIG. 40.

(a) If $9\sin^2\alpha < 8$, the equation

$$g^2t^2 - 3ugt\sin\alpha + 2u^2 = 0 \tag{3}$$

has no real roots and the expression

$$g^2t^2 - 3ugt\sin\alpha + 2u^2$$

is positive for all values of t. In this case, since $\dfrac{d(s^2)}{dt}$ is positive, s^2 and therefore s (which is positive) increases continuously from $t = 0$.

(b) If $9\sin^2\alpha > 8$, and if the roots of equation (3) are $t = t_1$ and $t = t_2$ where $t_2 > t_1$, the graph of the expression $t(g^2t^2 - 3gut\sin\alpha + 2u^2)$, i.e., of $g^2t(t - t_1)(t - t_2)$, is as shown in Fig. 40. From $t = 0$ to $t = t_1$, $\dfrac{d(s^2)}{dt}$ is positive and for this time s increases with t. From $t = t_1$ to $t = t_2$, $\dfrac{d(s^2)}{dt}$ is negative and for this period of time, $(t_2 - t_1)$, the distance s decreases with t. For $t > t_2$, $\dfrac{d(s^2)}{dt}$ is again positive.

$$t_2 - t_1 = \sqrt{\left(\frac{9u^2}{g^2}\sin^2\alpha - \frac{8u^2}{g^2}\right)} = \frac{u}{g}\sqrt{(9\sin^2\alpha - 8)},$$

so that the distance of the particle from O decreases for a period of time $\dfrac{u}{g}\sqrt{(9 \sin^2\alpha - 8)}$.

With t as the parameter, the parametric equations (1) and (2) of the path of the particle give

$$\frac{\mathrm{d}y}{\mathrm{d}x} = \frac{\mathrm{d}y}{\mathrm{d}t} \Big/ \frac{\mathrm{d}x}{\mathrm{d}t} = \frac{u \sin\alpha - gt}{u \cos\alpha}$$

and the equation of the tangent to the path at P is

$$y - ut \sin\alpha + \frac{1}{2}gt^2 = \frac{u \sin\alpha - gt}{u \cos\alpha}\,(x - ut \cos\alpha).$$

This line meets $x = 0$ where

$$y = ut \sin\alpha + \tfrac{1}{2}gt^2 - ut \sin\alpha + gt^2,$$

i.e. where
$$y = Y \text{ (say)} = \frac{3}{2}gt^2.$$

$$\therefore \quad \frac{\mathrm{d}^2 Y}{\mathrm{d}t^2} = 3g$$

so that the point at which the tangent to the path at P meets the y-axis moves with constant acceleration ($3g$ upwards).

*4.4. The Parabolic Path of a Projectile

Equation (4.14) shows that the path of a projectile, projected under the conditions we have assumed throughout this chapter, is a parabola. We now obtain the equation of the path referred to (downward) vertical and horizontal axes Ox and Oy through the highest point of the path (Fig. 41). The particle is projected from A with velocity u at an angle α with the horizontal and $P(x, y)$ is the point of the path reached by the particle at time t from the instant when the particle was at O. Then

$$x = \tfrac{1}{2}gt^2, \qquad y = ut \cos\alpha$$

so that the equation of the path is

$$y^2 = \frac{2u^2 x \cos^2\alpha}{g}. \tag{4.17}$$

The path of the projectile is thus seen to be a parabola with latus rectum $\dfrac{2u^2 \cos^2\alpha}{g}$, focus at $\left(\dfrac{u^2 \cos^2\alpha}{2g}, 0\right)$, and directrix $x = -\dfrac{u^2 \cos^2\alpha}{2g}$.

The length of the latus rectum is a function of the horizontal component of the velocity of projection. From equation (4.8) the height of O above A is $\dfrac{u^2 \sin^2 \alpha}{2g}$; therefore

the height of the directrix above A is $\dfrac{u^2 \sin^2 \alpha}{2g} + \dfrac{u^2 \cos^2 \alpha}{2g} = \dfrac{u^2}{2g}$.

Thus the height of the directrix above the point of projection is independent of the angle of projection of the particle and is equal

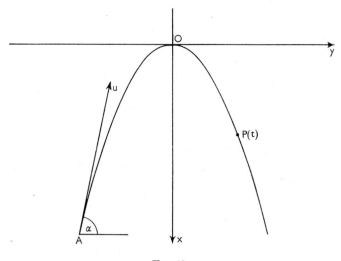

Fig. 41.

to the height which the particle would reach if it were thrown vertically upwards from A. It follows that the parabolic paths of all particles projected from A with speed u have the same directrix.

When the particle is at a point Q whose distance below the directrix is d, the horizontal component of its velocity is $u \cos \alpha$ and the vertical component of its velocity is

$$\sqrt{\left\{ u^2 \sin^2 \alpha - 2g \left(\frac{u^2}{2g} - d \right) \right\}}.$$

Therefore the speed of the particle at Q is

$$\sqrt{\left\{ u^2 \cos^2 \alpha + u^2 \sin^2 \alpha - 2g \left(\frac{u^2}{2g} - d \right) \right\}} = \sqrt{(2gd)}.$$

This speed is equal to the speed that would be acquired by the particle in falling from the directrix to Q.

Example. Three parallel vertical walls of heights h, H, h are at equal distances a apart. A ball is thrown in a vertical plane perpendicular to the walls so that it just clears their tops. Show that the ball will strike the ground at a distance $a\sqrt{\left(\dfrac{H}{H-h}\right)}$ from the middle wall. (N.)

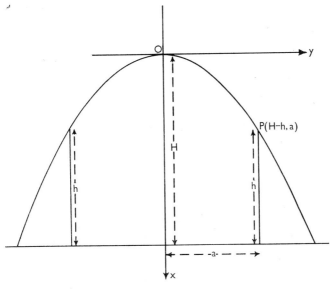

FIG. 42.

Suppose the ball to have been projected with velocity u at an angle α with the horizontal (Fig. 42). From (4.17) the equation of the path of the ball referred to vertical and horizontal axes of x and y through its highest point is $y^2 = \dfrac{2u^2 x \cos^2\alpha}{g}$. The symmetry of Fig. 42 shows that the vertex of the parabola of flight is at a height H above the plane of projection, and that $P(H-h, a)$ is a point on the parabola.

$$a^2 = \frac{2u^2 \cos^2\alpha}{g}(H-h).$$

$$\frac{2u^2 \cos^2\alpha}{g} = \frac{a^2}{H-h}$$

and the equation of the path may now be written

$$y^2 = \frac{a^2 x}{H - h} \, .$$

When $x = H$, $y = a\sqrt{\left(\dfrac{H}{H - h} \right)}$ and this value of y is the distance from
the middle wall at which the particle strikes the ground.

*EXERCISES 4.4.

*1. A particle is projected with a speed of 64 ft/sec and passes through a
point P whose horizontal distance from the point of projection is 96 ft and whose
vertical height above the point of projection is 28 ft. Prove that α, the angle
of elevation, is given by $\tan \alpha = 4/3$ and that the time taken from the instant
of projection for the particle to reach P is $2\frac{1}{2}$ sec.

Show also that the direction of motion of the particle at P makes the same
angle α with the downward vertical through P.   (N.)

*2. O, A and B are three collinear points on a piece of ground which is hori-
zontal, and A lies between O and B. A vertical wall of height $2h$ is erected at A,
and a parallel vertical wall of the same height is erected at B, both walls being
perpendicular to the line OAB. A particle is projected from O under constant
gravity in a vertical plane through the line OAB. It just clears the wall at A
and strikes the wall at B at a height h above the ground. If $OA = 2d$, $AB = d$,
prove that the particle was projected at an angle $\tan^{-1}(7h/3d)$ to the horizontal.
                                                                              (L.)

*3. The components of the initial velocity of a particle, projected under gravity
from a point O, are u, v referred to horizontal and upward vertical axes Ox,
Oy respectively. Show that the equation of its path referred to these axes
is $2u^2 y = 2uvx - gx^2$.

A particle is projected from a point in a horizontal plane so as just to clear
a vertical wall of height $\frac{1}{2} a$ at a distance a from the point of projection, and to
have a range $4a$ on the horizontal plane. Show that it must be projected at
an angle $\tan^{-1}(2/3)$ with the horizontal and find the speed of projection. (N.)

*4. A projectile, fired from a point A on horizontal ground, just clears an
obstacle 16 ft high at a horizontal distance 20 ft from A. If the projectile strikes
the ground at a point 80 ft from A, prove that the angle of projection α is
given by $15 \tan \alpha = 16$ and find the speed of projection.   (N.)

*5. A projectile is fired with velocity V from the edge of a vertical cliff of
height b and hits the sea at a distance a from the foot of the cliff. Show that
there are in general two possible directions of projection and that these will
be at right angles if

$$b V^2 = g a^2.$$

If $a = 216$ ft, $b = 162$ ft, and $V = 96$ ft/sec, verify that this condition is
satisfied, and find the two possible directions of projection.   (C.)

*6. Prove that there are two trajectories, each with initial velocity V, through
the point $P(a, h)$ if $(V^2 - gh)^2 > g^2(a^2 + h^2)$.

Verify that there are two trajectories when $V = 256$ ft/sec and P is the point
given by $a = 2h = 1024$ ft. Prove that the directions of motion at P in the

two trajectories include an acute angle whose tangent is 2 and that the times taken to reach P are in the ratio $\sqrt{5} : 1$. (O.C.)

*7. If the maximum range of a particle projected with speed V from a point O in a horizontal plane is 40 ft, prove that $V = 16\sqrt{5}$ ft/sec; and show that with this value of V an obstacle more than 15 ft high placed at a horizontal distance of 20 ft from O cannot be cleared by the particle. (N.)

*8. A heavy particle is projected from a point O at an angle of elevation α and describes a parabola, under gravity. If axes of coordinates are taken horizontally and vertically through O, prove that the equation of the parabola is

$$y = x \tan\alpha \left(1 - \frac{x}{R}\right)$$

where R is the horizontal range.

If the angle of elevation is $45°$ and the particle just clears the tops of two vertical masts, distant 40 yd apart and each 45 ft above the point of projection, calculate the value of R. (L.)

*9. A particle is projected with speed $(4ga/3)^{1/2}$ from a point on horizontal ground at distance a from the foot of a vertical wall of height $a/8$, the plane of projection being perpendicular to the wall. If the particle is to clear the wall, show that its angle of projection must lie between the values $\tan^{-1}(2/3)$ and $\tan^{-1} 2$.

Show also that the greatest and least distances from the wall of the point where the particle strikes the ground beyond the wall are respectively $3a/13$ and $a/15$. (L.)

*10. Two particles are projected with speed $\sqrt{(4ga)}$ from a point A in a horizontal plane, so as to pass by different paths through a point of which the horizontal and vertical distances from A are both equal to a. Show that they ultimately strike the plane again at points distant $a\sqrt{7}$ apart.

4.5. The Range on an Inclined Plane

A particle is projected from a point O in a vertical plane containing the line of greatest slope of a plane through O which is inclined at an angle θ to the horizontal. The particle is projected at an angle α with the horizontal and it strikes the inclined plane at a point P (Fig. 39). The components of the initial velocity of the particle parallel (up) and perpendicular to the plane respectively are $u \cos(\alpha - \theta)$, $u \sin(\alpha - \theta)$. The components of acceleration of the particle parallel (up) and perpendicular to the plane are respectively $-g \sin\theta$, $-g \cos\theta$.

For the component of the motion of the particle perpendicular to the inclined plane,

$$s = ut \sin(\alpha - \theta) - \tfrac{1}{2}gt^2 \cos\theta.$$

The particle strikes the plane again when $s = 0$, so that

the time of flight from O to P is $\dfrac{2u \sin(\alpha - \theta)}{g \cos\theta}$.   (4.18)

For this period of time the particle has been moving with uniform horizontal velocity $u \cos \alpha$, so that the horizontal distance from O to P is

$$ON = \frac{u \cos \alpha \times 2u \sin(\alpha - \theta)}{g \cos \theta} = \frac{2u^2 \cos \alpha \sin(\alpha - \theta)}{g \cos \theta}.$$

The range on the inclined plane is $OP = \dfrac{2u^2 \cos \alpha \sin(\alpha - \theta)}{g \cos^2 \theta}$. (4.19)

This range is a maximum, as α varies, when $\cos \alpha \sin(\alpha - \theta)$ is a maximum, i.e., when $\frac{1}{2}\{\sin(2\alpha - \theta) - \sin \theta\}$ is a maximum,

i.e. when $\qquad\qquad 2\alpha - \theta = \frac{1}{2}\pi,$

i.e. when $\qquad\qquad \alpha = \frac{1}{4}\pi + \frac{1}{2}\theta,$ (4.20)

i.e., when the direction of projection bisects the angle between the inclined plane and the vertical.

The maximum range on the inclined plane is

$$\frac{2u^2 \cdot \frac{1}{2}(1 - \sin \theta)}{g \cos^2 \theta} = \frac{u^2}{g(1 + \sin \theta)}.$$ (4.21)

In § 4.3 we showed that $P(x_1, y_1)$ is a point of limiting range when equation (4.16) has equal roots.

Examples. (i) A particle is projected with a given speed in a vertical plane from a point on an inclined plane so as to have the greatest possible range up the plane. Prove that, neglecting air resistance, the direction of motion of the particle as it strikes the plane is perpendicular to the direction of projection. (L.)

If the particle is projected with velocity u at an angle α with the horizontal, the equation of the path referred to horizontal and vertical axes through the point of projection is

$$y = x \tan \alpha - \frac{gx^2}{2u^2}(1 + \tan^2 \alpha)$$

and, if the particle passes through the point (x_1, y_1) in the plane,

$$gx_1^2 \tan^2 \alpha - 2u^2 x_1 \tan \alpha + 2u^2 y_1 + gx_1^2 = 0.$$

We have shown above that (x_1, y_1) is a point of limiting range if the roots of this equation in $\tan \alpha$ are equal, i.e. if

$$\tan \alpha = \frac{u^2}{gx_1}.$$

The direction of motion of the particle at any point is given by the gradient of its curve at that point, i.e. by $\dfrac{\mathrm{d}y}{\mathrm{d}x}$.

$$\therefore \tan\psi = \left(\dfrac{\mathrm{d}y}{\mathrm{d}x}\right)_{(x_1,\,y_1)} = \tan\alpha - \dfrac{g\,x_1}{u^2}(1 + \tan^2\alpha)$$

where ψ in the angle between the direction of motion and Ox. If, therefore, the particle has the greatest possible range up the plane,

$$\tan\psi = \tan\alpha - \dfrac{1}{\tan\alpha}(1 + \tan^2\alpha) = -\cot\alpha.$$

$$\therefore \quad \psi = \alpha + 90°.$$

Therefore the direction of motion of the particle as it strikes the plane is perpendicular to the direction of projection.

(ii) A particle is projected from a point O with velocity u at an angle α with the horizontal, so as to strike at right angles at P a plane inclined at an angle β to the horizontal. Prove that, if OP makes an angle θ with the horizontal,

$$\tan\alpha = \cot\beta + 2\tan\theta.$$

The initial component of velocity of the particle in a direction parallel to the inclined plane is $u\cos(\alpha - \beta)$, and its acceleration in this direction is $-g\sin\beta$ (Fig. 43). When the particle strikes the inclined plane at right angles its velocity in a direction parallel to that plane is zero.

$$\therefore \quad u\cos(\alpha - \beta) - gT\sin\beta = 0,$$

where T is the time of flight.

$$\therefore \quad T = \dfrac{u\cos(\alpha - \beta)}{g\sin\beta}. \qquad (1)$$

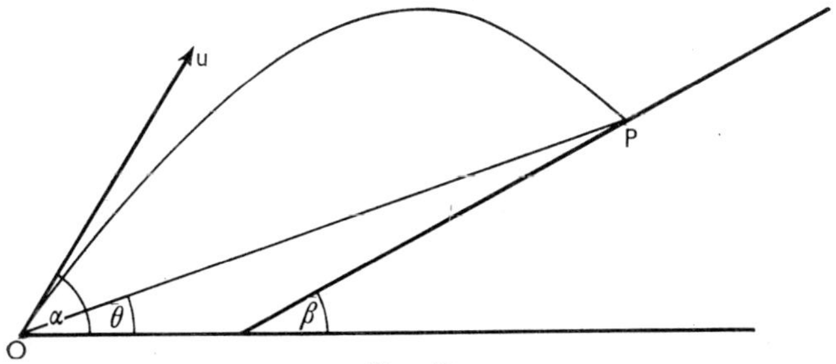

FIG. 43.

At time T from the instant of projection, the displacement of the particle in the direction perpendicular to OP vanishes.

$$\therefore \ uT\sin(\alpha - \theta) - \tfrac{1}{2}gT^2\cos\theta = 0.$$

$$\therefore \ T = \frac{2u\sin(\alpha - \theta)}{g\cos\theta}. \tag{2}$$

Equating the values of T given by (1) and (2) gives

$$2\sin(\alpha - \theta)\,\sin\beta - \cos\theta\cos(\alpha - \beta) = 0.$$

$$\therefore \ 2\sin\alpha\cos\theta\sin\beta - 2\cos\alpha\sin\theta\sin\beta - \cos\theta\cos\alpha\cos\beta -$$
$$- \cos\theta\sin\alpha\sin\beta = 0.$$

$$\therefore \ \sin\alpha\cos\theta\sin\beta = \cos\theta\cos\alpha\cos\beta + 2\cos\alpha\sin\theta\sin\beta.$$

$$\therefore \ \tan\alpha = \cot\beta + 2\tan\theta.$$

EXERCISES 4.5.

In each of questions 1 to 5 a particle is projected from a point O in a plane inclined at an angle θ to the horizontal. The particle is projected with velocity u at an inclination α to the horizontal, and in a plane containing a line of greatest slope of the inclined plane. Give answers where necessary, correct to 3 significant figures.

1. $u = 320$ ft/sec, $\alpha = 60°$ and $\theta = 30°$. Calculate the range on the inclined plane.

2. $u = 40$ ft/sec, $\alpha = 45°$ and $\theta = 30°$. Calculate the magnitude and direction of the velocity at which the particle strikes the plane.

3. $u = 80$ ft/sec, $\alpha = 60°$, $\theta = 45°$. Calculate the time of flight of the particle.

4. $u = 80$ ft/sec, $\theta = 30°$. Calculate the maximum range of the particle (i) up the plane, (ii) down the plane.

5. Calculate in terms of u, α, θ the greatest perpendicular distance from the inclined plane reached by the particle.

6. A particle is projected with velocity u from a point on a plane of slope β. Prove that the maximum range down the plane is $u^2/g(1 - \sin\beta)$.   (L.)

*7. A particle is projected with velocity u from the foot of a plane of inclination β, the direction of projection lying in the vertical plane through the line of greatest slope and making an angle α with the horizontal.
If the particle strikes the plane at right angles, prove that

$$1 + 2\tan^2\beta = \tan\alpha\tan\beta. \tag{O.C.}$$

*8. A particle is projected under gravity with velocity V from a point on a plane inclined at an angle α to the horizontal. Find its maximum range (i) up the plane, (ii) down the plane.
If r_1 and r_2 are these maximum ranges, prove that

$$\frac{1}{r_1} + \frac{1}{r_2}$$

is independent of the inclination of the plane.   (O.C.)

*9. A, B are two points on a line of greatest slope of a plane of inclination β, A being above B. A particle projected from A with velocity u can just reach B. Prove that the least velocity with which a particle can be projected from B so as to reach A is

$$u \tan \left(\frac{\pi}{4} + \frac{\beta}{2} \right),$$

and that the times of flight in the two cases are equal. (O.C.)

*10. A particle is projected under gravity with speed u at elevation α. Find the time when it is farthest from a plane inclined at an angle β to the horizontal through the point of projection, the vertical plane through the trajectory cutting the inclined plane in the line of greatest slope.

Find this greatest distance and show that the velocity parallel to the plane is then $u \cos \alpha \sec \beta$. (L.)

MISCELLANEOUS EXERCISES. IV

1. A stone is thrown upwards at an angle of 30° to the horizontal. If the greatest vertical height reached above the point of projection is 25 ft calculate
 (i) the speed of projection,
 (ii) the horizontal distance travelled by the stone before reaching the horizontal plane through the point of projection, and
 (iii) the time during which the stone is 24 ft or more above the point of projection. (L.)

2. A cat sitting on the top of a wall 9 ft high sees a mouse on the ground 12 ft away from the foot of the wall. If the cat jumps horizontally from the top of the wall and lands on the mouse, calculate
 (i) the speed with which the cat must leave the wall,
 (ii) its direction of flight on landing, giving the answer as an inclination to the horizontal, to the nearest half degree. (L.)

3. A bowler in a cricket match delivers the ball at a height of 6 ft above the ground at an angle of elevation α; the ball hits the wicket, 22 yd away, at a height of 8 in. above the ground. If the maximum height of the ball in its trajectory is 9 ft above the ground find (i) the value of $\tan \alpha$ and (ii) the tangent of the acute angle with the horizontal at which the ball hits the wicket. (O.C.)

4. A tower, 160 ft high, stands on horizontal ground. From its top a stone is thrown up, with a speed of 144 ft/sec, at an angle of 30° to the horizontal. Find the distance from the foot of the tower at which the stone strikes the ground, and its velocity (in magnitude and direction) at that instant. (L.)

5. An aircraft, diving at an angle of 30° to the horizontal at a speed of 320 ft/sec, releases a bomb which falls freely from a height of 1200 ft. Neglecting air resistance, calculate
 (i) the time taken by the bomb to reach the ground,
 (ii) the horizontal distance travelled by the bomb before striking the ground,
 (iii) the direction of motion of the bomb when it strikes the ground, giving your answer in degrees and minutes as an inclination to the horizontal. (L.)

6. A shell is observed to explode at the level of the gun from which it is fired after an interval of 10 sec; and the sound of the explosion reaches the gun after a further interval of 3 sec. Find the elevation of the gun and the speed with which the shell is fired. [Assume the velocity of sound to be 1100 ft/sec.]

(O.C.)

7. In a tennis court the service line is 39 ft from the base of the net which is 3 ft high. If a ball is served horizontally from the service line at a height of 7 ft above the ground so as just to clear the net, calculate

(i) the initial velocity of the ball,

(ii) the velocity of the ball in magnitude and direction when it strikes the ground beyond the net.   (L.)

[Neglect air resistance.]

8. A cricketer standing on horizontal ground throws a ball with a velocity whose horizontal and vertical components are 108 and 28 ft/sec respectively. The ball leaves his hand 8 ft above the ground. Calculate:

(i) after how many seconds the ball strikes the ground,

(ii) the horizontal distance travelled by the ball whilst in the air,

(iii) the speed with which the ball strikes the ground.   (L.)

9. A golf ball, at rest on the ground, is struck so that it starts to move with a velocity whose horizontal component is $3v$ ft/sec and whose upward vertical component is v ft/sec. In its flight the ball rises to a maximum height of 49 ft. Assuming that air resistance may be neglected and that the ground is horizontal, calculate

(i) the value of v;

(ii) the horizontal distance travelled by the ball before striking the ground;

(iii) the direction in which the ball is moving when at a height of 24 ft, giving your answer in degrees and minutes as an inclination to the horizontal.   (L.)

10. If the maximum range, on a horizontal plane, of a projectile fired from a gun is 3 miles, find the height to which the projectile rises above the point of projection.   (O.C.)

11. A boy throws a ball towards a wall 30 ft away from him. The top of the wall is 16 ft higher than his hand, and the horizontal and vertical components of the velocity of the ball when it leaves his hand are 20 and 35 ft/sec. Prove that the ball clears the wall.

Determine whether the ball will clear a wall 10 ft behind the first and 9 ft lower.   (O.C.)

12. Prove that in order that a projectile should pass, on its downward flight, at an angle of 45° to the horizontal, through a point 44 ft vertically above and 100 ft horizontally from its point of projection, it must be projected at an angle $\tan^{-1} 1\cdot 88$ to the horizontal. Find also the speed of projection.   (L.)

*13. Two points A, B are at the same horizontal level, and two bodies are projected simultaneously from A with the same velocity V. If they both pass through B, one after time t_1, and the other after time t_2, prove that

$$4V^2 = g^2(t_1^2 + t_2^2).$$ (L.)

*14. If a shell is projected with velocity V inclined at an angle α to the horizontal from a stationary ship to hit a floating stationary target, find the distance of the target from the ship.

If the target is being towed with velocity u directly away from the ship, prove that the angle of projection must be altered to θ, where

$$\sin 2\theta - \frac{2u}{V}\sin\theta = \sin 2\alpha.$$ (N.)

*15. A particle is projected at an angle of elevation α with a velocity u. Find its vertical and horizontal velocities after a time t. Find also the greatest height attained and the horizontal range.

If the horizontal range is equal in length to the latus rectum of the parabolic path, find the angle of projection with the horizontal. (N.)

*16. A particle P is projected from O with velocity V at angle of elevation α. Prove that the particle rises to a vertical height H above O given by

$$H = \frac{V^2}{2g}\sin^2\alpha.$$

A and B are two points on the trajectory at a vertical height $h(h < H)$ above O; at A and at B the acute angle between the direction of motion and the horizontal is θ. Prove that

$$\tan^2\theta = \frac{H-h}{H}\tan^2\alpha.$$

If the time in the trajectory between A and B is equal to the time for P to reach the highest point above O, prove that

$$4h = 3H.$$ (O.C.)

*17. A particle is projected with speed V ft/sec from a point O of a horizontal plane in a direction making an angle α with the horizontal. If $\alpha = 60°$, it is observed that when $t = 2$ sec the elevation of the particle as viewed from O is $45°$. Find the initial speed V, and the range on the horizontal plane. (N.)

*18. A particle is projected under gravity with given speed so that its range on the horizontal plane through the point of projection is a maximum. Prove that this range is equal to four times the greatest height above this plane attained by the particle.

Prove that, if the particle is projected from O at elevation α, and if after time t the particle is at P, then

$$\tan\beta = \tfrac{1}{2}(\tan\alpha + \tan\theta),$$

where β and θ are the inclinations to the horizontal of OP and of the direction of motion of the particle when at P. (N.)

*19. Prove that if a particle is projected with velocity, V, at an angle of elevation, α, to the horizontal, then the range, R, on a horizontal plane through the point of projection is given by

$$R = \frac{V^2}{g}\sin 2\alpha.$$

Prove that, if $R < V^2/g$, there are two possible angles of projection, α_1 and α_2 $(\alpha_2 > \alpha_1)$, which give the same range, R, and that if T_1 and T_2 are the corresponding times of flight, then

$$T_1 T_2 = 2R/g.$$

Also, if $\alpha_1 = 15°$, prove that $T_2 - T_1 = \dfrac{V\sqrt{2}}{g}$, and that, if two particles are projected simultaneously, one in the α_1-direction and the other in the α_2-direction, then the distance between them t sec after projection $(t < T_1)$ is Vt. (O.C.)

*20. A particle is projected with velocity V at an angle α above the horizontal and moves under gravity. Neglecting air resistance, calculate the square of its distance from the point of projection after a time t.

Show that, if $\sin\alpha$ is less than $\frac{2}{3}\sqrt{2}$, this distance increases steadily with time. (C.)

*21. A particle is projected at an angle α to the horizontal from a point at a horizontal distance x from the nearer of two obstacles which are each of height h and are a distance h apart. If it just clears both obstacles, show that

$$\tan\alpha = h(2x + h)/x(x + h). \qquad \text{(N.)}$$

*22. A heavy particle is projected from a point in an inclined plane, inclined at 2β to the *vertical*, and moves towards the upper part of the plane in the vertical plane through a line of greatest slope of the inclined plane; the initial velocity of the particle is $u\cos\beta$ and its initial direction of motion is inclined at β to the *vertical*. Prove that the time of flight of the particle is u/g, its range on the plane is $u^2/2g$, the velocity with which it strikes the plane is $u\sin\beta$, and its direction of motion has then turned through a right angle. (O.C.)

*23. A projectile is fired from a point on a cliff to hit a mark 200 ft horizontally from the point and 200 ft vertically below it. The velocity of projection is that due to falling freely under gravity through 100 ft from rest. Show that the two possible directions of projection are at right angles, and that the times of flight are approximately 2·7 and 6·5 sec. (O.C.)

*24. A particle is projected from O and just passes over each of two obstacles A and B at horizontal distances of 70 ft and 105 ft from O and at vertical heights of 60 ft and 30 ft above O respectively. Find the velocity of projection. (O.C.)

*25. The greatest horizontal range of a gun, capable of firing at all elevations, is 20 miles. When the gun is fired so that the range is a maximum, find

(i) the greatest height attained by the projectile, and

(ii) the height of the projectile when it has travelled 5 miles horizontally. (O.C.)

*26. A particle is projected with velocity V at an angle α to the horizontal. Find its height h above the point of projection when it has travelled a horizontal distance l; and find the greatest value of h, when V and l are given and α varies.

A particle may be projected, with a given velocity V but in any direction, from a given point on a horizontal plane. At a distance $a(< V^2/g)$ from the point of projection is a vertical wall. Shew that the points on the wall which it is possible to hit lie inside a parabola, whose vertex is at a height

$$\frac{V^2}{2g} - \frac{ga^2}{2V^2}$$

above the horizontal plane. (C.)

*27. A ball is projected vertically upwards with speed u from a point A on the ground. At the same instant a boy, standing at a horizontal distance a from A, throws a ball from a height b towards the other with speed v at an

angle α with the horizontal. Show that the second ball hits the first if α satisfies the equation
$$a \sin \alpha + b \cos \alpha = a u/v.$$

If $a = 12$ ft, $b = 5$ ft and $u = v$, find the value of α from this equation. (L.)

*28. A particle P is projected under gravity from a point O. Prove that, in the absence of air-resistance, the particle describes a parabola.

If the line OP meets at Q a fixed vertical line in the plane of the motion, show that Q descends with constant velocity. (L.)

*29. A projectile is fired from a fixed point O at an elevation α and hits a stationary target A, where OA is horizontal. Find the speed of projection V, assuming that there is no air resistance.

On another occasion the target starts to rise vertically from A with uniform speed U at the same instant as a projectile is fired from O at elevation α. If the moving target is to be hit, show that the speed of projection must be increased to W, where W is the positive root of the equation
$$W^2 - W U \operatorname{cosec} \alpha = V^2. \tag{N.}$$

*30. A shell is fired with velocity V at an inclination θ to the horizontal from a fort at sea level. Find the horizontal and the vertical distances of the shell from the fort t sec after firing. Hence find the range of the shell on the horizontal plane through the fort.

A target is towed with velocity v directly away from the fort. If the target is hit by the shell, show that when the shell is fired the distance between the target and the fort is
$$(V^2 \sin 2\theta - 2Vv \sin\theta)/g.$$

If the target had stopped at the moment the shell was fired, show that the shell would have passed over the target at a height h where
$$gh = 2(V \sin\theta - v \tan\theta)v \tan\theta. \tag{N.}$$

*31. A small object, projected towards a vertical rectangular screen perpendicular to the vertical plane of the path of the object, just clears it at the highest point of its path. The screen is a ft in front of the point of projection and the top of the screen is b ft higher than the point of projection. Find the vertical and horizontal components of the velocity of projection.

If the object is projected with the requisite velocity, but the vertical plane through the direction of projection, instead of being at right angles to the screen, makes an angle θ with the screen, prove that it will fail to clear the screen by $b (\operatorname{cosec}\theta - 1)^2$ ft. (O.C.)

*32. It is desired to project a particle so that it will just clear two given walls, of equal heights a, which are $2a$ apart. The speed of projection from ground level is to be $\sqrt{(agk)}$. Prove that, if the angle of projection is α, then the point of projection must be at a distance $a(k \sin\alpha \cos\alpha - 1)$ from the nearer wall and α must satisfy the equation
$$\sec^4 \alpha - (k^2 - 2k) \sec^2 \alpha + k^2 = 0.$$

Find the point of projection when $k = 4$, and prove that the greatest height attained by the particle is then $\frac{3}{2}a$. (O.C.)

8*

*33. A shot is fired with velocity v ft/sec from the top of a cliff h ft high and strikes the sea at a distance d ft from the foot of the cliff. Show that the possible times of flight are roots of the equation

$$\tfrac{1}{4} g^2 t^4 - (g\,h + v^2)\, t^4 + d^2 + h^2 = 0\,.$$

By considering the roots of this equation, or otherwise, show that the greatest value of d for given values of v and h is $v(v^2 + 2\,gh)^{1/2}/g$.   (O.C.)

*34. When a particle, projected with velocity V at an angle of elevation α, has described a horizontal distance x, the direction of its motion makes an angle θ with the horizontal, θ being taken positive when the particle is rising. Prove that

$$\tan\theta = \frac{V^2 \sin\alpha \cos\alpha - g\,x}{V^2 \cos^2\alpha}\,.$$

Prove also that the range on the horizontal plane through the point of projection is $\dfrac{V^2}{g}\sin 2\,\alpha$.

When the particle has described $\tfrac{2}{3}$ of its horizontal range it is moving at right angles to its initial direction. The maximum vertical height above the point of projection is 30,000 ft; find the value of V.   (O.C.)

*35. Two particles A and B are projected simultaneously in the same vertical plane with the same speed u from points C, D distant a apart, the line CD being horizontal. The particle A is projected at an inclination $\alpha\left(<\dfrac{\pi}{2}\right)$ to CD and B is projected vertically upwards. Find the distance between the particles at time t after projection and hence show that their least distance apart is $a\sqrt{\{(1 - \sin\alpha)/2\}}$ and find when this occurs.   (L.)

CHAPTER V

RELATIVE MOTION

5.1. Relative Position

The position of a particle may be determined by reference to its displacement from an arbitrarily chosen point in space. The position thus determined is defined as the position of the particle *relative to the chosen point*. The *frame of reference*, by means of which the position of a particle is defined, is an essential feature of the definition. Thus, for example, the position of a particle in a moving railway carriage relative to another particle in the carriage may be constant, whereas the position of the first particle relative to a point on the ground outside the carriage changes with the motion of the carriage relative to the ground outside it. Because of the varied motions within the solar system, the position of a body in that system is considered relative to the sun.

5.2. Relative Velocity

The velocity of a particle A relative to a particle B is defined as the rate of change of the displacement of A from B. Since the displacement of A from B is a vector, the velocity of A relative to B is also a vector.

When particle A is moving with velocity u and particle B is moving with velocity v in the same direction, Fig. 44(i), the component of the displacement of B from A *in the direction of the motion* is increasing at the rate $(v - u)$. The component of displacement of B from A in a direction at right angles to the direction of motion is constant. The velocity of B relative to A is therefore $v - u$ in the direction of the motion.

Similarly, when particle A is moving with velocity u and particle B is moving with velocity v in the opposite direction, Fig. 44(ii), the velocity of B relative to A is $(v + u)$ in the direction of the motion of B.

In each case the velocity of B relative to A is obtained by the *vector addition of the velocity of B to the reversed velocity of A*. When we obtain the velocity of B relative to A in this way we make use of a result which follows from the law of vector addition applied to the displacements concerned, i.e.

$$\overrightarrow{AB} = \overrightarrow{AC} + \overrightarrow{CB}.$$

Therefore, if C is the point of reference, and since, by definition, relative velocities are rates of change of relative displacements:

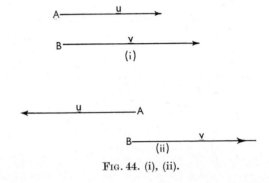

Fig. 44. (i), (ii).

The velocity of A relative to B is equal to the sum of the velocity of A relative to C and the velocity of C relative to B. (5.1)

Since C is a fixed point of reference this is equivalent to the statement:

The velocity of A relative to B is equal to the sum of the velocity of A and the velocity of B reversed. (5.2)

This reasoning is no less valid when the velocities of A and B are not parallel to one another and results (5.1) and (5.2) are true in this general case. The addition implied in result (5.2) is a vector addition which can be carried out either by the use of the triangle of vectors or by the use of the Law of Resolved Parts as discussed in Chapter II, § 2.1. Figure 45 illustrates the use of the triangle of vectors for obtaining the velocity of a particle A relative to a particle B. Triangle abc is a triangle of velocities in which

$$\overrightarrow{ab} + \overrightarrow{bc} = \overrightarrow{ac}.$$

$\overrightarrow{ab}$ represents the velocity of A, $\overrightarrow{bc}$ represents the velocity of B reversed and $\overrightarrow{ac}$ represents the velocity of A relative to B.

Notation

In the diagrams throughout this chapter we use the notation,

$_A V$ to denote the velocity of A,

$_B \underset{\smile}{V}$ to denote the velocity of B reversed,

$_A V_B$ to denote the velocity of A relative to B.

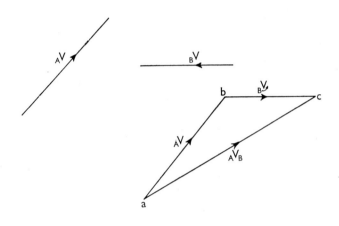

FIG. 45.

Reducing to Rest

The process of compounding the velocity of A with the reversed velocity of B can be considered as a process in which a velocity equal and opposite to that of B is superimposed on the whole system, thus "reducing B to rest".

Examples. (i) Town P is N. 30° E. on a straight road from town O, and town R is due East on a straight road from P. A cyclist is riding at 10 m.p.h. on the road from R to P and a pedestrian is walking at 4 m.p.h. on the road from O to P. Calculate the velocity of the pedestrian relative to the cyclist.

Figure 46 (i) shows the relative positions of the two roads, and Fig. 46 (ii) is a triangle of velocities in which the velocity of the pedestrian is added to the reversed velocity of the cyclist.

From this triangle,

$$AC^2 = AB^2 + BC^2 - 2AB \cdot BC \cos 120°$$
$$= 16 + 100 + 2 \cdot 4 \cdot 10 \cdot \tfrac{1}{2} = 156.$$
$$\therefore AC = 12 \cdot 49.$$
$$\therefore \sin BAC = \frac{10 \sin 120°}{12 \cdot 49}.$$
$$\therefore \angle BAC = 43° 53'.$$

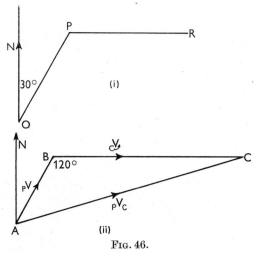

Fig. 46.

The velocity of the pedestrian relative to the cyclist is 12·5 m.p.h. in a direction N. 73° 53′ E.

(ii) A ship is moving due S. at 20 knots and from it a second ship B appears to be moving SW. at 15 knots. Calculate the velocity of B.

Figure 47 shows the vector triangle of velocities. $\overrightarrow{bc}$ represents the velocity of A reversed, $\overrightarrow{ac}$ represents the velocity of B relative to A and therefore $\overrightarrow{ab}$ represents the velocity of B.

$$ab^2 = ac^2 + cb^2 - 2ac \cdot cb \cos acb$$
$$= 225 + 400 + 2 \cdot 15 \cdot 20 \cdot \tfrac{1}{2}\sqrt{2} = 1049 \cdot 2.$$
$$\therefore ab = 32 \cdot 3\,(9).$$
$$\sin b = \frac{15 \sin 135}{32 \cdot 39}$$
$$\therefore b = 19° 7'.$$

Therefore B is moving at 32·4 knots in a direction S. 19°7′ W.

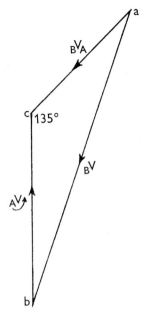

FIG. 47.

(iii) To a cyclist riding at 10 m.p.h. due N. the wind appears to
come from a direction 5° E. of N. When the cyclist rides at 10 m.p.h.
due E., the wind appears to come from the NE. Find the speed and
the true direction of the wind.

The cyclist then rides, still at 10 m.p.h., in such a direction that
the same wind appears to be coming from his right, at right angles
to his course. In what direction is he now riding?   (N.)

Figure 48 (i) is the triangle of velocities when the cyclist is riding N.

Figure 48 (ii) is the triangle of velocities when the cyclist is riding E.

Figure 48 (iii) is a composite triangle of velocities diagram, formed
by superimposing Fig. 48 (ii) on to Fig. 48 (i) so that the lines representing the true velocity of the wind coincide.

From Fig. 48 (iii),

$$QR = 10\sqrt{2}, \quad \angle RQS = 90° \quad \text{and} \quad \angle SRQ = 50°.$$

$$\therefore \ QS = 10\sqrt{2} \tan 50° = 16{\cdot}85.$$

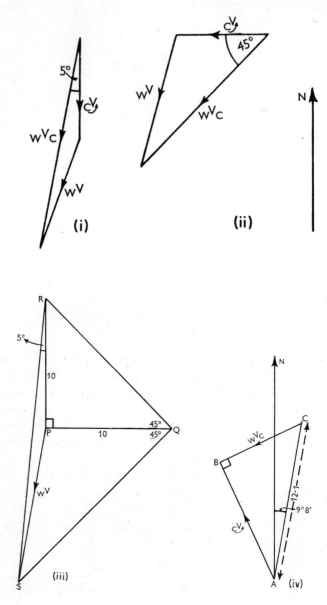

FIG. 48.

Therefore from triangle PQS,

$$\tan\frac{P-S}{2} = \frac{6\cdot85}{26\cdot85}\tan 67\tfrac{1}{2}°.$$

$$\therefore \frac{P-S}{2} = 31°\,38'.$$

$$\therefore P - S = 63°\,16'.$$

But $P + S = 135°.$

$$\therefore 2P = 198°\,16'.$$

$$\therefore P = 99°\,8'.$$

$$\therefore PS = \frac{16\cdot85\sin 45°}{\sin 99°\,8'} = 12\cdot0(7).$$

The wind is $12\cdot1$ m.p.h. from a direction $9°\,8'$ E. of N.

Figure 48(iv) is the triangle of velocities in the third case. $\overrightarrow{AB}$ represents the reversed velocity of the cyclist. Then

$$\cos CAB = \frac{10}{12\cdot07}.$$

$$\therefore \angle CAB \doteqdot 34°.$$

The cyclist is now riding in a direction $25°$ E. of S.

A graphical solution to each part of the question can be obtained by drawing Figs. 48(iii) and 48(iv) to scale.

(iv) The wind is blowing at a constant speed from a compass point $\gamma°$ W. of N. The trail of smoke from a ship steaming due north is in a direction $\alpha°$ E. of S. The trail of smoke from the ship when it is steaming due W., at the same speed, is in a direction $\beta°$ E. of S. Prove that

$$\tan\gamma°(1 + \tan\alpha°) = \tan\alpha°(1 + \tan\beta°). \qquad \text{(O.C.)}$$

The direction of the smoke trail is the direction of the air relative to the ship.

If P, Q [Fig. 49(i)] represent two positions of the ship, R represents the position when the ship is at Q of a particle of smoke emitted by the ship when it was at P, and if the velocities concerned are uniform, then $\overrightarrow{PQ}$ represents the velocity of the ship, $\overrightarrow{PR}$ represents the velocity of the air and therefore $\overrightarrow{QR}$ represents the velocity of the air relative to the ship. Since this relative velocity is constant, all the particles of smoke will lie along QR, which is the direction of the smoke trail.

Figure 49 (ii) is a composite one showing the triangle of velocities for the relative motion in each of the two cases. APC is the triangle

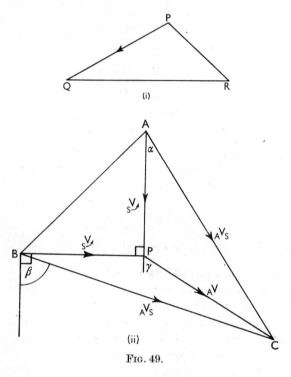

(i)

(ii)

FIG. 49.

of velocities when the ship is steaming N. and BPC is the triangle of velocities when the ship is steaming W.

In triangle APC, $\angle ACP = \gamma - \alpha$.

$$\therefore \frac{PC}{\sin \alpha} = \frac{AP}{\sin(\gamma - \alpha)}.$$

In triangle BPC, $\angle PCB = \beta - \gamma$.

$$\therefore \frac{PC}{\sin(90 - \beta)} = \frac{BP}{\sin(\beta - \gamma)}.$$

But $AP = BP$, and $\sin(90 - \beta) = \cos \beta$.

Therefore by division

$$\frac{\cos\beta}{\sin\alpha} = \frac{\sin(\beta-\gamma)}{\sin(\gamma-\alpha)}.$$

$$\therefore \cos\beta\sin\gamma\cos\alpha - \cos\beta\cos\gamma\sin\alpha = \sin\alpha\sin\beta\cos\gamma$$
$$- \sin\alpha\cos\beta\sin\gamma.$$

$$\therefore \tan\gamma - \tan\alpha = \tan\alpha\tan\beta - \tan\alpha\tan\gamma.$$

$$\therefore \tan\gamma(1 + \tan\alpha) = \tan\alpha(1 + \tan\beta).$$

(v) A ship A is sailing at 30 knots in a direction N. 40° E. and a second ship B is known to be sailing at 15 knots. If the bearing of B from A is observed to be always N. 60° E., find, graphically or otherwise, the two possible directions in which B may be sailing.   (L.)

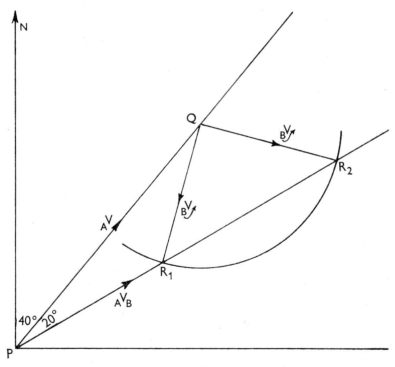

Fig. 50.

Figure 50 shows the two possible triangles of velocity for the motion of the ship A relative to the ship B. The possible directions of motion in which B may be sailing are R_1Q and R_2Q.

A graphical solution can be obtained by an accurate drawing to scale of Fig. 50.

Otherwise from a triangle PQR in which $PQ = 30$, $QR = 15$ and $\angle QPR = 20°$,

$$\frac{\sin R}{30} = \frac{\sin 20°}{15}.$$

$$\therefore \ \sin R = 0\cdot6840.$$

$$\therefore \ R = 43° 9' \quad \text{or} \quad 136° 51'.$$

Therefore B is sailing $16° 51'$ E. of N. or $76° 51'$ W. of N.

(vi) Two aircraft fly from an aerodrome, the first to a place due W. of the aerodrome and the second to a place due N. Each aircraft flies at speed v relative to the air and there is a wind of speed w blowing from the NE. Show that the magnitude of the velocity of the first aircraft relative to the second is $v\sqrt{2}$.

If $v = 10w$, find the direction of this relative velocity.   (L.)

Figure 51 is a composite diagram showing the triangle of velocities for each of the aircraft; ABC is a triangle of velocities for the first aircraft P. $\overrightarrow{AB}$ represents the velocity of the air relative to the ground $(_AV_G)$, $\overrightarrow{BC}$ represents the velocity of P relative to the air $(_PV_A)$, and, since $_PV_G - {_AV_G} = {_PV_A}$, $\overrightarrow{AC}$ represents the velocity of P

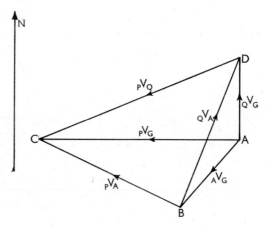

FIG. 51.

relative to the ground $(_PV_G)$. Similarly ABD represents the triangle of velocities for the second aircraft Q.

From triangle BDC,

since $$_PV_A - _QV_A = _PV_Q,$$

therefore $\overrightarrow{DC}$ represents $_PV_Q$.

From triangle ABC, $\dfrac{BC}{\sin 45°} = \dfrac{AB}{\sin ACB}$.

$$\therefore \sin ACB = \frac{AB\sin 45°}{v}.$$

From triangle ABD, $\dfrac{BD}{\sin 135°} = \dfrac{AB}{\sin ADB}$.

$$\therefore \sin ADB = \frac{AB\sin 135°}{v}.$$

$\angle ACB$ is acute because $\angle BCD = \angle BDC$.

$\angle ADB$ is acute because $\angle BAD = 135°$.

$$\therefore \angle ACB = \angle ADB.$$

$$\therefore ABCD \text{ is cyclic.}$$

$$\therefore \angle DCB = 45°; \therefore \angle DBC = 90°.$$

$$\therefore DC = BD\sqrt{2} = v\sqrt{2},$$

so that $_PV_Q = v\sqrt{2}$. Also

$$\frac{\sin BCA}{AB} = \frac{\sin 45°}{BC}.$$

But $AB = w$, $BC = v$, and therefore, if $v = 10\,w$,

$$\sin BCA = \frac{\sin 45°}{10} = 0.0707.$$

$$\therefore \angle BCA = 4° 3',$$

$$\therefore \angle ADC = 49° 3'.$$

Therefore the velocity of P relative to Q is in a direction $49° 3'$ W. of S.

EXERCISES 5.2.

1. An aeroplane whose air speed is 200 m.p.h. is to fly from A to a point B $40°$ E. of N. from A. The wind is blowing at 40 m.p.h. from the E. What direction must the pilot steer (a) going, (b) returning? (N.)

2. An aeroplane is flying due N. horizontally at 120 m.p.h. The pilot sees a train below which to him appears to be going SW. On looking at his map he finds that the railway runs NW. Find the speed of the train. (N.)

3. A ship is steaming on a course 30° E. of N. at a speed of 12½ knots, and a man walks backwards and forwards across the deck in a direction perpendicular to the ship's course at a speed of 5 ft/sec. Find the actual directions in which the man moves. [A knot is a speed of 6080 ft/hr.]   (O.C.)

4. A motor boat, which travels at 9 m.p.h. relative to the surface of the water, makes journeys to and fro from A to B, 3 miles E. of A. If the tide is flowing at 2½ m.p.h. from the NE. find, graphically or otherwise,

(i) the direction in which the boat must steer, i.e. the direction in which the axis of the boat must point, when travelling from A direct to B,

(ii) the time taken to travel from A to B,

(iii) the time taken for the return journey from B direct to A.   (L.)

5. A swimmer crosses a river of width 40 ft whose current flows at a uniform speed. In crossing as quickly as possible he takes 30 sec and is carried 30 ft down stream. Calculate

(i) the speed of the current,

(ii) the speed of the swimmer relative to the water.

Find also, graphically or otherwise, how long it will take the swimmer to swim in a straight line back to his starting point.   (L.)

6. The speed of an aircraft in still air is 240 m.p.h. On a certain day there is a wind of 60 m.p.h. from the E. Find the least time in which the aircraft can reach a point 500 miles SW. of its starting point.   (L.)

7. A ship is moving due S. with a speed 20 knots, and another appears to be approaching it from the NE. at a speed of 24 knots. What is the true speed and direction of the motion of the second ship?   (N.)

8. When a motor-cyclist is travelling along a straight stretch of road from S. to N. at a steady speed of 30 m.p.h. the wind appears to him to come from a direction N. 40° E. When he returns along the same road at the same speed the wind appears to come from a direction S. 30° E. Find, by drawing or otherwise, the true magnitude and direction of the wind.   (C.)

9. A man can swim in a river to a point 120 yd upstream and back again in 3½ min, the current running at 3 ft/sec. How long will he take to swim across the river, which is 100 yd wide, from a point on one bank to a point immediately opposite on the other bank?   (L.)

10. A ship is moving due W. at 20 knots and the wind appears to blow from 22½° W. of S. The ship then steams due S. at the same speed and the wind then appears to blow from 22½° E. of S. Find the speed of the wind and the true direction from which it blows, assuming that they remain constant.   (N.)

11. When a motor launch moves northwards at 20 knots a pennant on its mast-head points due E. On the return journey, when the speed is 20 knots southwards, the pennant points N. 10° 12′ E. Find the speed and direction of the wind, assuming them to be unchanged throughout.   (N.)

12. A cyclist is travelling due E. with speed V along a straight and level road, and to him the wind appears to blow from the S. When he doubles his speed the wind appears to blow from the SE. Find the actual velocity of the wind, in magnitude and direction, and the direction from which it appears to blow when the cyclist has trebled his speed.   (N.)

13. An aeroplane, which can travel at 200 m.p.h. in still air, sets out at 9 a.m. to go from a point A to a point B, 300 miles due N. of A. The wind is blowing at 25 m.p.h. from due W. Calculate the ground speed of the areoplane and the course set by the pilot.

When the aeroplane is halfway from A to B, the speed of the wind suddenly increases (without any change of direction) and the pilot is obliged to change his course by 5° in order to continue travelling in the line AB. Find by calculation (i) the time at which he encounters the new conditions, (ii) the new wind speed.   (C.)

14. A ship steaming NE. at 16 m.p.h. enters a current flowing due E. at 3 m.p.h. By how much must she change her direction, and at what speed must she steam relative to the water, in order to continue to make 16 m.p.h. to the NE.?   (O.C.)

15. When a motor-cyclist is travelling along a straight stretch of road from S. to N. at a steady speed of 30 m.p.h. the wind appears to him to come from a direction N. 40° E. When he returns along the same road at the same speed the wind appears to come from a direction S. 30° E. Find, by drawing or otherwise, the true magnitude and direction of the wind.   (C.)

5.3. Problems of Relative Position and Interception

Problems in which the positions and relative positions of two moving vehicles in stated circumstances are required are best reduced to problems of *relative motion*. Each of the motions concerned is considered as motion relative to one or the other of the vehicles, which one is thus "reduced to rest".

In general, the problems are best solved with the help of diagrams.

1. *The relative velocity diagram* which is used to find the velocity of one vehicle relative to the other.

2. *The relative position diagram* on which the *relative* positions of the vehicles in the stated circumstances are indicated.

3. *The position diagram* in which the corresponding positions relative to the original frame of reference are indicated.

Time is a factor which is constant with reference to corresponding displacements indicated in the relative position diagram and the position diagram. It follows that

$$_A D_B : {}_A D = {}_A V_B : {}_A V, \qquad (5.3)$$

where

$_A D_B$ is the *magnitude* of the displacement of A relative to B,

$_A D$ is the *magnitude* of the displacement of A in the original framework,

$_A V_B$ is the *magnitude* of the velocity of A relative to B,

$_A V$ is the *magnitude* of the velocity of A in the original framework.

T.M.S.F.I.   9

Examples. (i) A ship A is steaming due S. at 6 knots and a ship B is steaming due E. at 8 knots. At noon, the distance between the ships is 5 nautical miles and the bearing of B from A is S. 30° W Find

(a) the velocity of B relative to A,

(b) the distance between the ships when they are nearest each other,

(c) the position of B when the ships are nearest each other,

(d) the time at which the ships are nearest each other.

(a) Figure 52 (i) shows the relative velocity diagram.

$$_BV_A = 10, \ \sin\alpha = \tfrac{4}{5}.$$

Therefore the velocity of B relative to A is 10 knots, N. 53° 8′ E.

(b) Figure 52 (ii) shows the relative position diagram with A reduced to rest. A, B are the initial positions of A and B and BX is the line through B parallel to the velocity of A relative to B, i.e. BX is the *relative track of B*. The ships are nearest together when B is at a position N relative to A where N is the foot of the perpendicular from A on the relative track of B.

$$AN = AB \sin ABN = 5 \sin 23° 8′ = 1 \cdot 964.$$

Therefore the shortest distance between the ships is 1·96 nautical miles.

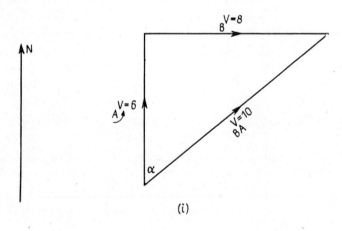

(i)

Fɪɢ. 52 (i).

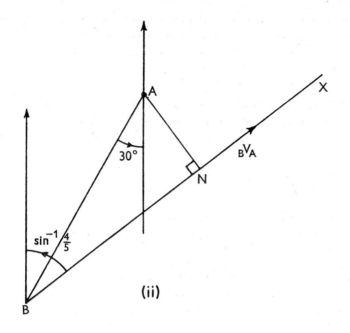

(ii)

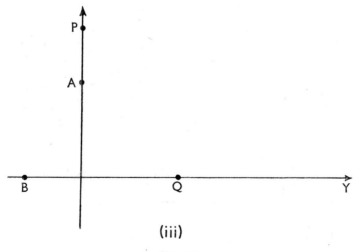

(iii)

FIG. 52.

9*

(c) Figure 52 (iii) shows the position diagram in which A, B are the initial positions of A and B and BY is the track of B. The position of B when the ships are nearest each other is Q in BY, where

$$BQ = \tfrac{8}{10} BN = \tfrac{8}{10} \times 5 \cos 23° 8' = 3·68.$$

Therefore when the ships are nearest each other, B is 3·68 miles E. of its initial position.

(d) Referring to Fig. 52 (ii), the ships are nearest each other at h hours past noon, where

$$h = \frac{BN}{\left|\text{velocity of } B \text{ relative to } A\right|} = \frac{4·598}{10} \doteq 0·460.$$

Therefore the ships are nearest each other at 27·6 min past noon.

(ii) A batsman at B plays the ball along the ground in a direction S. 15° E. at an average speed of 40 ft/sec. A fieldsman F standing at a point 40 yd S. 15° W. from B starts to run at the instant when the batsman strikes the ball and, running in a straight line at an average speed of 25 ft/sec, intercepts the ball. No part of the ground within the boundaries is more than 75 yd from B. Show that F intercepts the ball at a distance of about 32·2 yd from B. Show also that if the ground were large enough F, running in a straight line at the same average speed, could intercept the ball at a distance of about 81·5 yd from B.

Figure 53 (i) is the relative position diagram in which the ball is reduced to rest at B. Since F intercepts the ball, his movement is represented in this diagram by the relative direction FB.

Figure 53 (ii) is the relative velocity diagram. The direction $Q_1 P$ is the direction of the velocity of F relative to the ball, $\overrightarrow{RP}$ represents the reversed velocity of the ball and $\overrightarrow{Q_1 R}$, $\overrightarrow{Q_2 R}$ represent 25 ft/sec in each of the possible directions of the velocity of F.

For triangle PQR, $PR = 40$, $RQ = 25$ and $\angle QPR = 30°$,

$$\frac{40}{\sin PQR} = \frac{25}{\sin 30°}.$$

$$\therefore \sin PQR = \tfrac{4}{5}, \quad \angle PQR = 53° 8' \quad \text{or} \quad 126° 52'.$$

$$\therefore \angle PQ_1 R = 53° 8' \quad \text{and} \quad \angle PQ_2 R = 126° 52'.$$

$$\therefore PQ_1 = \frac{25 \sin 96° 52'}{\sin 30°} \text{ ft} = 49·65 \text{ ft},$$

$$PQ_2 = \frac{25}{\sin 30°} \sin 23° 8' \text{ ft} = 19·64 \text{ ft}.$$

If the fieldsman runs in the direction Q_1R, he covers a relative distance 40 yd [Fig. 53 (i)] at a velocity relative to the ball of 49·65 ft/sec in time $\dfrac{120}{49\cdot65}$ sec. In this time the ball travels

$$\frac{120}{49\cdot65} \times 40\,\text{ft} = 96\cdot70\,\text{ft}.$$

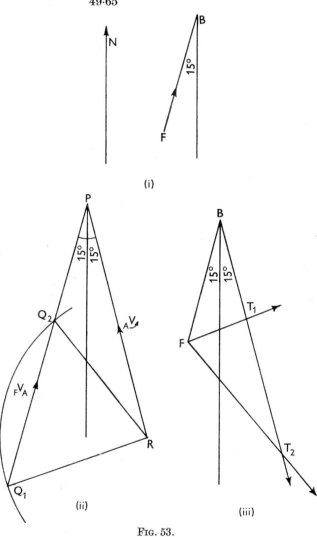

(i)

(ii)

(iii)

FIG. 53.

The ball is intercepted at about 32·2 yd from B. If the fieldsman runs in the direction Q_2R, he covers a relative distance 40 yd at a velocity relative to the ball of 19·64 ft/sec in time $\dfrac{120}{19\cdot64}$ sec. In this time the ball travels

$$\frac{120}{19\cdot64} \times 40\,\text{ft} = 244\cdot4\,\text{ft} \doteq 81\cdot5\,\text{yd}.$$

The ball is intercepted (if the ground is large enough) at about 81·5 yd from B.

Figure 53 (iii) is the position diagram showing the possible points of interception T_1 and T_2.

(iii) To a cruiser C steaming N. at V knots an enemy battleship B, distant a sea-miles to the W. appears to be moving SE. at $V\sqrt{2}$ knots. Find the true velocity of B, and show that when the vessels are nearest to one another C is NE. of B.

If C is within firing range of B when the vessels are not more than b sea-miles apart, where $b < a$, show that C is liable to be hit at any moment within an interval of time lasting $\sqrt{(2b^2 - a^2)}/V$ hours. (N.)

Figure 54 (i) is the relative velocity diagram for the motions of the two ships, $\overrightarrow{AB}$ represents the reversed velocity of the cruiser, $\overrightarrow{BC}$ represents the velocity of the battleship, and $\overrightarrow{AC}$ represents the velocity of the battleship relative to the cruiser. Therefore the velocity of the battleship is V knots E.

Figure 54 (ii) is the relative position diagram in which the cruiser is reduced to rest at C and BX is the relative track of the battleship. The cruiser is within firing range of the battleship during the (relative) progress of the latter from P_1 to P_2 along BX where $CP_1 = CP_2 = b$.

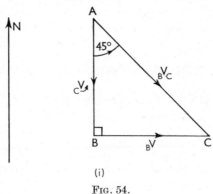

(i)

FIG. 54.

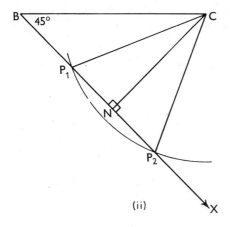

FIG. 54.

But

$$CN = CB \sin 45° = \frac{a\sqrt{2}}{2}.$$

$$\therefore\ P_1 P_2 = 2\sqrt{(b^2 - \tfrac{1}{2}a^2)} = \sqrt{(4b^2 - 2a^2)}.$$

Therefore the cruiser is within firing range of the battleship for a time

$$\frac{P_1 P_2}{|\text{relative velocity}|} = \frac{\sqrt{(4b^2 - 2a^2)}}{V\sqrt{2}} = \frac{\sqrt{(2b^2 - a^2)}}{V} \text{ hours}.$$

(iv) A wind is blowing towards the direction of N. θ E. An aeroplane, on the course N. α W., passes over two points A and B, B being due N. of A; on arrival over B the course is altered to S. β E. and the aeroplane passes over a point C due E. of B. Prove that

$$\tan\theta = \sin\alpha \sec\beta.$$

If $AB = BC$ and T_1, T_2 are the times taken for flying over the distances AB, BC respectively, prove that

$$T_1/T_2 = \tan\tfrac{1}{2}(\alpha + \beta). \qquad\qquad \text{(O.C.)}$$

Figure 55 is a composite relative velocity diagram for the two legs of the course in which $_pV_G$ represents the velocity of the aeroplane relative to the ground and $_A V_G$ the velocity of the air relative to the ground. From triangles PSR and PSQ

$$\frac{PS}{\cos\beta} = \frac{RS}{\cos\theta},$$

$$\frac{PS}{\sin\alpha} = \frac{SQ}{\sin\theta}.$$

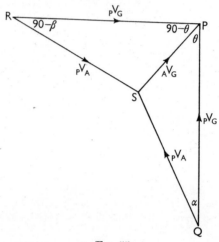

Fig. 55.

Therefore, if we assume that the magnitude of $_P V_A$ is constant over the two legs of the course, i.e. that $RS = SQ$,

$$\frac{\sin\alpha}{\cos\beta} = \frac{\sin\theta}{\cos\theta},$$

i.e. $\sin\alpha \sec\beta = \tan\theta.$

For the first leg of the course,

$$PQ = \frac{PS \sin(\theta + \alpha)}{\sin\alpha},$$

and for the second leg

$$PR = \frac{PS \sin(\theta + \beta)}{\cos\beta}.$$

$$\text{Time of flight} = \frac{\text{Displacement relative to the ground}}{\text{Magnitude of velocity relative to the ground}}.$$

$$\therefore T_1 = \frac{AB \sin\alpha}{PS \sin(\theta + \alpha)}, \quad T_2 = \frac{BC \cos\beta}{PS \sin(\theta + \beta)}.$$

Therefore when $AB = BC$,

$$\frac{T_1}{T_2} = \frac{\sin\alpha\sin(\theta+\beta)}{\cos\beta\sin(\theta+\alpha)}$$

$$= \frac{\sin\alpha\sin\theta\cos\beta + \sin\alpha\cos\theta\sin\beta}{\cos\beta\sin\theta\cos\alpha + \cos\beta\cos\theta\sin\alpha}$$

$$= \frac{\sin\alpha\tan\theta\cos\beta + \sin\alpha\sin\beta}{\cos\beta\tan\theta\cos\alpha + \cos\beta\sin\alpha}.$$

But $\tan\theta = \sin\beta\,\sec\beta$.

$$\therefore \frac{T_1}{T_2} = \frac{\sin^2\alpha + \sin\alpha\sin\beta}{\sin\alpha\cos\alpha + \sin\alpha\cos\beta} = \frac{\sin\alpha + \sin\beta}{\cos\alpha + \cos\beta}$$

$$= \frac{2\sin\frac{1}{2}(\alpha+\beta)\cos\frac{1}{2}(\alpha-\beta)}{2\cos\frac{1}{2}(\alpha+\beta)\cos\frac{1}{2}(\alpha-\beta)}.$$

$$\therefore \frac{T_1}{T_2} = \tan\frac{1}{2}(\alpha+\beta).$$

EXERCISES 5.3.

1. An enemy aeroplane is notified to a pilot who is at a point A, as being 40 miles NE. of him and flying due W. at 150 m.p.h. If the pilot flies at 200 m.p.h. what course should he set to intercept the enemy, and after what time will he meet him? (N.)

2. An aeroplane A is flying NE. at a steady speed of 300 m.p.h. on a day when there is no wind. At 12 noon it is 120 miles due W. of an aeroplane B which flies at 450 m.p.h. What course should B set to intercept A as quickly as possible? At what time will B then intercept A? (L.)

3. A ship A is travelling due W. at 12 m.p.h. and at a certain instant a ship B is 4 miles due N. of A. Half an hour later the distance apart of the ships has reached its minimum value, and B then bears NW. from A.

Calculate the velocity of B assuming it to be constant.

Show that after a further hour the bearing of B from A is S. $\tan^{-1}3$ W. (L.)

4. A ship is sailing due N. at 20 knots. It observes at noon another ship, on a bearing N. 45° E. and at a distance of 5 sea-miles, sailing due W. at 15 knots. At what time are the ships closest together and how far are they then apart?

For how long a time is the distance between the ships less than 5 sea-miles?

[Answers should be given to the nearest minute and to the nearest tenth of a sea-mile.] (L.)

5. Two straight roads cross at a point O. A motorist is travelling at 30 m.p.h. towards O along the first road AO. At the instant when he is 5 miles away from O, a cyclist, travelling at 10 m.p.h., leaves O along the second road OB. If the angle AOB is 30°, determine graphically or otherwise, the time that elapses before they are at their minimum distance apart. (L.)

6. Two ships leave the same port; one steams 30° W. of N. at 12 knots and the other, leaving 6 hr later, steams due W. at 15 knots. Their radio allows them to communicate with each other up to 400 sea miles. How long, after the first ship leaves the port, may the ships remain in touch with each other? (L.)

7. Two straight roads intersect at O. At a certain instant a motorist on the first road is 10 miles due north of O and travelling towards O at 40 m.p.h., while a cyclist on the second road is leaving O and travelling at 10 m.p.h. in the direction 60° E. of N. Assuming their speeds to remain constant, find their shortest distance apart and the time that elapses before this is attained. (L.)

8. A boat A is sailing NE. at 3 m.p.h. A motor boat B, whose speed is 5 m.p.h., is 3 miles due S. of A at 8 a.m. Determine, by drawing or calculation, the direction in which B must steer in order to intercept A as soon as possible, and find when they meet. (C.)

9. At 4 p.m. the bearing and distance of a steamer, proceeding due N. at 10 knots, from a destroyer are 45° W. of N. and 38 nautical miles respectively. The destroyer, whose speed is 30 knots, is ordered to intercept the steamer at the earliest possible moment. Find, either by calculation or by means of a carefully drawn diagram, the course steered by the destroyer and the time at which the steamer is intercepted. (O.C.)

MISCELLANEOUS EXERCISES. V

1. The wind is blowing at 15 m.p.h. from the E. when a cyclist begins to cycle at 10 m.p.h. due N. on a level road. What velocity (in magnitude and direction) will the cyclist think the wind has? (N.)

2. A ship A is travelling NE. at 20 m.p.h. and a ship B is travelling NW. at 10 m.p.h. At a certain instant B is 5 miles due E. of A. Find the distance and bearing of A from B when the ships are closest together. Find also the bearing of A from B when the ships are next 5 miles apart. (L.)

3. A cruiser which can steam at 30 knots receives a report that an enemy vessel, steaming due N. at 20 knots, is 29 nautical miles away in a direction 30° N. of E. Show (1) graphically, (2) by calculation, that the cruiser can overtake the vessel in almost exactly 2 hr. (O.C.)

4. A destroyer, steaming N. 30° E. at 30 knots, observes at noon a steamer, which is steaming due N. at 12 knots, and overtakes the steamer at 12·45 p.m. Find the distance and bearing of the steamer from the destroyer at noon. (O.C.)

5. A ship which has a speed of 10 m.p.h. in still water steams from a point A, which is 5 miles due S. of a lighthouse L, to a point B, which is 5 miles due E. of L, through a current flowing at 3 m.p.h. in the direction 15° N. of E. If the course set to take the ship along the line AB is φ N. of E., prove that

$$\sin(\varphi - 45°) = \tfrac{3}{20}.$$

Find, to the nearest minute, (i) the time for the run from A to B, and (ii) the time for the return from B to A, the current being assumed to be unaltered. (O.C.)

***6.** Two smooth wires OX, OY are fixed in a vertical plane so that O is the lowest point of each wire, XOY is a right angle and OX makes an acute angle θ with the horizontal. Two small rings threaded one on each wire are released simultaneously from rest. Find the magnitude and direction of the velocity of one ring relative to the other after time t, assuming that neither has reached O.

Find also the magnitude and direction of the acceleration of one ring relative to the other. (L.)

7. Two aircraft A and B fly at the same height and at constant speeds on straight and level courses. At noon aircraft B is 100 miles due W. of aircraft A and is flying NE. at 400 m.p.h. Aircraft A is flying NW. at 300 m.p.h. Find the least distance between A and B and the time at which they are nearest to one another. (N.)

8. Two cars, A and B, are travelling along straight roads which cross at right angles at O, their constant velocities being 40 m.p.h. westwards and 30 m.p.h. northwards respectively. At the instant when B is passing through O the car A is 250 yd from O and moving towards it. Find
(i) the velocity of B relative to A,
(ii) the least distance between the cars,
(iii) the distances of the cars from O when they are nearest to one another. (N.)

9. A wind is blowing with velocity v from a direction N. θ E. To a car travelling due E. with velocity u, the wind appears to blow from a direction N. α E. Prove that
$$\tan\alpha = (u + v\sin\theta)/v\cos\theta.$$

To a car travelling due west with velocity u, the wind appears to blow from a direction N. β W. Prove that
$$2\tan\theta = \tan\alpha - \tan\beta.$$

If $\tan\alpha = 2\tan\beta$, prove that, when the car is travelling due east, the headwind against it has velocity $u/3$. (L.)

10. Two footballers, A and B, are running with equal speeds along parallel lines in the same direction, and an opposing player is running towards them with an equal speed along a parallel line equidistant from the first two lines. Show that if, when A reaches the stationary ball, the three players are at the vertices of an equilateral triangle, A must project the ball with a speed, relative to the ground, at least $\sqrt{(7/3)}$ times his own speed, in order that player B receives the pass. (Assume that B and C continue to move as described after the ball is passed.) (L.)

11. An equilateral triangular course is marked out by buoys A, B, C in a broad straight reach of a river, the buoy C being upstream and the line AB perpendicular to the current. A motor launch follows the course $ABCA$. If V is the speed of the launch in still water and u the speed of the current, show that while the launch is moving along AB it is pointed at an angle θ to AB on the upstream side, where $\sin\theta = u/V$.
Find the angle between BC and the direction in which the launch is pointed while it is moving along BC. Show that when it reaches C the launch turns through $120°$. (N.)

12. A river half a mile wide flows between parallel banks at a rate of 2 m.p.h. A man, who rows at $2\frac{1}{2}$ m.p.h. in still water, wishes to cross from a point A on one bank to a point B on the other, AB being perpendicular to the direction of flow. Find the angle between AB and the direction in which he must head the boat, and find also the time he takes to get across.
On the return journey from B the man finds that the speed of the river has increased to 3 m.p.h. He heads the boat so as to reach a point C on the bank from which he first started as near as possible to A. Find the distance AC. (N.)

13. A ship is steaming due N. at speed u and the wind appears to blow from the direction θ E. of N., where $0° < \theta < 45°$. The ship turns and steams due S. at the same speed u and the wind now appears to blow from the direction θ S. of E. Find the magnitude and direction of the true wind velocity. (L.)

14. At 6 a.m. a ship is at A, 8 nautical miles due S. of a lighthouse L. Given that the ship's speed in still water is 10 knots, find, graphically or otherwise, the course to be steered through a current, flowing in the direction N. 30° E. at 3 knots, so as to pass through the position K which is 10 nautical miles due E. of L. Find also, to the nearest minute, the time of arrival at K.

If the current remains unchanged, find how long it will take the ship to go from K to A. (O.C.)

15. A man can row at a speed v through still water and wishes to cross a straight river flowing with speed u. Prove that he can reach the point A directly opposite to him if and only if $v > u$.

If $v < u$ and he rows so as to reach a point B on the opposite bank as near as possible to A, find the ratio of AB to the width of the river. (L.)

16. An aircraft, travelling in cloud at an air speed of 240 m.p.h. is steered due E. by compass. Ten minutes after starting a break in the cloud reveals that it is directly above a place 6 miles N. and 48 miles E. of the starting point. Find, graphically or otherwise, the speed and direction of the wind, supposed constant. (L.)

17. A swimmer in a river finds that he can cover a distance d upstream in time t_1 and the same distance downstream in time t_2. Show that the speed of the current is

$$\frac{(t_1 - t_2)d}{2t_1 t_2}.$$

If the width of the river is also d, show that he would take a time $\sqrt{(t_1 t_2)}$ to swim across it, starting from a point on one bank and crossing in a straight line to the point directly opposite on the other bank. (The speed of the current is constant throughout.) (N.)

18. (i) Rain is falling vertically. From a train travelling at 15 m.p.h. the rain appears to fall at 60° to the horizontal. Find the speed of the rain. Find also its apparent direction when the train is travelling at 45 m.p.h.

(ii) If the wind is blowing at 40 m.p.h. from NW., find graphically the course a pilot should set, with an air-speed of 160 m.p.h., in order to fly due N. What is his ground-speed in this case? (L.)

19. A particle P moves round the circumference of a circle of radius a with a constant speed v, being initially at a point A on the circumference. At the same instant another particle Q commences to move from A along the tangent at A, in the same direction, with constant velocity v. Find the magnitude of the relative velocity of P with respect to Q when t sec have elapsed and show that its direction is perpendicular to AP.

After what time does this relative velocity first attain its greatest magnitude? (C.)

20. A motor-launch travels at a constant speed of 25 m.p.h. relative to the water and has sufficient fuel for 10 hr. It travels due W. for 5 hr and sets a return course so that it travels towards a point A 50 miles due N. of the original starting point. If throughout there is a constant current of 7 m.p.h. from the N., show, graphically or otherwise, that the launch will fail to reach A. Find the distance from A at which the launch stops. (L.)

*21. An aeroplane whose speed is V in still air flies horizontally due N. from A to B in a wind blowing with speed w from a direction θ E. of N. If $AB = a$, show that the time taken is

$$\frac{a}{V^2 - w^2} \{\sqrt{(V^2 - w^2 \sin^2 \theta)} + w \cos \theta\}.$$

If the complete course of the aeroplane is a horizontal square $ABCD$, no time is lost at the corners and the wind remains unchanged, show that the total time taken is

$$\frac{2a}{V^2 - w^2} \{\sqrt{(V^2 - w^2 \sin^2 \theta)} + \sqrt{(V^2 - w^2 \cos^2 \theta)}\}. \tag{N.}$$

*22. A model aircraft is capable of maintaining a speed of 20 m.p.h. in still air. It describes a horizontal circuit which is in the form of an equilateral triangle of side $\frac{1}{4}$ mile, there being a wind of speed 5 m.p.h. blowing parallel to one side of the circuit, but in the direction opposite to that in which the aircraft traverses this side. Find the average speed with which the aircraft traverses the circuit.
(L.)

*23. An aircraft flies straight from an aerodrome A to an aerodrome B and immediately back to A. The distance AB is a and the bearing of B from A is θ W. of N. There is a wind blowing at speed u from due S. and the speed of the aircraft relative to the air is nu $(n > 1)$. Show that the time taken for the flight is

$$\frac{2a\sqrt{(n^2 - \sin^2 \theta)}}{(n^2 - 1)u}. \tag{L.}$$

*24. Three thin rods AB, BC, CA are fastened together to form a triangular frame ABC in which ACB is a right angle. The frame is fixed so that A is vertically above B. Small smooth rings slide along AC and CB, starting simultaneously from rest at A and C respectively. Prove that the rings reach C and B simultaneously, and find

   (i) the acceleration of the higher ring relative to the lower;
   (ii) the shortest distance between the rings during the motion;
   (iii) the locus of the point midway between the rings. (L.)

*25. A particle P moves, with uniform velocity $p\sqrt{5}$, from the point $A \equiv (-a, 0)$ to the point $B \equiv (a, a)$, where coordinates refer to fixed rectangular axes. As P leaves A, another particle Q leaves the point $(0, -a)$ with velocity $5p$, and moves in the positive direction along the axis of y with uniform retardation f. Prove that, when the velocity of Q relative to P is a minimum, the distance PQ is $\pm\left(a - \dfrac{8p^2}{f}\right)\sqrt{2}$, and show that the velocity of the retarded particle is then equal to p. (O.C.)

26. To an observer on a ship sailing N. at 12 knots a constant wind appears to have a speed of 16 knots; to an observer on a nearby ship sailing W. at 16 knots the wind's apparent speed is 12 knots. Find, graphically or otherwise, how many possibilities there are for the actual speed and wind direction, and in each case find the speed and direction. (N.)

CHAPTER VI

THE MOMENT OF A FORCE

6.1. The Law of the Lever

Thus far, we have considered

(a) the relation between forces acting on a particle in equilibrium, and

(b) the relation between forces acting on a rigid body in equilibrium in the case in which these forces are reduced to three forces which are not all parallel, when we were able to deduce that the three forces act through a point. We made the assumption, however, that the resultant weight of the rigid body is a single force acting through a point called the Centre of Gravity of the body which is fixed relative to the body.

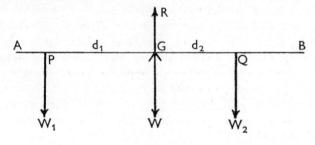

FIG. 56.

Figure 56 shows a thin uniform rod in equilibrium supported horizontally on a smooth support at its centre of gravity G and carrying masses of weights W_1 and W_2 respectively at P and Q. The points P and Q are on opposite sides of G: $PG = d_1$, $GQ = d_2$.

The rod is in equilibrium under the action of the following forces:

(i) its weight W vertically downwards through G,

(ii) the reaction R, between the support and the rod, vertically upwards at G,

132

(iii) the weights W_1 and W_2 acting vertically downwards at P and Q respectively. (Strictly, these forces do not act on the rod but on the respective masses. If the masses are resting on the rod, the reactions between the masses at P, Q and the rod are W_1, W_2 respectively. If the masses are connected to the rod by light strings, the forces acting on the rod are the tensions in the strings, again equal to W_1, W_2 respectively.)

All the forces acting on the rod are thus either vertically upwards or vertically downwards and therefore, since the rod is in equilibrium, $R = W + W_1 + W_2$. If, however, the mass of weight W_1 were moved nearer to G, equilibrium would be broken by the rod turning in a clockwise direction about G. This tendency of a force to turn a rigid body about an axis is called the *turning effect* of the force. Experiment shows that, when the rod in this example is in equilibrium,

$$W_1 d_1 = W_2 d_2.$$

The product $W_1 d_1$ is defined as the *moment* of the force W_1 about G and it is the measure of the turning effect of W_1 about G.

Thus, the *Moment of a Force about a point is the product of the force and the perpendicular distance of the point from the line of action of the force.* The moment of a force about a line (i.e. about an axis) is defined as the product of the resolved part of the force at right angles to the given line and the shortest distance between the line of action of the force and the given line. In this book we consider systems of coplanar forces only, so that a reference to moment about a point is equivalent to a reference to moment about an axis through that point perpendicular to the plane of the forces. The moment of a force about a point is a directed quantity which can either be counterclockwise (positive in this book) or clockwise (negative in this book).

If a rigid body is in equilibrium under the action of a number of coplanar parallel forces, the sum of the moments of the forces about any point in their plane is zero.

This is the *Law of the Lever*.

Units

Since the moment of a force about a point is the product of force and distance, the units in which moment is measured are:

(a) the *foot-poundal* or the *foot-pound-weight* in the FPS system,

(b) the *centimetre-dyne* or the *centimetre-gram-weight* in the CGS system of units.

In § 6.2 the relation between the Law of the Lever and the Parallelogram of Forces is considered.

Examples. (i) A thin uniform rod AB of length 2 ft and mass 10 lb is supported horizontally at its centre of gravity G and masses of 5 lb, 8 lb are attached to the rod at P, Q respectively, where $AP = 8$ in., $AQ = 15$ in. A third mass of 4 lb is attached to the rod at a point R so that the rod is in equilibrium. Calculate the distance AR and the reaction between the rod and the support.

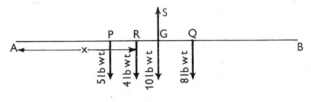

Fig. 57.

Suppose $AR = x$ in.; then, since the sum of the moments of the forces about G is zero (Fig. 57),

$$5 \times 4 - 8 \times 3 + 4(12 - x) = 0.$$

$$\therefore x = 11.$$

$$\therefore \text{ the distance } AR \text{ is 11 in.}$$

The sum of the forces acting on the rod is zero and so the reaction at the support is $S = 5 + 4 + 10 + 8 = 27$ lb wt.

(ii) A thin uniform rod AB of length $2l$ ft is suspended by a light inextensible string attached to the rod at C. The distance AC is $\frac{1}{2}l$ ft and the string is vertical (Fig. 58). The rod is balanced when masses of $7W/2$ lb and W lb respectively are suspended from A and B. Find the mass of the rod and the tension in the supporting string.

The rod is now suspended by two similar strings attached at C and B respectively and a mass of $4W$ lb is suspended from a point D of the rod between C and B (Fig. 59). Show that, if the breaking tension of either string is $6W$ lb, and if the rod and the masses now rest in equilibrium, $BD < 3l/8$.

Let the mass of the rod be X lb so that its weight is X lb wt. acting at its mid-point M.

The sum of the moments about C of the forces acting on the rod is zero.

$$\therefore \frac{7W}{2} \cdot \frac{l}{2} - X \cdot \frac{l}{2} = W \cdot \frac{3l}{2}.$$

$$\therefore X = \tfrac{1}{2}W,$$

i.e. the mass of the rod is $\tfrac{1}{2}W$ lb.

The sum of the (vertical) forces acting on the rod is zero.

$$\therefore T = 5W,$$

i.e. the tension in the string is $5W$ lb wt.

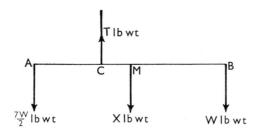

Fig. 58.

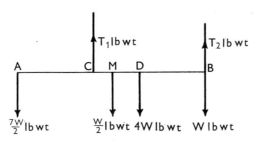

Fig. 59.

In the second case, if the tensions in the strings at C and B respectively are T_1 lb wt. and T_2 lb wt.,

$$T_1 + T_2 = 9W.$$

The sum of the moments of the forces about C is zero.

$$\therefore T_2 \cdot \frac{3l}{2} = 4W \left(\frac{3l}{2} - BD \right).$$

(The sum of the moments of the forces $7W/2$ lb wt., $\frac{1}{2}W$ lb wt. and W lb wt. about C is zero.)

$$\therefore \; T_2 = 4W - \frac{8W \cdot BD}{3l}.$$

$$\therefore \; T_1 = 5W + \frac{8W \cdot BD}{3l}.$$

Since the breaking tension of either string is $6W$,

$$\therefore \; 5W + \frac{8W \cdot BD}{3l} < 6W.$$

$$\therefore \; BD < 3l/8.$$

The necessary condition $T_2 < 6W$ is satisfied whatever the position of D between B and C.

(iii) A non-uniform thin rod is balanced in two successive trials as follows:

(a) suspended by an inextensible string attached to the mid-point, with a mass of 10 gm attached at a distance of 10 cm to the right of the mid-point,

(b) suspended by the string attached to a point 10 cm to the left of the mid-point, with a mass of 2 gm attached at the mid-point.

Find the mass of the rod and the position of its centre of gravity.

Let the mass of the rod be M gm and let the centre of gravity of the rod be x cm to the left of the mid-point. Then, in each case, the sum of the moments about the point of suspension of the forces acting on the rod is zero.

$$\therefore \; \text{(a)} \; 10 \times 10 = Mx,$$

$$\text{(b)} \quad 2 \times 10 = M(x - 10).$$

$$\therefore \; M = 8, \quad x = 12\tfrac{1}{2}.$$

The rod has a mass of 8 gm and its centre of gravity is $12\frac{1}{2}$ cm to the left of its mid-point.

(iv) A thin uniform circular disc marked as a clock-face, with XII at the highest point, is free to rotate in a vertical plane about a horizontal axis through its centre. Masses of W lb, $2W$ lb, $3W$ lb, $4W$ lb respectively are attached to the rim of the disc at the points corresponding to the hours XII, IV, VI, VIII. Find the position of the disc in equilibrium.

Figure 60 shows the forces acting on the disc in its position of equilibrium, other than the weight of the disc and the reaction between the support and the disc, neither of which forces have a moment about the axis of support. The sum of the moments of these forces about the axis is zero.

$$\therefore \quad 2\,Wa\sin(120-\theta) + 3\,Wa\sin\theta = 4\,Wa\sin(60-\theta) + Wa\sin\theta,$$

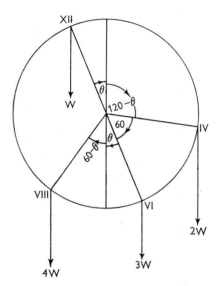

FIG. 60.

where a is the radius of the disc.

$$\therefore \quad \sqrt{3}\cos\theta + \sin\theta + 3\sin\theta = 2\sqrt{3}\cos\theta - 2\sin\theta + \sin\theta,$$

$$\therefore \quad 5\sin\theta = \sqrt{3}\cos\theta,$$

$$\therefore \quad \tan\theta = \frac{\sqrt{3}}{5}.$$

$$\therefore \quad \theta = 19°\,6' \quad \text{or} \quad 199°\,6'.$$

The disc rests in equilibrium with its XII–VI diameter inclined at 19° 6' anticlockwise to the vertical or 160° 54' clockwise to the vertical.

10*

EXERCISES 6.1.

1. Two men support by vertical forces a uniform horizontal pole MN, of length 12 ft and mass 36 lb, holding it at points X and Y, where $MX = 1$ ft. $NY = 2$ ft. If a load of mass 270 lb is suspended from a point P of the pole, where $MP = 5$ ft find the force exerted by each of the men on the pole. (N.)

2. A non-uniform beam XY, of length 10 ft and mass M lb, rests horizontally on supports at X and Y. The forces exerted on the supports at X and Y are 24 lb wt. and R lb wt. respectively. If the centre of gravity of the beam is 6 ft from X, find M and R. (N.)

3. A non-uniform beam LM, of length 8 ft and mass 40 lb, rests horizontally on supports at L and N, where $LN = 6$ ft. The force exerted on the support at N is 20 lb wt. Find the distance of the centre of gravity of the beam from L.

If a mass of 10 lb is now hung from M, find the force exerted by the beam on the support at L. (N.)

4. A uniform plank AB, of length 6 ft and mass 20 lb, is supported by a knife edge at C, where $AC = 4$ ft. When loads of mass x lb and y lb are hung from A and B respectively the plank rests in equilibrium in a horizontal position and the force exerted on the knife edge is 60 lb wt. Calculate x and y. (N.)

5. A uniform beam AB, of length 20 ft and mass 50 lb, is supported horizontally by means of two vertical strings, one at each end. A mass of 20 lb is hung from the beam at C, where $AC = 6$ ft. Find the tensions in the two strings. (N.)

6. A uniform plank AB, of mass 56 lb and length 18 ft, lies on a horizontal roof in a direction at right angles to the edge of the roof. The end B projects 4 ft over the edge. A man of mass 140 lb walks out along the plank. Find how far along the plank he can walk without causing the plank to tip up.

Find also the mass which must be placed on the end A so that the man can reach B without upsetting the plank. (N.)

7. A non-uniform rod AB, 10 ft long, balances about a point 4 ft from A when a load of 25 lb is suspended from the end A, and about a point $2\frac{2}{3}$ ft from B when the same load is suspended from B. Find the distance from A of the point about which the rod balances when loads of 25 lb are suspended from A and B simultaneously. (N.)

8. A uniform rod $ACDB$ of weight W and length $2l$ rests in a horizontal position on two pegs at C and D respectively, where $AC = a$ and $DB = b$. If a weight nW is placed between C and D at a distance x from A, find the reactions at C and D. Show also that, if $a > b$ and $l > (n + 1) a$, the weight nW can be placed at any point between A and B without disturbing the equilibrium. (N.)

9. A horizontal bar ABC, 12 ft long and of mass 60 lb, has its centre of gravity at D where $AD = 5$ ft. The bar is hung from spring balances at A, B and C where $AB = 8$ ft.

   (i) If the balance at B reads 25 lb wt., what will be the readings of the balances at A and C?

   (ii) How far must the balance at B be moved in order that all three readings may be the same? (L.)

10. A light rod ABC, in which $AB = BC$, has a particle of weight W affixed to the mid-point of AB. The rod is kept at rest in a horizontal position by the action of three like vertical forces applied at A, B and C. The force at B is four times the force at C. Calculate the force at A.   (N.)

11. A faulty balance has a fulcrum not quite at the middle of the beam, whose weight is negligible. An object is balanced by a 7 lb wt. when put in one scale-pan, and by a 6 lb wt. when put in the other scale-pan. Find the true weight of the object.   (N.)

12. A uniform beam, 6 ft long and of mass 40 lb, is supported in a horizontal position by two vertical strings, each connecting an end of the beam with a fixed point above the beam. Neither string can support a tension of more than 30 lb wt. Find the greatest load which will not cause either of the strings to break, wherever it is placed on the beam, and determine the portion of the beam on which a load of 15 lb can be placed without causing either of the strings to break.   (O.C.)

13. A uniform rod AB, of length 8 ft and mass 12 lb, supports a load of 7 lb hung from B. The system is kept in equilibrium with AB horizontal by two vertical strings, one attached to the rod at A and the other at a point C between A and B. Find the least possible length of AC.   (L.)

14. A uniform rod AB, of length 6 ft and mass 10 lb, is suspended horizontally by two vertical inextensible strings attached to it at A and C, where $AC = x$ ft. A mass of 12 lb is hung from a point of the rod distant $2\frac{1}{2}$ ft from A. Find the limits between which x must lie (a) if the strings are strong enough to support the rod and the mass under all circumstances, (b) if the breaking tension in each is 15 lb wt. In each case give the greatest and least tensions in the string attached to A.   (L.)

15. A uniform beam AB is 6 ft long and of mass 24 lb. Its rests on two vertical supports at C and D, CD being a distance of 3 ft, and the pressures on the supports at C and D are 16 lb wt. and 8 lb wt. respectively. Find the lengths of AC and DB, assuming that A is nearer to C than to D.   (O.C.)

16. A framework consists of a regular hexagon $ABCDEF$ of thin uniform rods each of weight W with five uniform rods each of weight W joining the centre O of the hexagon to five of its vertices, A, B, C, D, E. The framework is free to rotate in a vertical plane about an axis through O. Find its position of equilibrium.

*17. A non-uniform thin circular disc of weight W and radius r is free to rotate in a vertical plane about an axis through a point A on its circumference. The disc can be held in equilibrium

(a) with its diameter AB horizontal, by means of a vertical force P acting at B,

(b) with its diameter AB vertical and B below A by means of a vertical force P acting at a point C on its circumference where $\angle CAB = \theta$. Prove that the centre of gravity of the disc is at G where $\tan GAB = \frac{1}{2}\sin 2\theta$ and

$$AG = \{Pr\sqrt{(4 + \sin^2 2\theta)}\}/W.$$

*18. A non-uniform rod AB, 100 cm long, carries loads of 50 gm at A, 80 gm at B, and 30 gm at the middle point. It is found to balance if placed horizontally across a knife-edge 40 cm from A. If the 80-gm mass is removed, the system balances about a point 20 cm from A. Find the mass of the bar and the distance of its mass-centre from A.   (N.)

*19. Two equal uniform rods AB, BC are rigidly joined at B and form a right angle. The system is suspended by means of a string attached to A and to a fixed point. Prove that, in the position of equilibrium, BC makes with the horizontal an angle of $\cot^{-1}3$.

The point of support is lowered so that the end C of the rod BC rests on a smooth horizontal table and BC is inclined to the horizontal at an angle θ. Prove that the tension of the supporting string is

$$\frac{3\cos\theta - \sin\theta}{2\,(\cos\theta - \sin\theta)}\,W,$$

where W is the weight of each rod.   (O.C.)

*20. A uniform beam ABC, of weight $4W$ and length $3a$, rests horizontally on supports at A and B where $AB = 2a$. Two persons, whose weights are W and $2W$, stand on the beam at distances x and y respectively from A. Calculate the load borne by each support in terms of W, a, x and y.

If the support at A cannot bear a load greater than $3W$, show that equilibrium is possible only if

$$2a \leqslant x + 2y \leqslant 8a.$$ (N.)

6.2. The Resultant of a System of Parallel Forces

We define the *resultant* of a system of coplanar forces acting on a rigid body as the single force which is equal to the vector sum of the forces of the system *and which has a moment about each point in the plane which is equal to the algebraic sum of the moments about that point of the forces of the system.* This definition assumes the existence of such a resultant force in all cases except the one discussed below.

The Resultant of Two Parallel Forces

(a) The forces P and Q are *like* and parallel. A line at right angles to the lines of action of the forces cuts the line of action of P at A and the line of action of Q at B [(Fig. 61 (i)]. If the resultant R of P and Q cuts AB at D, from the definition quoted above,

the sum of the moments of P and Q about D is zero.

$$\therefore\ P.AD = Q.BD.$$
$$\therefore\ \frac{AD}{BD} = \frac{Q}{P}.$$

From elementary geometry we deduce that the resultant would similarly divide any other line joining a point in the line of action of P to a point in the line of action of Q.

Also, from the definition, $R = P + Q$.

The resultant of two like parallel forces is a parallel force equal to the vector sum of the two forces, whose line of action divides a line joining the lines of action of the two forces inversely in the ratio of the forces.

(b) The forces P and Q are parallel and *unlike*. A line at right angles to the lines of action of the forces cuts the line of action of P at A and the line of action of Q at B [Fig. 61 (ii)]. $P > Q$ and the resultant R of P and Q cuts BA produced at D.

Then, by definition, the sum of the moments of P and Q about D is zero.

$$\therefore Q.BD = P.AD.$$

$$\therefore \frac{AD}{BD} = \frac{Q}{P}.$$

Also, by definition, $R = P - Q$.

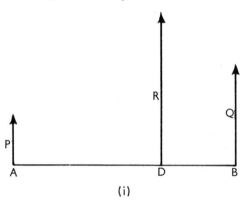

(i)

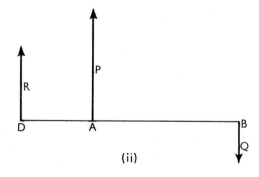

(ii)

FIG. 61.

The resultant of two unequal, unlike parallel forces is a parallel force equal to the vector sum of the two forces, whose line of action divides a line joining the lines of action of the two forces externally, inversely in the ratio of the forces.

(c) The forces P are unlike and equal. A line drawn at right angles to the lines of action of the forces cuts the lines of action at A and B respectively [Fig. 61 (iii)].

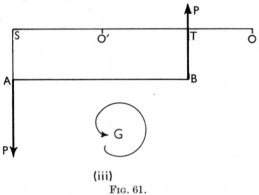

(iii)

FIG. 61.

There is no single force resultant of the system which satisfies our definition.

If O is a point in the plane of the forces and if OTS, perpendicular to the lines of action of the forces, cuts the lines of action at T and S respectively,

the moment of the system about O is $P.SO - P.TO = P.AB$. Similarly, if O' is in ST between S and T,

the moment of the system about O' is $P.O'T + P.SO' = P.AB$.

The moment of a system of two equal and unlike parallel forces is thus constant about all the points in the plane, and equal to the product of one of the forces and the perpendicular distance between them. Such a system is called a *couple*.

A couple as defined here is replaceable by any system which has the same constant moment about *all the points in the plane*. (The converse property, that a system whose moment is constant about all points in the plane has a zero vector sum, is easily proved.) For this reason it is possible, and frequently expedient, to consider a couple only in terms of its constant moment and not in terms of two parallel unlike forces. We then indicate a couple in a force diagram as shown in Fig. 61 (iii) where $G = P \cdot AB$.

Couples are directed quantities (anticlockwise positive, clockwise negative) and the *resultant* of a number of couples is a couple of moment equal to the algebraic sum of the moments of the component couples.

The Relation between the Parallelogram of Forces and the Resultant of two Parallel Forces

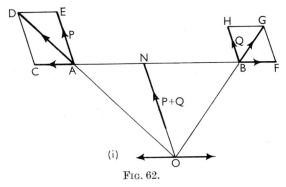

FIG. 62.

Figure 62 (i) shows vectors $\overrightarrow{AE}$ and $\overrightarrow{BH}$ representing two unequal like parallel forces P and Q acting through A and B. The points F in AB produced and C in BA produced are such that $BF = AC$. Parallelograms $BFGH$ and $ACDE$ are completed. The lines DA and GB meet, when produced, at O; also ON, parallel to each of the forces P and Q, meets AB at N.

Then, for vectors at A,

$$\overrightarrow{AE} = \overrightarrow{AD} - \overrightarrow{AC},$$

and, for vectors at B

$$\overrightarrow{BH} = \overrightarrow{BG} - \overrightarrow{BF},$$

But

$$(\overrightarrow{AC} \text{ at } A) + (\overrightarrow{BF} \text{ at } B) = 0.$$

$$\therefore (\overrightarrow{AE} \text{ at } A) + (\overrightarrow{BH} \text{ at } B) = (\overrightarrow{AD} \text{ at } A) + (\overrightarrow{BG} \text{ at } B)$$

$$= (\overrightarrow{AD} \text{ at } O) + (\overrightarrow{BG} \text{ at } O)$$

$$= (\overrightarrow{AE} + \overrightarrow{AC} + \overrightarrow{BH} + \overrightarrow{BF}) \text{ at } O$$

$$= (\overrightarrow{AE} + \overrightarrow{BH}) \text{ at } O$$

$$= (P + Q) \text{ at } O$$

in the common direction of P and Q.

From the similar triangles ONB and BHG,

$$\frac{NB}{ON} = \frac{HG}{BH},$$

and from the similar triangles ONA and AED,

$$\frac{AN}{ON} = \frac{DE}{AE}.$$

Therefore by division and since $HG = DE$,

$$\frac{AN}{NB} = \frac{BH}{AE} = \frac{Q}{P}.$$

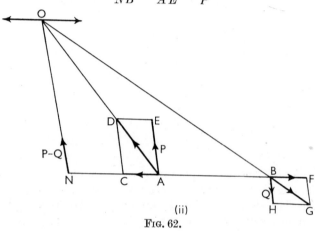

(ii)

FIG. 62.

Figure 62 (ii) illustrates the case in which the forces are parallel and unlike. The construction is similar to that of Fig. 62 (i).

For vectors at A,

$$\overleftarrow{AE} = AD - \overrightarrow{AC}.$$

For vectors at B,

$$\overrightarrow{BH} = \overrightarrow{BG} - \overrightarrow{BF}.$$

$$
\begin{aligned}
\therefore (\overrightarrow{AE} \text{ at } A) + (\overrightarrow{BH} \text{ at } B) &= (\overrightarrow{AD} \text{ at } A) + (\overrightarrow{BG} \text{ at } B) \\
&= (\overrightarrow{AD} \text{ at } O) + (\overrightarrow{BG} \text{ at } O) \\
&= (\overrightarrow{AE} + \overrightarrow{AC} + \overrightarrow{BH} + \overrightarrow{BF}) \text{ at } O \\
&= (\overrightarrow{AE} + \overrightarrow{BH}) \text{ at } O \\
&= (P - Q) \text{ at } O \text{ in the direction of } P.
\end{aligned}
$$

From the similar triangles BNO and GHB,

$$\frac{BN}{NO} = \frac{HG}{BH}$$

and from the similar triangles NAO and CAD,

$$\frac{NA}{NO} = \frac{AC}{CD}.$$

$$\therefore \frac{BN}{NA} = \frac{CD}{BH} = \frac{P}{Q}.$$

When $P = Q$ the construction fails, since in this case GB is parallel to AD.

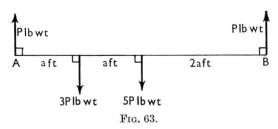

FIG. 63.

Examples. (i) Find the resultant of the system of parallel forces shown in Fig. 63. Find also the magnitude, direction and position of the single force, which, added to the system, would make the system equivalent to a counterclockwise couple of moment G ft lb wt.

The resultant is parallel to the forces of the system. Let it be a force of R lb wt. in a like direction to the force of $5P$ lb wt. and let it act through X in AB distance b ft from A.

The resultant is equal to the vector sum of the forces of the system.

$$\therefore R = 6P.$$

The moment of the resultant about A is equal to the sum of the moments of the system about A.

$$\therefore Rb = 3P.a + 5P.2a - P.4a.$$

$$\therefore 6Pb = 9Pa.$$

$$\therefore b = 3a/2.$$

The resultant is a force of $6P$ lb wt. acting in a parallel (like) direction to the force of $5P$ lb wt. acting through a point in AB distant $3a/2$ from A.

Let Q lb wt. acting through a point in AB distant c ft from A be the force which reduces the system to a couple of moment G ft lb wt. counterclockwise.

The vector sum of the forces of a system which reduces to a couple is zero,

$$\therefore\ Q = 6P \text{ and the direction of the force } Q \text{ lb wt. is}$$

parallel (like) to the direction of both the forces P lb wt. The moment of the couple about every point in the plane is G ft lb wt. counterclockwise. Therefore the sum of the moments of the system about A is G ft lb wt. counterclockwise.

$$\therefore\ 6P \cdot c + P \cdot 4a - 3P \cdot a - 5P \cdot 2a = G.$$

$$\therefore\ c = (G + 9Pa)/6P.$$

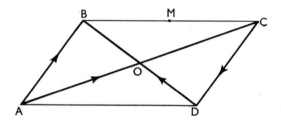

Fig. 64.

(ii) $ABCD$ is a parallelogram. Prove that forces completely represented by the lines AB, CD, AC, DB have a resultant $2AB$ in magnitude and position. (O.C.)

AC and BD intersect at O and M is the mid-point of BC (Fig. 64).

$$(\overrightarrow{AC} + \overrightarrow{DB}) \text{ at } O = 2(\overrightarrow{DO} + \overrightarrow{OC}) \text{ at } O$$

$$= 2\overrightarrow{DC} \text{ at } O.$$

$$(\overrightarrow{CD} \text{ at } D) + (2\overrightarrow{DC} \text{ at } O) = \overrightarrow{DC} \text{ at the point which divides } CM$$
$$\text{externally in the ratio } 2:1$$

$$= \overrightarrow{DC} \text{ at } B.$$

$$(\overrightarrow{AB} \text{ at } B) + (\overrightarrow{DC} \text{ at } B) = 2\overrightarrow{AB} \text{ at } B.$$

Therefore the resultant of the system is represented by $2AB$ in magnitude, direction and position.

(iii) Forces of magnitude 12 lb wt., 8 lb wt., 5 lb wt. act along the sides AB, BC, CA respectively of an equilateral triangle ABC of side 2 ft in directions indicated by the order of the letters. A force of P lb wt. acts along BM the perpendicular from B to AC and a force of Q lb wt. acts through B in a direction parallel to AC. Calculate the values of P and Q for which the system reduces to a couple and calculate the value of the couple in this case.

The sum of the components of the system parallel to AC is (Fig. 65)

$$(12 \cos 60° + 8 \cos 60° - 5 + Q) \text{ lb wt.} = (5 + Q) \text{ lb wt.}$$

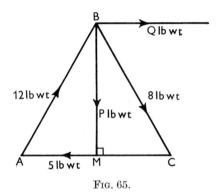

FIG. 65.

The sum of the components of the system perpendicular to AC is

$$(12 \sin 60° - 8 \sin 60° - P) \text{ lb wt. in the direction } MB$$

$$= (2\sqrt{3} - P) \text{ lb wt. in the direction } MB.$$

If the system reduces to a couple,

$$5 + Q = 0, \quad \therefore Q = -5;$$
$$2\sqrt{3} - P = 0, \quad \therefore P = 2\sqrt{3}.$$

The moment of the system about B is $5\sqrt{3}$ ft lb wt. clockwise. Therefore the moment of the couple to which the system reduces when $Q = -5$ and $P = 2\sqrt{3}$ is $5\sqrt{3}$ ft lb wt. clockwise.

(iv) A uniform rod AB, of length $2a$ and weight W, is smoothly hinged to a vertical wall at A and is supported in a horizontal position by a light elastic string of natural length $2a$ fastened to the rod at B and to the wall at a point C vertically above A where $AC = 2a$. The rod is now held in equilibrium inclined at 120° to AC by means of a couple G. Calculate G in terms of W and a.

In the first position of equilibrium, if T_1 is the tension in the string, the sum of the moments of the forces on the rod about A is zero [Fig. 66(i)].

$$\therefore\ T_1 a \sqrt{2} = W a.$$

$$\therefore\ T_1 = W/\sqrt{2}.$$

By Hooke's Law

$$\frac{W}{\sqrt{2}} = \frac{\lambda(2\sqrt{2}-2)\,a}{2a},$$

where λ is the modulus of elasticity.

$$\therefore\ \lambda = \frac{W}{2-\sqrt{2}} = \frac{(2+\sqrt{2})\,W}{2}.$$

In the second position of equilibrium, if T_2 is the tension in the string [Fig. 66(ii)],

$$T_2 . 2a \sin 30° = G + W a \sin 60°.$$

$$\therefore\ \lambda\left(\frac{4a\cos 30° - 2a}{2a}\right) 2a \sin 30° = G + W a \sin 60°.$$

$$\therefore\ G = \left\{\frac{2+\sqrt{2}}{2}\,(\sqrt{3}-1) - \frac{\sqrt{3}}{2}\right\} W a.$$

$$\therefore\ G \doteqdot 0.38\, W a.$$

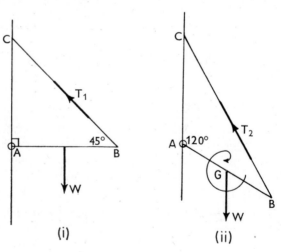

(i)   (ii)

Fig. 66.

EXERCISES 6.2.

Where possible in each of questions 1 to 12 find the resultant of the forces shown in the diagram, giving its position in terms of its distance from A, where AB is the positive direction, and an upward force is measured as positive. If there is no single force resultant, state whether the system is in equilibrium or reduces to a couple, and in the latter case state the moment of the couple.

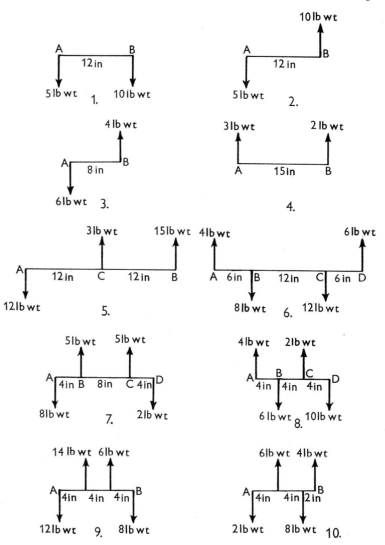

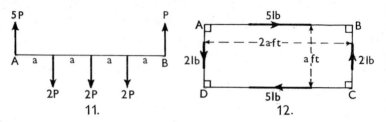

11.   12.

13. In the triangle ABC, $AC = CB$ and $\angle ACB = 120°$. Forces P, P and $P\sqrt{3}$ act along the sides AC, CB, AB respectively in the directions indicated by the order of the letters. Prove that the resultant of the system is parallel to AB and show that its line of action bisects AC and CB.

14. Forces P, $2P$, $4P$, P, $2P$, $4P$ act along the sides of a regular hexagon $ABCDEF$ of side a taken in order and in the directions indicated by the order of the letters. Show that the resultant is a couple and find its moment.

15. Three parallel forces P, $-(1 + b)P$ and bP act through points $(0, a)$, $(a, 0)$, (a, a) in a coordinate plane and in a direction making an angle θ with the positive x direction. Show that, in general, the system is equivalent to a couple and find the moment of the couple in terms of P, a, b, θ. Prove that the system is in equilibrium if $\tan \theta = -(1 + b)$.

16. A non-uniform rod AB of mass 10 lb can rotate freely in a vertical plane about an axis through its mid-point. The rod is maintained in equilibrium with B to the right of, and higher than A at an angle of $60°$ to the horizontal, by means of an anticlockwise couple of 15 ft lb wt. Find the position of the centre of gravity of the rod.

17. A uniform rod AB of weight W and length $2a$ is smoothly hinged at one end A to a vertical wall. The rod is kept in equilibrium inclined at an angle θ with the downward vertical by means of a couple. State the moment of the couple and state also the magnitude and direction of the force exerted by the hinge on the rod at A.

18. A uniform circular disc of radius r is free to rotate about an axis through its centre O perpendicular to its plane. A mass W lb is attached at a point P on the rim of the disc and a vertically upward force of W lb wt. is applied to the disc by means of an inextensible string at a point Q on the rim, where obtuse angle $POQ = \theta°$. The disc is held in equilibrium by means of a couple G so that PO makes an angle $\alpha°$ (less than $90°$) below the horizontal and OQ is above the horizontal. Find the moment of G in terms of W, r, θ and α and find α in terms of θ when the magnitude of G is least. If $\theta = 120$, find α when the magnitude of G is greatest.

6.3. Equilibrium of a Rigid Body acted upon by a System of Coplanar Forces

If a rigid body is in equilibrium under the action of a system of coplanar forces, then

(i) the vector sum of the forces is zero,

(ii) the forces have no resultant turning effect.

The first of these conditions ensures that the forces acting on the body are in equilibrium or that they reduce to a couple. If, therefore, condition (i) is satisfied and if also the resultant moment of the system about any one point in the plane is zero, condition (ii) is also satisfied. We have stated in § 2.7 that condition (i) is satisfied if the sums of the resolved parts of the forces in any two directions separately vanish.

These two conditions form the basis of a fundamental method for considering the equilibrium of a rigid body acted upon by a system of coplanar forces. A more detailed analysis of this method is discussed in Volume II.

Examples. (i) A uniform rod AB, of length $2a$ and weight W, is hinged to a vertical post at A and is supported in a horizontal position by a string attached at B and to a point C vertically above A; a weight w is hung from B. Prove that, if the reaction of the hinge at A is at right angles to BC, then

$$AC = 2a \Big/ \left(1 + \frac{2w}{W}\right). \qquad \text{(O.C.)}$$

The forces acting on the rod are as shown in Fig. 67. The reaction at the hinge at A has horizontal and vertical components X and Y respectively and the string is inclined at an angle θ to the horizontal. The rod is in equilibrium.

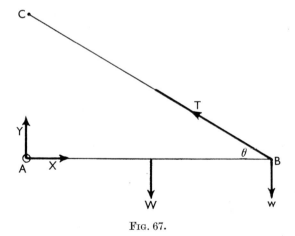

Fig. 67.

1. The sum of the horizontal components of the forces is zero.

$$\therefore X = T\cos\theta.$$

2. The sum of the vertical components of the forces is zero.

$$\therefore Y + T\sin\theta = W + w.$$

3. The sum of the moments of the forces about A is zero.

$$\therefore T.2a\sin\theta = W.a + w.2a.$$

From equations (2) and (3)

$$T\sin\theta = \frac{W+2w}{2}, \quad Y = \frac{W}{2}.$$

If the reaction at A is at right angles to BC,

$$\tan\theta = \frac{X}{Y}.$$

Therefore from equation (1),

$$\tan\theta = \frac{T\cos\theta}{Y}.$$

$$\therefore \tan\theta = \frac{W+2w}{2\sin\theta}\cdot\frac{\cos\theta}{Y} = \frac{W+2w}{2\sin\theta}\cdot\frac{2\cos\theta}{W}.$$

$$\therefore \tan^2\theta = 1 + \frac{2w}{W}.$$

$$\therefore AC = AB\tan\theta = 2a\left/\left(1+\frac{2w}{W}\right)\right..$$

(ii) A uniform square lamina $ABCD$ of side 2 ft and mass 7 lb can turn freely in a vertical plane about the point A which is fixed. It is kept in equilibrium, with D uppermost and the diagonal AC horizontal, by means of a force P lb wt. acting from B to C in the side BC, together with a couple. If the reaction at A is 13 lb wt., find the magnitude of P and the moment of the couple.   (N.)

Since the lamina is in equilibrium, if X, Y are the horizontal and vertical components respectively of the reaction at A, and G ft lb wt. is the moment of the couple, then (Fig. 68):

1. The sum of the horizontal components of the forces is zero.

$$\therefore X = P/\sqrt{2}.$$

2. The sum of the vertical components of the forces is zero.

$$\therefore Y + P/\sqrt{2} - 7 = 0.$$

3. The sum of the moments of the forces about A is zero.

$$\therefore 2P + G = 7\sqrt{2}.$$

4. The resultant reaction at A is 13 lb wt.

$$\therefore \sqrt{(X^2 + Y^2)} = 13.$$

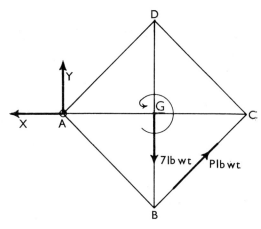

FIG. 68.

From equations (1), (2) and (4),

$$\sqrt{\left(\frac{P^2}{2} + 49 - P.7\sqrt{2} + \frac{P^2}{2}\right)} = 13.$$

$$\therefore P^2 - P.7\sqrt{2} + 49 = 169.$$

$$\therefore P^2 - P.7\sqrt{2} - 120 = 0.$$

$$\therefore P = 12\sqrt{2} \text{ since the data implies that } P \text{ is positive.}$$

$$\therefore G = -17\sqrt{2}.$$

The couple is a *clockwise* couple of moment $17\sqrt{2}$ ft lb wt.

EXERCISES 6.3.

1. A uniform ladder PQ, of mass 48 lb and length 25 ft, rests with P on a smooth horizontal floor and Q against a smooth vertical wall. The end P is attached by a string of length 7 ft to the junction of the wall and the floor. Find the tension in the string.

If the tension in the string is not to exceed 49 lb wt., find how far a man of mass 150 lb can ascend the ladder.　(N.)

2. A uniform horizontal rod AB, of length 3 ft and mass 20 lb, is freely pivoted at B to a vertical wall, and the end A is joined by a cord, inclined at

11*

$30°$ to the horizontal, to a point of the wall above B. If a lamp of mass 30 lb is suspended from A, find the tension in the cord.

If the breaking tension of the cord is 200 lb wt., find the greatest permissible distance from B at which an additional load of 135 lb wt. can be hung from the rod AB. (N.)

3. A rod AB of length 8 ft, whose weight may be neglected, is smoothly hinged to a vertical wall at A and has a load of 10 lb suspended from the end B. It is kept in a horizontal position by a string CD attached to a point C in the rod 4 ft from A, and to a point D in the wall 3 ft vertically above A. Find (i) the tension in the string, (ii) the magnitude and direction of the force at the hinge. (L.)

4. A uniform rod AB, of mass 2 lb, carries a load of 3 lb wt. at the end B. The rod is smoothly hinged at A to a vertical wall and is supported in a horizontal position by a light string which joins B to a point C on the wall vertically above A, the angle ABC being $60°$. Find the tension in the string BC and the magnitude and direction of the force at the hinge A. (C.)

5. A uniform plank, of mass 20 lb, rests with its upper end against a smooth vertical wall and its lower end on a smooth horizontal surface. The plank is held in equilibrium in a vertical plane, at an angle of $60°$ with the horizontal, by means of a light cord, fixed at right angles to the plank and in the same vertical plane with it, and attached to a point on the line of intersection of the vertical wall and the horizontal surface. Calculate the reactions at the ends of the plank and the tension in the cord. (C.)

6. A heavy uniform beam AB, 8 ft long and of mass 4 cwt is lifted on to a lorry by means of a chain attached to B whilst the end A rests on rough horizontal ground. The chain passes over a pulley C fixed above the lorry, the beam and chain being in the same vertical plane. The beam is in equilibrium when the angle between the beam and the ground is $25°$ and the angle ABC is $135°$. Find

(i) the magnitude and direction of the reaction between the beam and the ground,

(ii) the tension in the chain. (L.)

7. A uniform square lamina $ABCD$, of weight W, whose sides are 5 ft long, can turn freely in a vertical plane about the point A which is fixed. The point A is 4 ft in front of a smooth vertical wall perpendicular to the plane of the lamina. The lamina rests with B against the wall. Find the reaction at B and prove that the reaction at A is

$$\frac{W\sqrt{37}}{6}.$$

Find also the least weight which, suspended from D, will make the lamina turn away from the wall. (O.C.)

8. A uniform rod AB of weight W can turn freely about a smooth fixed hinge at A and has fixed to it a small smooth ring of negligible weight at B. A light inextensible string has one of its ends attached to a point C on the same level as A and such that $AC = AB$. The string passes through the ring and carries at its other end a particle of weight $W/10$ which hangs freely. If the system is in equilibrium so that CAB is an acute angle α, prove that $\cos \frac{1}{2}\alpha = \frac{3}{4}$, and find the vertical and horizontal components of the reaction of the hinge on the rod at A.　　　　　　　　　　　　　　　　　　　　　　　　　(N.)

9. Two uniform rods, AB, BC, each 1 ft long, of mass 1 lb and 2 lb respectively, are freely jointed at B. The rod AB can move freely about A, which is fixed. Find where a vertical force must act on BC so that both rods may be horizontal.　　　　　　　　　　　　　　　　　　　　　　　(N.)

10. A uniform straight rod AB, whose centre of gravity is C, is of mass 10 lb, and is inclined at $30°$ to the horizontal. The rod is acted upon by a force of 20 lb wt. vertically upwards at its higher end B, by a force of 10 lb wt. vertically downwards at A, and by such horizontal forces at B and C that the rod is in equilibrium. Prove that the horizontal forces at B and C are equal in magnitude, and find their magnitude.　　　　　　　　　　　　(N.)

6.4. Graphical Representation of the Moment of a Force

A force $\lambda \overrightarrow{BC}$ acting in the line BC has a moment $\lambda BC.AP$ about A (Fig. 69). The moment of the force is therefore represented by $(2\lambda) \times$ (the area of the $\triangle ABC$).

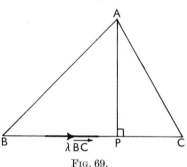

Fɪɢ. 69.

Example. Prove that the resultant of forces which are represented in magnitude, direction, and *position* by the sides AB, BC, CA of a triangle ABC is a couple whose moment is represented by twice the area of the triangle (Fig. 70).

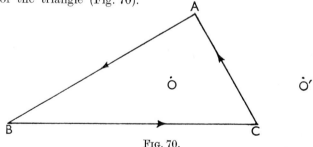

Fɪɢ. 70.

If O is a point inside the triangle, the sum of the moments of the forces of the system about O is represented by,

$$2 \text{ (area of } \varDelta AOB + \text{area of } \varDelta OBC + \text{area of } \varDelta OCA)$$
$$= 2 \text{ area of } \varDelta ABC.$$

The moment of the system is therefore constant about all points inside the triangle, and this is a sufficient condition for the system to reduce to a couple of moment represented by twice the area of $\varDelta ABC$.

For O' outside the triangle, for example in the position shown in Fig. 70, the sum of the moments of the forces about O' is represented by

$$2 (\varDelta BCO' + \varDelta ABO' - \varDelta ACO') = 2 \varDelta ABC.$$

The result which we have proved in this example can be generalized to the following:

The resultant of a system of coplanar forces represented in magnitude, direction and position by the sides of a polygon taken in order round the polygon is a couple whose moment is represented by twice the area enclosed by the polygon.

MISCELLANEOUS EXERCISES. VI

1. A load of mass 72 lb is suspended from a point T of a uniform horizontal pole LM, of mass 40 lb and length 12 ft. The pole is carried by two men, one at each end. If the man supporting the end L exerts an upward force of 44 lb wt., calculate the length of TM. (N.)

2. A uniform beam AB, of length 28 ft and mass 84 lb, is hinged at A so that it can turn freely in a vertical plane. The beam is held in equilibrium in a horizontal position by means of a light rope attached to a point C, which is 7 ft vertically above A, and to a point D in AB such that AD is 24 ft. Find the tension in the rope. Find also, in magnitude and direction, the force exerted on the hinge at A.

If a load of mass x lb is hung from B and if the rope breaks under a tension exceeding 300 lb wt., find the greatest possible value of x. (N.)

3. A uniform square lamina $ABCD$ of weight W is freely suspended at A. A particle of weight w is attached to the lamina at B, and the system rests in equilibrium with AB inclined to the vertical at an angle of $30°$. Find the ratio of w to W.

If now an additional particle of weight $2w$ is attached to the lamina at D, find an equation for the inclination of AD to the vertical in the new position of equilibrium. Prove that this inclination is greater than $30°$. (O.C.)

4. A light uniform rod AB, of length $2l$, rests in a horizontal position on supports at A and B. The rod carries loads of 10 lb at its middle point and 15 lb at the point of trisection nearer to B. P is a point of the rod distant x from A.

Find formulae for the moment about P of all forces, reaction included, acting on the part AP of the rod when (i) $x < l$, (ii) $l < x < \dfrac{4l}{3}$, (iii) $\dfrac{4l}{3} < x < 2l$. Draw a graph to show the variation of the moment as x varies from 0 to $2l$.

(O.C.)

5. A uniform plank AB of length 20 ft is of mass 40 lb and has a mass of 20 lb attached to it at B. The plank passes under a smooth peg C and over a smooth peg D. CD is horizontal, AC is 6 ft and CD is 2 ft. Calculate the reaction between each of the pegs and the plank. Calculate also the least weight that should be attached to the plank, loaded with 20 lb at B as before, for equilibrium to be broken and state, in this case, the point at which the weight should be attached. (L.)

6. Eight feet of a plank, 24 ft long and of mass 200 lb, project over the side of a quay. What load must be placed on the end of the plank so that a man of mass 150 lb may be able to walk to the other end without the plank tipping over? (O.C.)

7. A uniform beam rests in a horizontal position supported at a point distant 2 ft from one end and carrying a load of 10 lb suspended from this end. The pressure on the support is 30 lb wt. Determine the weight and length of the beam. (O.C.)

8. A uniform rod AB, of mass 2 lb, carries a load of 3 lb at the end B. The rod is smoothly hinged at A to a vertical wall and is supported in a horizontal position by a light string which joins B to a point C on the wall vertically above A, the angle ABC being 60°. Find the tension in the string BC and the magnitude and direction of the force at the hinge A. (C.)

9. A uniform horizontal beam is pivoted about a horizontal axis through its middle point so that the beam can rotate in a vertical plane, but in order to move the beam a couple of 6 ft lb wt. is necessary to overcome friction at the pivot. A mass of 20 lb is suspended from a point on the right-hand half of the beam and distant $1\frac{1}{2}$ ft from the pivot. Find the greatest and least values of a load W lb which will keep the beam in equilibrium in the horizontal position when suspended from a point distant 2 ft from the pivot on the left-hand half of the beam.

If $W = 15$, find how many inches it may be moved along the beam without disturbing equilibrium. (L.)

10. A uniform wire of length $6a$ and weight W is bent so as to form three sides AB, BC, CD of a square. It is freely suspended from A; prove that, in equilibrium, AB makes an angle $\tan^{-1} \frac{3}{4}$ with the vertical.

If a horizontal force is now applied at C so as to maintain the wire in equilibrium with BC horizontal and below A, find the magnitude of this force, and the magnitude and direction of the pressure on the support at A. (O.C.)

11. Forces of magnitude 1, 2, 3 and 6 lb wt. act along the sides AB, BC, CD and DA of a square $ABCD$ of side 2 ft. Two other forces P and Q act along the diagonals AC and BD respectively. All six forces act in the senses indicated by the orders of the letters. Determine the values of P and Q in order that the system may reduce to a couple and calculate the moment of this couple. (L.)

12. A uniform rod AB of mass 10 lb and length 4 ft is freely pivoted at A. At B a mass of 5 lb is attached. The rod is held inclined to the vertical by a force of 8 lb wt. acting at B perpendicular to the rod. Calculate

    (i) the inclination of the rod to the vertical,

    (ii) the horizontal and vertical components of the reaction of the pivot at A on the rod, and

    (iii) the resultant reaction at A of the pivot on the rod.　　(L.)

13. A uniform ladder of mass 100 lb rests with its upper end in contact with a smooth vertical wall and its lower end in contact with smooth horizontal ground, being prevented from slipping by a horizontal force exerted by a string fixed to its lower end. If the breaking tension of the string is 25 lb wt., calculate the greatest possible inclination of the ladder to the vertical.　(N.)

14. A uniform bar AB, 3 ft long and of mass 4 lb, has a cord 5 ft long attached to its ends. The cord passes through a smooth ring O fixed in a smooth vertical wall; the rod is placed in a vertical plane perpendicular to the wall with the end A against the wall and vertically below O. Prove that the rod will be in equilibrium if OA is 2 ft; and show that the tension of the string is 3 lb wt.　　(O.C.)

15. A straight uniform rigid rod AB, of weight $2W$, is freely hinged at one end A to a fixed point. A light inextensible string is attached to the rod at B, passes over a small smooth fixed peg at C, AC being horizontal, and carries at its other end a weight W which hangs freely. In the position of equilibrium $AB = BC$. Calculate the inclination of the rod AB to the horizontal.　　(N.)

16. A uniform straight rod of length l and weight W is freely hinged at one end to a fixed point. The rod is kept in equilibrium, at an inclination of 60° to the vertical, by a couple in the vertical plane which contains the rod. Calculate the moment of the couple in terms of W and l.

Find also the inclination of the rod when in equilibrium under the action of a couple of half this moment, and prove that the reaction at the hinge is the same in both cases.　　(N.)

17. Two smooth planes are each inclined at 45° to the upward vertical, their line of intersection being horizontal. A cube of weight W and edge a is placed with one edge on each plane and its lowest face inclined at an angle θ to the horizontal. Show that the couple required to keep the cube in position is $Wa \sin \theta$.　　(N.)

18. A uniform circular lamina, whose plane is vertical, is free to rotate about a horizontal axis through the centre O. At points A, B, C on the circumference, which are at the vertices of an equilateral triangle, particles of weights w_1, w_2, w_3 respectively are fixed to the lamina so that the system is in equilibrium.

    (i) If OC is horizontal, prove that

$$2w_3 = w_1 + w_2.$$

    (ii) If θ is the acute angle which OA makes with the vertical, and if OA, OB are on the same side of the vertical through O, prove that

$$\tan \theta = \frac{(w_3 - w_2)\sqrt{3}}{2w_1 - w_2 - w_3}.$$

(N.)

19. Two uniform rods AB, BC, rigidly jointed at B so that ABC is a right angle, hang freely in equilibrium from a fixed point A. The lengths of the rods are a, b, and their weights are wa, wb. Prove that, if AB makes an angle θ with the vertical,

$$\tan\theta = \frac{b^2}{a^2 + 2ab} \, . \tag{O.C.}$$

20. A uniform rod AB, of weight W and length $2a$, is pivoted to a fixed point at its end A, and its other end B is attached by a light spring of natural length a to a fixed point C at a distance $2a$ vertically above A. If in equilibrium the spring is of length $3a/2$, show that its modulus is $3W/4$.

Find the length of the spring when the system is in equilibrium, with a mass of weight W_1 suspended from B. (L.)

*21. A square lamina $ABCD$, of negligible weight, can turn freely in its own vertical plane about a smooth hinge at the corner A. Weights W, $2W$ and $3W$ are suspended from B, C and D respectively. The diagonal AC is inclined to the downward vertical at an acute angle θ and B is below the level of D, the lamina being kept in equilibrium by a horizontal force P applied at C. Show that

$$P = W(1 + 4\tan\theta).$$

If the pull on the hinge is in the direction AC, find the angle θ. (N.)

*22. A lamina of mass m consists of a uniform rectangle of metal $PQRS$ with $PQ = SR = 2a$, $PS = QR = 2b$. A particle of mass M ($>m$) is attached to the lamina at S. When the lamina hangs freely under gravity from a horizontal peg at the middle point of PQ, the angle made by PS with the vertical is α. When it hangs freely under gravity from a horizontal peg at P, the angle made by PS with the vertical is β. Find expressions for $\tan\alpha$ and $\tan\beta$ in terms of m, M, a and b.

Show that if an additional particle of mass $\frac{1}{3}(M - m)$ is attached at Q, and if the lamina is suspended in turn from each of the two pegs, then the angles made by PS with the vertical will be equal. (C.)

*23. A uniform rod AB, of weight W and length $2a$, is pivoted to a fixed point at its end A, and its mid-point C is attached by a light spring of natural length a to a fixed point D at a distance a vertically above A. If in equilibrium the spring is of length $5a/4$, show that its modulus is $5W$.

Find the point of the rod from which a mass of weight W_1 should be suspended in order that the rod may be in equilibrium in a horizontal position and show that, for this to be possible, $W_1 \geqq W(8 - 5\sqrt{2})/4$. (L.)

*24. A uniform rod AB of length $2a$ and weight w is smoothly hinged at one end A. It rests at an angle of $45°$ to the horizontal against a smooth support at C, placed so that $AC = x$ and B is below the level of A. Find, in terms of w, a, and x, the pressure of the support on the rod and the horizontal and vertical components of the reaction at the hinge.

Show that if $x = \frac{1}{2}a$, the resultant reaction at the hinge is horizontal and equal to w. Find the value of x (in terms of a) for which the resultant reaction at the hinge is equal in magnitude to the pressure of the support on the rod. (C.)

*25. Two uniform rods AB, BC, each of weight W and length $2a$, are smoothly hinged at B and rest in one horizontal line on supports at P and Q, where $PB = x$ and $BQ = y$. Prove that

$$\frac{1}{x} + \frac{1}{y} = \frac{2}{a},$$

and that $y \geqq 2a/3$.

If the support at P cannot withstand a load greater than $\frac{3}{4}W$, prove that $y \leqq 4a/5$.   (N.)

*26. A light rod AB, 5 ft long, is hung from a peg O by two light strings OA, OB, which are 4 ft and 3 ft long respectively. A weight w_1 is fixed to the rod at A and a weight w_2 at B, where $w_1 > w_2$. Show that in the position of equilibrium the inclination of the rod to the vertical is θ where

$$\tan\theta = \frac{12(w_1 + w_2)}{16w_1 - 9w_2}$$

and find in terms of w_1 and w_2 the tension in the string OA.

*27. A uniform equilateral triangular lamina ABC, of weight W, has the vertex A hinged to a fixed point, about which it can turn freely in a vertical plane, and rests with AB vertical, B being above A, and the vertex C in contact with a smooth vertical wall. Find the reaction between the lamina and the wall, and the magnitude and direction of the reaction at A.   (O.C.)

CHAPTER VII

CENTRES OF GRAVITY

7.1. Definition

We have already defined the centre of gravity of a rigid body as that point, *fixed relative to the rigid body, through which the resultant weight of the body acts no matter what the position of the body.* Thus far we have assumed the existence of such a point.

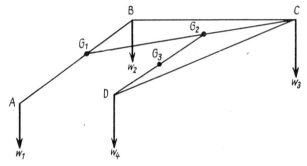

FIG. 71.

Consider a rigidly connected system of particles, A, B, C, D, ... of weights w_1, w_2, w_3, w_4, ... (Fig. 71).

The resultant of the downward vertical forces w_1 at A and w_2 at B is

$$(w_1 + w_2) \text{ at } G_1 \text{ in } AB, \text{ where } \quad \frac{AG_1}{G_1B} = \frac{w_2}{w_1}.$$

The resultant of $(w_1 + w_2)$ at G_1 and w_3 at C is

$$(w_1 + w_2 + w_3) \text{ at } G_2 \text{ in } G_1C, \text{ where } \quad \frac{G_1G_2}{G_2C} = \frac{w_3}{w_1 + w_2}.$$

The resultant of $(w_1 + w_2 + w_3)$ at G_2 and w_4 at D is

$$(w_1 + w_2 + w_3 + w_4) \text{ at } G_3 \text{ in } G_2D, \text{ where } \quad \frac{G_2G_3}{G_3D} = \frac{w_4}{w_1 + w_2 + w_3}.$$

161

The point G_3 is fixed relative to A, B, C and D and it is independent of the position of the rigid system $ABCD$ in relation to the vertical direction of the weights of the particles.

Similarly the resultant weight of a system of particles of weights $w_1, w_2, w_3, \ldots, w_n$ acts at a point G_{n-1} which is fixed relative to the position of the particles. This point, G_{n-1}, is a unique one, for if there were another such point, say P_{n-1}, then $G_{n-1}P_{n-1}$ would be the line of action of the resultant weight and therefore vertical for all positions of the rigid system.

7.2. The Centre of Gravity of a Finite Number of Coplanar Particles

Let a set of coplanar particles of weights $w_1, w_2, w_3, \ldots, w_n$ have positions in relation to rectangular axes in the plane: (x_1, y_1), (x_2, y_2), (x_3, y_3), $\ldots$, (x_n, y_n). Let these positions of the particles be fixed relative to each other and relative to the axes. The centre of gravity $(\bar{x}, \bar{y})$ of the system is in the plane of the particles and is fixed relative to the particles (Fig. 72). Let the system be in the position in which the plane of the particles is vertical and the y-axis is vertical. Then the sum of the moments of the weights of the particles about O is equal to the moment of the resultant weight of the particles about O.

$$\therefore \ \sum_{1}^{n} w_r x_r = \bar{x} \sum_{1}^{n} w_r.$$

$$\therefore \ \bar{x} = \frac{\displaystyle\sum_{1}^{n} w_r x_r}{\displaystyle\sum_{1}^{n} w_r}. \tag{7.1}$$

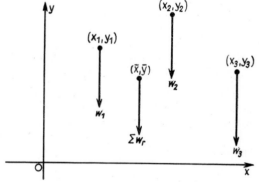

FIG. 72.

If the system is now rotated so that the plane of the particles remains vertical and the x-axis is vertical, we obtain the result

$$\bar{y} = \frac{\sum\limits_{1}^{n} w_r y_r}{\sum\limits_{1}^{n} w_r}. \tag{7.2}$$

Example. Particles of masses 5 lb, 4 lb, 8 lb, 3 lb are situated at the vertices A, B, C, D respectively of a regular hexagon $ABCDEF$. It is required to place particles at E and F so that the centre of gravity of the system of particles shall be at M, the mid-point of the line joining O, the centre of the hexagon, to F. Find the mass of each of these two particles.

Let the masses to be placed at E and F be m_1 lb and m_2 lb respectively and let the length of the side of the hexagon be $2a$ ft. Refer the system to rectangular axes with O as origin and OF as x-axis, (Fig. 73).

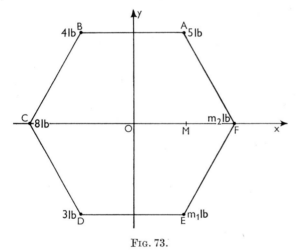

FIG. 73.

If $(\bar{x}, \bar{y})$ are the coordinates of the centre of gravity of the system, then, from equations (7.1) and (7.2),

$$\bar{x} = \frac{5 \times a + m_2 \times 2a + m_1 \times a - 3 \times a - 8 \times 2a - 4 \times a}{m_1 + m_2 + 20}$$

$$= \frac{2m_2 a + m_1 a - 18a}{m_1 + m_2 + 20},$$

$$\bar{y} = \frac{5 \times a\sqrt{3} + m_2 \times 0 - m_1 \times a\sqrt{3} - 3 \times a\sqrt{3} + 8 \times 0 + 4 \times a\sqrt{3}}{m_1 + m_2 + 20}$$

$$= \frac{6a\sqrt{3} - m_1 a\sqrt{3}}{m_1 + m_2 + 20}.$$

Therefore, if the centre of gravity is to be at M, i.e. at $(a, 0)$, we must have

$$\bar{y} = 0, \quad \therefore \ m_1 = 6,$$

$$\bar{x} = a, \quad \therefore \ \frac{2m_2 a + m_1 a - 18a}{m_1 + m_2 + 20} = a, \quad \therefore \ m_2 = 38.$$

Masses of 6 lb and 38 lb must be placed at E and F respectively.

Centre of Mass

The Centre of Mass of a coplanar system of particles $m_1, m_2, \ldots, m_n$, whose positions in relation to rectangular axes in the plane are $(x_1, y_1), (x_2, y_2), \ldots, (x_n, y_n)$, is *defined* as the point $(\bar{x}, \bar{y})$, where

$$\bar{x} = \frac{\sum_{1}^{n} m_r x_r}{\sum_{1}^{n} m_r}, \tag{7.3}$$

$$\bar{y} = \frac{\sum_{1}^{n} m_r y_r}{\sum_{1}^{n} m_r}. \tag{7.4}$$

With the assumptions we have made in this chapter,

(i) that the weight of each particle is proportional to its mass,

(ii) that the weights of the particles are parallel forces, the centre of mass of a system of particles coincides with the centre of gravity of the system.

EXERCISES 7.2.

In each of the exercises 1–8, find the position of the centre of mass of the system described, giving the answer in the terms suggested.

1. Particles of masses 5, 8, 12. 15 lb at A, B, C, D respectively where $ABCD$ is a straight line and $AB = BC = CD = 2$ ft. (Distance from A.)

2. Particles of masses 5, 8, 12, 15 lb at A, B, C, D respectively where $ABCD$ is a square of side 1 ft. (Distances from AB, AD.)

3. Particles of mass 2, 5, 3, 5, 3, 2 lb at A, B, C, D, E, F respectively where $ABCDEF$ is a regular hexagon of side 2 ft. (Distances from BE and the line through the centre of the hexagon at right angles to BE.)

4. Particles of mass 5, 13, 12 lb at A, B, C respectively where ABC is a triangle in which $AC = 13$ in., $AB = 5$ in., and $BC = 12$ in. (Distances from AB and BC.)

5. Particles of mass m, $2m$, $2m$, m at the vertices A, B, C, D respectively of a rhombus $ABCD$ in which $AB = a$, $\tan ABC = \frac{24}{7}$. (Distances from BD, AC.)

6. Particles of mass $2m$, m, $2m$, m at A, B, C, D respectively where $BA = BC$ and $DA = DC$, the lines AC and BD intersect at M, $BM = a$, $DM = 2a$. (Distance from D.)

7. Particles of mass m, $2m$, $3m$, $2m$, $2m$ at A, B, C, D, O respectively, where $ABCD$ is a rectangle, $AB = 2a$, $BC = 2b$ and AC and BD intersect at O. (Distances from AB, AD.)

8. Particles of mass $4m$, $3m$, $5m$ at A, B, C on the circumference of a circle of centre O and radius r where $\angle AOB = \angle BOC = \angle COA$. (Distance from O and $\angle BOG$ where G is the centre of mass.)

9. Particles of mass m, km, m, km are at the vertices A, B, C, D respectively of a trapezium $ABCD$ in which AB is parallel to DC and $AB = AD = BC = \frac{1}{2}DC$. Prove that the centre of mass of the particles is at the mid-point of HK where H and K are the mid-points of AB and CD respectively. Another particle of mass M is to be placed at H so that the centre of mass of the system becomes the point of intersection of the diagonals of the trapezium. Calculate M in terms of k and m.

10. Particles of mass $4m$, $5m$, m, $5m$ are at the vertices A, B, C, D respectively of a quadrilateral $ABCD$. Referred to coordinate axes through A the coordinates of these vertices are $A(0, 0)$, $B(4, 7)$, $C(6, 8)$ and $D(8, 4)$. Prove that the centre of mass of the particles divides KL internally in the ratio $1:4$ where K and L are the centroids of the triangles ABD and BCD respectively.

11. Particles of mass ka, kb, kc are at the vertices A, B, C respectively of a triangle ABC, right angled at A, whose sides, in the usual notation, are of lengths a, b and c. Prove that the centre of mass of the particles lies on the bisector of the angle A of the triangle and find its distance from A in terms of a, b and c.

12. Particles of mass $3m$, $4m$, x, y are at A, B, C and D, in that order, on the circumference of a circle, of radius r and centre O, so that $\angle AOB = \angle DOC = 60°$ and $\angle BOC = \angle AOD = 120°$. M is the mid-point of the chord BC. Find x and y in terms of m if the centre of mass of the particles is to be at the mid-point of OM.

7.3. The Centre of Gravity of a Rigid Body

If a (continuous) rigid body is considered as being an aggregate of particles, we can calculate the position of its centre of gravity by the methods of the Integral Calculus applied to the definitions of §7.2, extending these definitions to three dimensions where this is necessary. (The sums in these definitions are replaced by definite integrals.) We consider these methods in § 7.7 of this chapter where we obtain the positions of the centres of gravity of bodies of various shapes. The list which follows is a list of positions of centres of gravity, some of which will be obtained in § 7.7, but all of which will be used here.

1. *A thin uniform rod.*

We have already assumed that *the centre of gravity of a thin uniform rod is at its mid-point,* a result which clearly follows from symmetry combined with the formula $\bar{x} = \dfrac{\sum w_1 x_1}{\sum w_1}$.

2. *A uniform lamina in the shape of a parallelogram.*

We define a lamina as a solid body whose third dimension is so small as to be negligible when compared with each of the other two dimensions. In this case, *the centre of gravity of the lamina is at the point of intersection of the diagonals.*

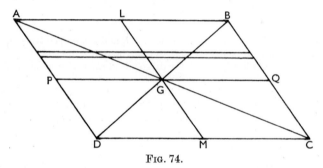

FIG. 74.

In Fig. 74, L, M are the mid-points of the opposite sides AB and DC of the parallelogram $ABCD$; P, Q are the mid-points of AD and BC. From symmetry we deduce that the centre of gravity of the lamina lies in PQ and also lies in LM. The centre of gravity of the lamina is therefore at G, the intersection of LM and PQ, and G is also the point of intersection of the diagonals of the parallelogram.

3. *A uniform triangular lamina. The centre of gravity is at the point of intersection of the medians.*

If we consider the lamina as composed of thin strips such as RS, each parallel to BC, and if we then consider the case when the number of such strips increases without limit, since the centre of gravity of each strip is at its mid-point which lies on AL, the median through A, we deduce that the centre of gravity of the lamina lies on AL (Fig. 75). Similarly we deduce that the centre of gravity lies on the median BM; it is therefore at G, the intersection of AL and BM. The medians of a triangle are concurrent at a point of trisection of each of them. In this case

$$AG : GL = BG : GM = CG : GN = 2 : 1.$$

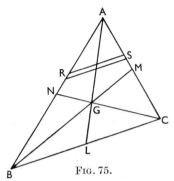

FIG. 75.

4. Three particles of equal mass. The centre of gravity is at the centroid of the triangle of which the particles form the vertices.

We define the *centroid* of a plane figure as that point which would be the centre of mass of a uniform lamina in the shape of the plane figure. The centroid of a solid figure is that point which would be the centre of mass of the corresponding uniform solid body.

Suppose the weight of each particle to be w. The resultant of the weights of the particles at B and C is a force of $2w$ vertically downwards acting through L, the mid-point of BC (Fig. 75). The resultant of the force $2w$ at L and the weight of the particle at A is a vertically downward force of $3w$ at the point G which divides AL in the ratio $2:1$. This is the centroid of the triangle ABC.

5. A uniform solid right prism.

The centre of gravity is the mid-point of the line joining the centroids of the two parallel faces.

6. A uniform solid pyramid.

The centre of gravity is the point which divides in the ratio 3 : 1 the line joining the vertex to the centroid of the base. (In the case of the tetrahedron, or triangular pyramid, it is proved by the methods of pure geometry that all four such lines are concurrent at a point of quadrisection of each of them.) In the limiting case, when the number of faces of the pyramid tends to infinity, we find that the centre of gravity of a uniform solid cone is $\frac{3}{4}$ of the way along the axis, from the vertex.

7. *A uniform solid hemisphere.*

The centre of gravity is on the radius of symmetry distance $\frac{3}{8}r$ from the centre of the base, where r is the radius of the hemisphere.

8. *A lamina in the shape of a uniform circular sector.*

The centre of gravity is on the radius of symmetry distance $\dfrac{2r \sin \alpha}{3\alpha}$ from the centre of the circle of which the sector is part, where r is the radius and 2α the angle of the sector.

9. *A thin uniform wire in the shape of a circular arc.*

The centre of gravity is on the radius of symmetry and distant $\dfrac{r \sin \alpha}{\alpha}$ from the centre of the circle of which the arc is part, where r is the radius of the arc and 2α the angle subtended by the arc at the centre of the circle.

7.4. The Centre of Gravity of a Compound Body

If a compound body is made up, either by addition or subtraction, of bodies whose weights and centres of gravity are known, the position of the centre of gravity of the compound body can be calculated.

(1) If the body is made up of parts of weight $w_1, w_2, w_3, \ldots, w_n$ the coordinates of whose centres of gravity (supposed coplanar) referred to arbitrarily chosen rectangular axes are (x_1, y_1), (x_2, y_2), (x_3, y_3), $\ldots$, (x_n, y_n), then the centre of gravity of the body is at $(\bar{x}, \bar{y})$ where

$$\bar{x} \sum w_1 = \sum w_1 x_1.$$
$$\therefore \bar{x} = \sum (w_1 x_1)/\sum w_1$$

and similarly

$$\bar{y} = \sum (w_1 y_1)/\sum w_1.$$

(2) If the body is the remainder when a body of weight w_2 with centre of gravity at (x_2, y_2) is removed from a body of weight w_1 with centre of gravity at (x_1, y_1) and if $(\bar{x}, \bar{y})$ is the centre of gravity of the remainder, then

$$(w_1 - w_2)\bar{x} + w_2 x_2 = w_1 x_1.$$
$$\therefore \bar{x} = \frac{w_1 x_1 - w_2 x_2}{w_1 - w_2}$$

and similarly

$$\bar{y} = \frac{w_1 y_1 - w_2 y_2}{w_1 - w_2}.$$

This result can clearly be extended when more than one subtraction takes place.

Examples. (i) A piece of uniform wire of length $2r(\alpha + 1)$ is bent into a closed plane figure consisting of a circular arc of length $2r\alpha$ and two radii each of length r. Find the distance of the centre of gravity of the whole wire from the centre of the circle.

Consider the positions of the centres of gravity of the parts of the wire in relation to rectangular axes through the centre of the circle with the x-axis along the radius of symmetry (Fig. 76). The centre of gravity of the whole wire will lie on this radius. The wire is uniform and therefore its weight varies as its length.

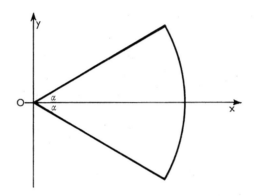

FIG. 76.

Part	Weight	x-coordinate of C of G
Circular arc	$2r\alpha$	$(r\sin\alpha)/\alpha$
Two radii	$2r$	$(r\cos\alpha)/2$

Therefore, if $\bar{x}$ is the distance of the centre of gravity from the centre of the circle,

$$\bar{x} = \frac{2r\alpha \cdot \dfrac{r\sin\alpha}{\alpha} + 2r \cdot \dfrac{r\cos\alpha}{2}}{2r(\alpha + 1)}$$

$$= \frac{r(2\sin\alpha + \cos\alpha)}{2(\alpha + 1)}.$$

12*

(ii) ABC is a uniform triangular lamina, and AD is a median. A point P is taken on AD, and the triangle PBC is removed. If the centre of gravity of the remainder is at P, find the ratio $PD:AD$.

(N.)

$$\frac{\text{Area of } \triangle ABC}{\text{Area of } \triangle PBC} = \frac{AD}{PD}. \quad \text{(Fig. 77)}$$

$$\therefore \frac{\text{Mass of lamina } ABC}{\text{Mass of lamina } PBC} = \frac{AD}{PD}.$$

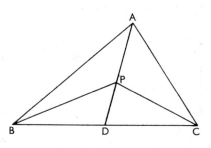

FIG. 77.

The centre of gravity of each lamina lies on AD.

Part	Weight	Distance of C of G from D
Triangle ABC	kAD	$\dfrac{1}{3}AD$
Triangle PBC	kPD	$\dfrac{1}{3}PD$
Remainder	$k(AD-PD)$	$\dfrac{\frac{1}{3}AD^2 - \frac{1}{3}PD^2}{AD-PD}$

Therefore, since the centre of gravity of the remainder is at P,

$$\frac{\frac{1}{3}(AD^2 - PD^2)}{AD - PD} = PD.$$

$$\therefore \ AD + PD = 3PD.$$

$$\therefore \ PD:AD = 1:2.$$

(iii) A uniform solid is formed of a hemisphere of radius a and a cone of base radius a and height a, with their circular bases coincident. The solid is placed inside a closed circular cylindrical canister of radius a and length $2a$ made of uniform material of negligible thickness, so that the axis of the solid coincides with that of the cylinder. If the weight of the canister is equal to that of the conical part of the solid find the position of the centre of gravity of the whole configuration.

Find the position of the centre of gravity of the remaining configuration when the circular ends of the canister are removed. (L.)

(1) By symmetry the centre of gravity of the canister is at the mid-point of its axis and the centre of gravity of the whole body lies on the axis (Fig. 78).

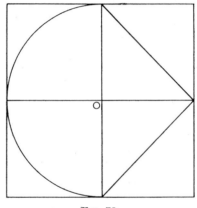

FIG. 78.

Part	Weight in terms of the density ϱ	Distance of C of G from O
Hemisphere	$\dfrac{2}{3}\pi a^3 \varrho$	$-\dfrac{3}{8}a$
Cone	$\dfrac{1}{3}\pi a^3 \varrho$	$+\dfrac{1}{4}a$
Canister	$\dfrac{1}{3}\pi a^3 \varrho$	0
Whole system	$\dfrac{4}{3}\pi a^3 \varrho$	$\dfrac{\pi a^4 \varrho(-\frac{1}{4}+\frac{1}{12})}{\frac{4}{3}\pi a^3 \varrho}=-\dfrac{1}{8}a$

The centre of gravity of the whole body is on the axis distance $\frac{1}{8}a$ from O on the hemisphere side.

(2) When the ends of the canister are removed the removed mass is one-third of the total mass of the canister, i.e. $\frac{1}{9}\pi a^3 \varrho$. The centre of gravity of the remainder is on the axis, distant x from O, where

$$x = \frac{\frac{4}{3}\pi a^3 \varrho\left(-\frac{1}{8}a\right) - \frac{1}{9}\pi a^3 \varrho\,(0)}{\frac{4}{3}\pi a^3 \varrho - \frac{1}{9}\pi a^3 \varrho} = -\frac{3a}{22}.$$

The centre of gravity is on the axis distant $3a/22$ from O on the hemisphere side.

(iv) A uniform lamina is in the form of the quadrilateral whose vertices are the points $(4, 0)$, $(5, 0)$, $(0, 12)$, $(0, 3)$ referred to rectangular axes. Find the coordinates of the centre of mass of the lamina.

Find also the coordinates of the centre of mass of a uniform wire bent into the form of the perimeter of the quadrilateral.   (L.)

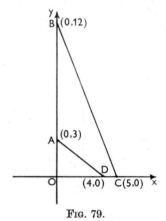

FIG. 79.

(1)   Area of triangle $ABD = 18$ units², (Fig. 79)
      area of triangle $BDC = 6$ units²,

therefore, from § 7.3 (4), the mass of the triangular lamina ABD can be replaced by three equal masses of 6 units at the points A, B, D respectively, and the mass of the triangular lamina BDC can be replaced by three equal masses of 2 units at the points B, D, C respectively. Hence, for the purpose of finding the centre of mass, the mass of the quadrilateral lamina $ABCD$ can be replaced by masses of

6 units at A, 8 units at B, 2 units at C and 8 units at D. If, now, the
centre of mass of the quadrilateral lamina is $(\bar{x}, \bar{y})$,

$$\bar{x} = \frac{6 \times 0 + 8 \times 0 + 2 \times 5 + 8 \times 4}{6 + 8 + 2 + 8} = \frac{7}{4},$$

$$\bar{y} = \frac{6 \times 3 + 8 \times 12 + 2 \times 0 + 8 \times 0}{24} = \frac{19}{4}.$$

The centre of mass of the lamina is $\left(\dfrac{7}{4}, \dfrac{19}{4}\right)$.

Alternatively

We can consider the quadrilateral $ABCD$ of area 24 units², as
obtained by subtracting the triangle OAD, of area 6 units², from the
triangle OBC of area 30 units². Then, *either* by using method (2) of
p. 168 *or* by finding the centre of mass of particles with masses $8, -2, 10$,
$10, -2$ placed at O, A, B, C, D respectively we obtain the above result.

This method of replacing a uniform lamina by particles for the
purposes of finding the centre of gravity is of general applicability
and can be used to great advantage (e.g. in Exercises 7.4).

(2) The length of AD is 5 units and the length of BC is 13 units.
The uniform wire bent into the shape of a quadrilateral can be
replaced by masses of 9 units at $(0, 7\frac{1}{2})$, the midpoint of AB, 13 units
at $(2\frac{1}{2}, 6)$, 1 unit at $(4\frac{1}{2}, 0)$ and 5 units at $(2, 1\frac{1}{2})$ and, if $(\bar{x}_1, \bar{y}_1)$ are
the coordinates of the centre of mass,

$$\bar{x}_1 = \frac{9 \times 0 + 13 \times 2\frac{1}{2} + 1 \times 4\frac{1}{2} + 5 \times 2}{28} = \frac{47}{28} = 1\frac{19}{28},$$

$$\bar{y}_1 = \frac{9 \times 7\frac{1}{2} + 13 \times 6 + 1 \times 0 + 5 \times 1\frac{1}{2}}{28} = \frac{153}{28} = 5\frac{13}{28}.$$

The centre of mass of the wire is $\left(1\dfrac{19}{28}, 5\dfrac{13}{28}\right)$.

EXERCISES 7.4.

1. A cubical tank without a lid is of edge $1\frac{1}{2}$ ft and stands on a horizontal
floor. The uniform thin sides and base of the tank are of total mass 120 lb.
The tank is filled with liquid. If the mass of 1 ft³ of the liquid is 64 lb, find,
in inches, the height of the centre of gravity of the tank and the contained
liquid above the floor.   (N.)

2. A table, which rests on a horizontal floor, consists of a thin top of mass
10 lb supported on three uniform vertical legs, each of mass 2 lb and length
32 in. Find the height of the centre of gravity of the table above the floor. (N.)

3. A kite-shaped quadrilateral lamina $ABCD$ has the diagonal $AC = 8$ in.,
the angles BAC and BCA both 60°, and the angles ACD and CAD both 45°.
Calculate the distance of the mass-centre from AC.   (N.)

4. $ABCD$ is a rectangular sheet of paper in which $AB = 12$ in., $BC = 36$ in., and E is a point in AD such that $ED = DC$. The triangle EDC is folded over about EC so that it is in contact with the plane area $AECB$. Find the distances of the centre of gravity of the folded sheet from AB and BC. (N.)

5. A chessboard $ABCD$ 8 in. square is divided into sixty-four squares of side 1 in. The eleven squares whose centres are nearest to the corner C are cut away. Show that the distance from A of the centre of gravity of the remainder is 4·949 in. ($\sqrt{2} = 1·414$.) (O.C.)

6. A uniform sheet of metal is in the form of a square of side a, and the middle points of the sides, taken in order, are, A, B, C and D. The corner O lies between C and D. The triangular piece with AB as hypotenuse is removed from the sheet, and the triangular piece with BC as hypotenuse is folded back along BC so as to lie flat on the remainder of the sheet. Taking OC and OD as axes of x and y respectively find, in terms of a, the coordinates of the centre of gravity of the sheet so formed. (N.)

7. A uniform circular lamina of radius $3a$ and centre O has a hole in the form of an equilateral triangle of side $2a$ with one vertex at O. Prove that the distance of the centre of gravity from O is

$$\frac{2a}{9\pi - \sqrt{3}}.$$ (N.)

8. Prove that the distance of the centre of gravity of a uniform cube of edge a from one corner of the cube is $(a\sqrt{3})/2$.

Eight equal uniform cubes of edge a are placed together to form a larger cube of edge $2a$. If one of the small cubes is removed, prove that the distance from the centre of the large cube of the centre of gravity of the remainder is $(a\sqrt{3})/14$. (N.)

9. A uniform circular disc ABC of radius r has its centre at O. With centre A and radius r an arc BOC is drawn, and the portion $BOCA$ removed from the original disc. Find the centre of gravity of the remaining part of the disc. (N.)

10. A uniform square lamina $ABCD$ of side $2a$ is folded along two straight lines, the first fold bringing A to O, the centre of the square, and the second fold bringing B to O. Find the distance from O of the centre of gravity of the folded lamina. (O.C.)

11. Assuming that the distance from the bounding diameter of the centre of gravity of a uniform semicircular lamina of radius a is $4a/(3\pi)$, prove that the centre of gravity of a lamina in the form of a quadrant of a circle of radius a is distant $4a\sqrt{2}/(3\pi)$ from the centre.

Hence find the position of the centre of gravity of the remainder when a quadrant is removed from a circular lamina of radius a. (N.)

12. The diagonals of a plane quadrilateral $ABCD$ intersect at O. E is the mid-point of BD and F is a point on AC such that $CF = AO$. Prove that the centroid of the quadrilateral trisects EF. (L.)

7.5. The Position of a Freely Suspended Body

If a body is freely suspended, it rests in equilibrium under the action of its resultant weight, acting vertically downward through its centre of gravity, and the tension in the supporting string (Fig. 80).

These two forces are, therefore, equal, opposite and in the same straight line and the body must rest in equilibrium with its centre of gravity vertically below the point of suspension.

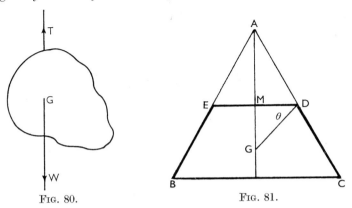

FIG. 80.   FIG. 81.

Example. A uniform lamina is in the form of an equilateral triangle ABC. The mid-points of AC, AB are respectively D and E. The triangular portion ADE is removed and $BCDE$ is suspended freely by a string attached at D. Prove that in the position of equilibrium DE makes an acute angle θ with the vertical where

$$\tan\theta = \frac{5\sqrt{3}}{9}.$$ (N.)

The centre of gravity of the lamina $BCDE$ is on the axis of symmetry, the line through A perpendicular to BC, meeting ED at M (Fig. 81). Let the mass of the original lamina be 4 units and let the side of the equilateral triangle be $2a$.

Then,

Lamina	Mass	Displacement of C of G from M
$\triangle ABC$	4	$a\left(\dfrac{2\sqrt{3}}{3} - \dfrac{\sqrt{3}}{2}\right) = \dfrac{a\sqrt{3}}{6}$
$\triangle ADE$	1	$\dfrac{-a\sqrt{3}}{6}$
Quadrilateral $BCDE$	3	$\dfrac{\dfrac{4 \cdot a\sqrt{3}}{6} - 1\left(-\dfrac{a\sqrt{3}}{6}\right)}{3} = \dfrac{5a\sqrt{3}}{18}$

When the lamina is suspended freely by a string attached at D, the line DG is vertical, $\angle EDG = \theta$, and

$$\tan\theta = \frac{MG}{MD} = \frac{5a\sqrt{3}}{18} \bigg/ \frac{a}{2} = \frac{5\sqrt{3}}{9}.$$

EXERCISES 7.5.

1. $ABCD$ is a thin uniform rectangular sheet such that AB is 6 ft and BC is 4 ft. If a square of edge 2 ft with one corner at A is cut away, find the centre of gravity of the remainder.

If the sheet is held in a vertical plane by means of a string attached at C, what angle will CB make with the vertical in the position of equilibrium? (N.)

2. A right-angled triangle AOB is made with thin rods OB 3 ft, OA 4 ft, AB 5 ft long. Find the distance from OA and OB of the centre of gravity of the three rods.

If the triangle is suspended from the point A show that OA will make an angle of about 22° with the vertical. (N.)

3. A thin uniform flat plate is in the form of an isosceles triangle PQR, where $PQ = QR = 6$ in., $\angle PQR = 90°$. Find the distance of the centre of gravity of the plate from PQ.

If the plate hangs from P in equilibrium under gravity, find the inclination of PQ to the downward vertical. (N.)

4. A thin uniform flat plate is in the shape of a square $ABCD$ of side 6 in. with an isosceles triangle CDE described externally on the side CD; $\angle CED = 90°$. Find the distance of the centre of gravity of the plate from AB.

If the plate hangs from B in equilibrium under gravity, find the inclination of BA to the downward vertical. (N.)

5. $ABCD$ is a square lamina of negligible mass and E, F are the mid-points of AB, BC respectively. Particles of masses 4, 5, 6, 7, and 8 lb are attached at E, B, F, C, and D respectively. The system is suspended from A. Find the angle between the diagonal AC and the vertical in the position of equilibrium. (O.C.)

6. A thin uniform wire is bent into the form of a closed plane pentagon $ABCDE$ in which $AB = BC = AE = ED = 5$ in., $BE = 8$ in., $CD = 2$ in. and the angles C and D are equal. Find the distance from A to the centre of mass of the wire.

When suspended freely from a point F in AB the wire is in equilibrium with AB horizontal; find the distance AF. (L.)

7. State the position of the centre of gravity of a uniform triangular sheet. Such a sheet with sides 5, 6, 7 in. hangs in a vertical plane by means of a vertical string attached at a point on the longest side. Find by drawing, or otherwise, the position of that point if the longest side is to be horizontal. (N.)

8. A light regular hexagon $ABCDEF$ has particles of mass 2, 4, 8, 6, 10 lb at the angular points F, E, D, C, B respectively. If it is suspended freely from the point A, find the angle that AF makes with the horizontal in the position of equilibrium. (N.)

9. Two uniform rods AB and BC, of equal lengths $2a$ and of equal weights, are rigidly connected at B. If the rod BC is horizontal when the rods are suspended from A, prove that $\cos ABC = \frac{1}{3}$, and find the distance of their centre of gravity from A.   (N.)

10. A rectangular sheet $ABCD$ of metal of uniform thickness has $AB = 4a$ and $BC = 3a$. A point X of the sheet is taken such that $XB = XC$ and a piece of the sheet in the form of the isosceles triangle XBC is removed. The remainder is then suspended from B and it is found that BX is vertical. Prove that the area of the triangle XBC is $3(3-\sqrt{3})a^2$.   (C.)

11. A uniform lamina, of weight W, consists of a circular disc, centre O and radius OA $(= a)$, from which a circular portion on OA as diameter has been removed. Prove that the centre of gravity of the lamina is at a distance $\frac{1}{6}a$ from O.

BC is the diameter perpendicular to OA; a particle, of weight $\frac{1}{3}W$, is attached at C. When the system is freely suspended from B and is at rest, find the tangent of the acute angle θ which OB makes with the vertical.   (O.C.)

12. A lamina in the form of a rhombus $ABCD$ consists of two uniform equilateral triangles ABC and ACD, of masses $2M$ and M respectively. The lamina is freely suspended from A; prove that, in the position of equilibrium, the angle which AC makes with the vertical is $\tan^{-1}\left(\dfrac{\sqrt{3}}{9}\right)$.

Find also the mass to be suspended from D so that, in the subsequent position of equilibrium, AC is vertical.   (O.C.)

13. Two equal uniform heavy rods AB and BC, each of weight W, are rigidly jointed at B so that $ABC = 90°$. The system hangs freely from A in a vertical plane. Show that AB makes an angle $\tan^{-1}\frac{1}{3}$ with the downward vertical.

What weight must be added to the end C for the angle to become $\tan^{-1}\frac{1}{2}$?   (O.C.)

14. One end of a uniform solid circular cylinder of radius a and length $2h/3$ made of the same material as the cone is welded symmetrically to the base of the cone. The system is suspended from a point on the base of the cone and is in equilibrium with a slant side of the cone horizontal. Prove that, if α denotes the semi-vertical angle of the cone, then

$$\tan \alpha = \tfrac{1}{6}\sqrt{5}.   \text{(O.C.)}$$

15. Prove that the centre of gravity of a uniform triangular lamina is the point of intersection of the medians of the triangle and show that it coincides with the centre of gravity of three equal particles placed at the vertices of the triangle.

Hence, or otherwise, prove that the centre of gravity of a uniform trapezium, of weight W, in which $AB = 2a$, $CD = 2b$, and $AD = BC$ is at a distance

$$\frac{(a + 2b)EF}{3(a + b)}$$

from E, where E and F are the mid-points of AB and CD respectively.

A particle of weight w is attached at D and the system is suspended by a string attached at F; in the position of equilibrium F is vertically above A. Prove that, if $b = 2a$, then $w = 2W/9$.   (O.C.)

7.6. The Equilibrium of a Body at Rest on a Horizontal Plane

When a body rests with a plane face in contact with a smooth horizontal plane, it is in equilibrium under the action of two forces only. These two forces are the normal reaction of the plane on the body and the weight of the body acting through its centre of gravity. The two forces must therefore be equal, opposite and in the same straight line. If the geometrical configuration of the body is such that the vertical through the centre of gravity cuts the plane base of

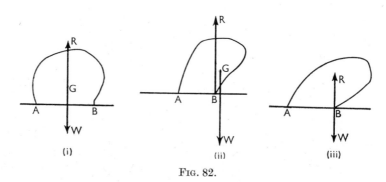

Fig. 82.

the body [Fig. 82 (i)], equilibrium is possible and the resultant reaction between the horizontal plane and the body is equal to the weight W of the body and acts vertically upwards through the point of the plane vertically below G. On the other hand, if the vertical through the centre of gravity falls outside the plane base [Fig. 82 (ii)], the two forces cannot act in the same line and equilibrium is not possible; in this latter case, the body topples about B (in the clockwise sense). Figure 82 (iii) shows the forces in the limiting case where the vertical through the centre of gravity of the body just passes through the edge of the plane base.

(If the plane is not smooth, the force of friction between the body and the plane is nevertheless zero, because there is no other horizontal force acting on the body. We discuss friction in Chapter IX).

Examples. (i) A right section of a solid triangular prism is a triangle ABC obtuse-angled at C. The prism is placed on a rough horizontal table with the face through BC on the table. Prove that the prism will not fall over about the edge through C provided that $a + b \cos C$ is positive.   (O.C.)

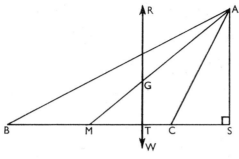

FIG. 83.

The vertical through the centroid G of triangle ABC meets BC at T, the line AM is a median and the perpendicular through A to BC meets BC produced at S (Fig. 83).

The prism will not fall over if

$$MT \leq MC,$$

i.e. if $\tfrac{1}{3}MS \leq MC,$

i.e. if $\tfrac{1}{3}\{\tfrac{1}{2}a + b \cos(\pi - C)\} \leq \tfrac{1}{2}a,$

i.e. if $\tfrac{1}{3}(\tfrac{1}{2}a - b \cos C) \leq \tfrac{1}{2}a,$

i.e. if $a + b \cos C \geq 0.$

(ii) A homogeneous rigid body consists of a right circular cylinder, of height h and radius a, whose base is attached to the plane face of a hemisphere, of radius $2a$, so that the axis of the cylinder passes through the mid-point of a radius of the base of the hemisphere. If the body rests in equilibrium with the curved surface of the hemisphere in contact with a horizontal plane, prove that the axis of the cylinder makes an angle $\tan^{-1}\left(\dfrac{2ah}{8a^2 - h^2}\right)$ with the vertical.   (L.)

Figure 84 represents a vertical section of the body through that diameter of the plane face of the cylinder which is also a radius of the hemisphere. Because the body is symmetrical about this plane its centre of gravity will lie within the plane.

If $(\bar{x}, \bar{y})$ are the coordinates of the centre of gravity of the body referred to axes of x along this diameter, and y *downwards* through the centre of the hemisphere, then

$$\bar{x} = \frac{\pi a^2 h \times a}{\pi a^2 h + 16 \pi a^3/3} = \frac{3ah}{3h + 16a},$$

$$\bar{y} = \frac{\pi a^2 h \times \left(-\dfrac{h}{2}\right) + \dfrac{16}{3}\pi a^3 \times \dfrac{3a}{4}}{\pi a^2 h + \dfrac{16}{3}\pi a^3} = \frac{3(8a^2 - h^2)}{2(3h + 16a)}.$$

When the body rests in equilibrium with its curved surface in contact with a horizontal plane, its centre of gravity is vertically above the point of contact with the plane. Hence, referring to Fig. 84, where P is the point of contact with the horizontal plane, this plane is the tangent plane at P, OP is vertical, and

$$\tan\theta = \frac{\bar{x}}{\bar{y}} = \frac{2ah}{8a^2 - h^2}.$$

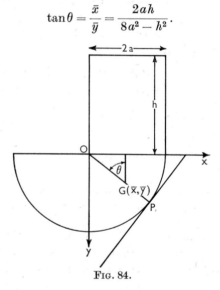

FIG. 84.

(iii) A uniform solid right circular cylinder of radius $\frac{1}{2}$ in. and height 20 in. has one of its plane ends attached to one face of a cylindrical disc of the same uniform material, of radius 4 in. and thickness 1 in., so that the centres of the two faces in contact are coincident. Find how far the centre of mass of the body thus formed is from the other face of the disc.

If the body stands with this face of the disc in contact with an inclined plane which is sufficiently rough to prevent any slipping, show that the body will topple if the inclination of the plane to the horizontal exceeds an angle α given by $\tan \alpha = 4/3$.   (N.)

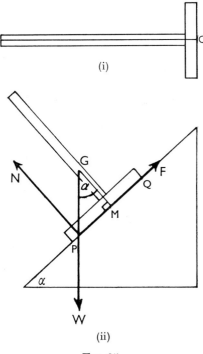

(i)

(ii)

Fig. 85.

Figure 85(i) represents a section of the body by a plane through the axis of the cylinder. The centre of gravity of the body will lie on the common axis of the cylinder and the disc.

If $\bar{x}$ is the distance of the centre of gravity from O,

$$\bar{x} = \frac{5\pi \times 11 + 16\pi \times \frac{1}{2}}{21\pi} = 3.$$

When the body rests on the inclined plane, Fig. 85(ii), its equilibrium is under the action of three forces, the force of friction F, its weight W acting vertically downwards through the centre of gravity G, and the normal reaction N of the plane on the body. If equilibrium is to be maintained, these three forces must act at a point.

Equilibrium is not therefore possible unless the vertical through G, the centre of gravity of the body, falls within the base PQ. Angle $PGM = \alpha$ where M is the mid-point of PQ and α is the angle of inclination of the plane.

Therefore, for equilibrium,

$$MG \tan \alpha \leq PM,$$

i.e. $$3 \tan \alpha \leq 4,$$

i.e. $$\tan \alpha \leq \tfrac{4}{3},$$

and so the body topples if $\alpha > \tan^{-1}(4/3)$.

EXERCISES 7.6.

1. A uniform flat plate of mass 8 lb is in the form of a square $ABCD$ of side 6 in.; E is the mid-point of AB. The triangular portion BEC is removed. Find the mass of the trapezium $AECD$. The centre of gravity of this trapezium is distant x in. and y in. from AD and AE respectively. Show that $x = 2\tfrac{1}{3}$ and find y.

The trapezium is placed in a vertical position with the side AE on a horizontal plane. Find the mass of the particle which must be placed at C for the trapezium to be on the point of overturning.   (N.)

2. A circular table of mass 20 lb has four legs spaced at equal distances round its edge. Prove that the greatest load which can be placed on the table with the certainty that the table will not be overturned (no matter where the load is placed) is about 48 lb $4\tfrac{1}{2}$ oz.

[Take $\sqrt{2} = 1 \cdot 4142$.]   (O.C.)

3. An isosceles triangle is cut off a corner of a uniform square lamina. Show that the remainder can stand on a shortened edge if the part cut off is $0 \cdot 5$ of an edge, but not if the part cut off is $0 \cdot 6$ of an edge.   (O.C.)

4. The radii of the ends of a frustum of a uniform right circular cone of vertical angle 2α, are a and $3a$. If the frustum can rest in equilibrium with its curved surface in contact with a horizontal plane, show that $30 \cos^2 \alpha \geq 13$.   (L.)

5. A stool has a uniform solid square seat of side 30 cm and thickness 2 cm. The four legs, each 25 cm long and having as cross-section a square of side 3 cm, are made of uniform solid material of density k times that of the seat. The legs are attached exactly at the corners of the seat, the top of which is 27 cm above the floor. Obtain an equation for the height of the centre of gravity of the stool above the floor. If the greatest angle through which the stool can be tilted on two legs without overbalancing is $\tan^{-1}(\tfrac{3}{4})$, find the value of k.   (N.)

6. A frustum of a uniform solid right circular cone of vertical angle 2α and of height h is obtained by cutting the cone by a plane parallel to the base at a distance h/n from the vertex. Find the distance of the centre of gravity of the frustum from the vertex of the cone.

The frustum is placed with its curved surface in contact with a horizontal plane. Show that it will remain in equilibrium if

$$\frac{4(n^3 - 1)}{3(n^4 - 1)} < \cos^2\alpha.$$ (L.)

7. From a uniform solid right circular cylinder, of radius r and height h, a right circular cone is bored out. The base of the cone coincides with one end of the cylinder and the vertex O is at the centre of the other end. Show that the centre of mass of the remainder of the cylinder is at a distance $3h/8$ from O.

The bored-out cylinder is placed with O uppermost on a horizontal plane which is rough enough to prevent slipping; the plane is then gradually tilted. Show that the cylinder topples when the inclination of the plane to the horizontal exceeds $\tan^{-1}(8r/5h)$. (N.)

8. A uniform solid is formed of a right circular cylinder, of height h and base radius a, joined to a hemisphere of radius a, the bases coinciding. Find h in terms of a if this solid can rest with any point of its spherical surface in contact with a horizontal plane. (C.)

9. ABC is a uniform triangular lamina in which $AB = AC$. A triangular part ADE is cut away, D and E being the mid-points of AC and AB respectively. Find the distance of the centre of gravity of the lamina $EBCD$ from BC in terms of the perpendicular distance, h, of ED from BC.

Show that, if the lamina is placed with CD on a horizontal plane with the plane of $EBCD$ vertical, the lamina will not topple about D if

$$14h^2 \geqq 9b^2,$$

where $DC = b$. (O.C.)

10. A hollow vessel of uniform small thickness consists of a cone and hemisphere joined at their circular rims, the cone and hemisphere being on opposite sides of the plane of the rims and of different materials. The semi-vertical angle of the cone is $\tan^{-1}\frac{1}{4}$, and it is found that, when the vessel is placed on a horizontal plane with a generator of the cone in contact with the plane, the vessel will not rest in this position. Show that the ratio of the densities of hemisphere and cone is greater than $19\sqrt{17} : 6$. (L.)

(The centre of mass of the curved surface of a thin hollow right circular cone of height h is on the axis at a point distant $\frac{2}{3}h$ from the vertex and the centre of mass of the curved surface of a thin hemispherical shell bisects the radius of symmetry.)

7.7. The Centres of Gravity of Some Common Solids

The position of the centre of mass of a continuous body, regarded as an aggregate of particles, can be found by using the methods of the Integral Calculus. The limits of the sums involved in the formulae

$$\bar{x} = \frac{\sum\limits_{1}^{n} m_r x_r}{\sum\limits_{1}^{n} m_r}, \quad \bar{y} = \frac{\sum\limits_{1}^{n} m_r y_r}{\sum\limits_{1}^{n} m_r}$$

are replaced by definite integrals.

A Uniform Right Pyramid

We define a right pyramid as one in which the perpendicular from the vertex meets the base at its centroid. Figure 86 represents a right pyramid $OABCD$ with a quadrilateral base $ABCD$ of area K. The perpendicular ON from the vertex to the base is of length h.

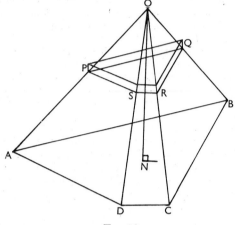

Fig. 86.

$PQRS$ is a section of the pyramid parallel to the base and distance x from the vertex O. A thin right prism is constructed with base $PQRS$ and thickness δx. We consider the mass of the pyramid as being the limiting sum, as $\delta x \to 0$, of the masses of all such prisms.

We assume from propositions of pure geometry

  (i) that $PQRS$ is a similar figure to $ABCD$,

 (ii) that the areas of such parallel sections of the pyramid are proportional to the squares of their distances from the vertex,

(iii) that the line joining the vertex of a pyramid to the centroid of the base passes through the centroid of every section parallel to the base.

The centre of mass of the whole pyramid will be in ON, and, if $\bar{x}$ is its distance from O,

$$\bar{x} = \frac{\displaystyle\lim_{\delta x \to 0} \sum_{x=0}^{h} \left(\varrho \frac{K x^2}{h^2} \delta x . x \right)}{\displaystyle\lim_{\delta x \to 0} \sum_{x=0}^{h} \left(\varrho \frac{K x^2}{h^2} \delta x \right)},$$

where ϱ is the density of the pyramid.

$$\therefore \; \bar{x} = \int\limits_0^h x^3\,\mathrm{d}x \Big/ \int\limits_0^h x^2\,\mathrm{d}x = \frac{3h}{4}.$$

The centre of mass of the pyramid is on the line joining the vertex to the centroid of the base and it divides that line in the ratio 3 : 1.

The proof given above is applicable to all such pyramids, whatever the shapes of their bases. If the pyramid is not a right pyramid, i.e. if the line joining its vertex to the centroid of the base is not at right angles to the base, a similar demonstration shows that the distance of the centre of mass from the vertex in a direction at right angles to the base is three-quarters of the perpendicular distance of the vertex from the base. Here again, the centre of mass lies on the line joining the vertex to the centroid of the base and a simple application of the properties of similar triangles now shows the centre of mass to be the point in this line which divides it in the ratio 3:1.

A Uniform Solid Cone

This is a limiting case of a uniform pyramid and its centre of mass is therefore on its axis and divides its axis in the ratio of 3:1 from the vertex.

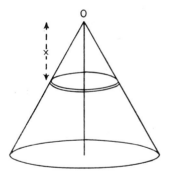

Fig. 87.

This result can be obtained directly, as follows. Figure 87 represents a uniform cone of base-radius R, height h, and density ϱ. A section of the cone parallel to the base is distant x from the vertex. The mass

13*

of a thin disc with this section as base and thickness δx is $\dfrac{\varrho\,\pi x^2 R^2 \delta x}{h^2}$.
Then, if $\bar{x}$ is the distance of the centre of mass from O,

$$\bar{x} = \frac{\lim\limits_{\delta x \to 0} \sum\limits_{x=0}^{h} \varrho\,\pi\,\dfrac{x^2 R^2}{h^2}\,\delta x . x}{\lim\limits_{\delta x \to 0} \sum\limits_{x=0}^{h} \varrho\,\pi\,\dfrac{x^2 R^2}{h^2}\,\delta x} = \frac{\displaystyle\int_0^h \dfrac{\varrho\,\pi R^2}{h^2}\,x^3\,\mathrm{d}x}{\displaystyle\int_0^h \dfrac{\varrho\,\pi R^2}{h^2}\,x^2\,\mathrm{d}x} = \frac{3h}{4}.$$

A Uniform Solid Hemisphere

Figure 88 represents a uniform hemisphere of radius R and density ϱ. A section of the hemisphere parallel to the base is distant x from the base. The mass of a disc with this section as base and thickness δx is $\varrho\,\pi(R^2 - x^2)\,\delta x$. The centre of mass of the hemisphere lies on the radius of symmetry of the hemisphere, and, if $\bar{x}$ is the distance of the centre of mass from the centre of the base,

$$\bar{x} = \frac{\lim\limits_{\delta x \to 0} \sum\limits_{x=0}^{R} \pi\varrho\,(R^2 - x^2)\,\delta x . x}{\lim\limits_{\delta x \to 0} \sum\limits_{x=0}^{R} \varrho\,\pi(R^2 - x^2)\,\delta x} = \frac{\displaystyle\int_0^R \pi\varrho\,(R^2 - x^2)\,x\,\mathrm{d}x}{\displaystyle\int_0^R \pi\varrho\,(R^2 - x^2)\,\mathrm{d}x}$$

$$= \left[\frac{R^2 x^2}{2} - \frac{x^4}{4}\right]_0^R \Big/ \left[R^2 x - \frac{x^3}{3}\right]_0^R = \frac{3}{8}\,R.$$

The centre of mass lies on the radius of symmetry distant $3R/8$ from the centre of the base.

A Uniform Hemispherical Shell

Consider a hemispherical shell which is half of a uniform spherical shell of negligible thickness, and which is of centre O, radius r, and surface density σ. Figure 89 represents a section through O at right

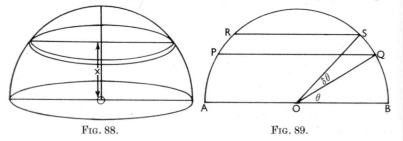

FIG. 88.   FIG. 89.

angles to the circle represented by AB. Two small circles on the surface of the hemisphere and parallel to the 'base' are represented by PQ and RS. Angle $QOB = \theta$ and angle $QOS = \delta\theta$. The mass of the band of surface bounded by the circles PQ and RS is approximately $\sigma\, 2\pi r \cos\theta.r\delta\theta$.

The centre of mass of the shell lies on the radius of symmetry through O.

Then, if this centre of mass is distant $\bar{x}$ from O,

$$\bar{x} = \frac{\displaystyle\lim_{\delta\theta\to 0} \sum_{\theta=0}^{\frac{1}{2}\pi} \sigma.2\pi r \cos\theta.r\delta\theta.r\sin\theta}{\displaystyle\lim_{\delta\theta\to 0} \sum_{\theta=0}^{\frac{1}{2}\pi} \sigma.2\pi r \cos\theta.r\delta\theta} = \frac{r\displaystyle\int_0^{\frac{1}{2}\pi} \sin\theta\cos\theta\,\mathrm{d}\theta}{\displaystyle\int_0^{\frac{1}{2}\pi}\cos\theta\,\mathrm{d}\theta}$$

$$= -r\left[\frac{\cos 2\theta}{4}\right]_0^{\frac{1}{2}\pi} \Big/ \left[\sin\theta\right]_0^{\frac{1}{2}\pi} = \frac{1}{2}r.$$

The centre of mass is the mid-point of the radius of symmetry. (This follows directly from the proposition of pure geometry which states that the area of the surface of a zone of a sphere is equal to the area of the corresponding zone of the circumscribing cylinder.)

A Uniform Lamina in the Shape of a Sector of a Circle

Figure 90 represents a uniform lamina in the shape of a sector of a circle of radius r and surface density σ. The angle of the sector is 2α, OM is its radius of symmetry, OP and OQ are radii of the sector such that $\angle MOP = \theta$ and $\angle POQ = \delta\theta$.

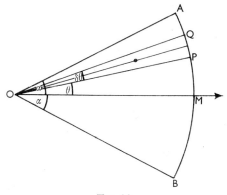

FIG. 90.

The centre of mass of the lamina lies in OM. The mass of the sector POQ is approximately $\sigma \frac{1}{2} r^2 \delta\theta$. The distance of the centre of mass of the sector POQ from an axis in the plane of the lamina through O perpendicular to OM is approximately $\frac{2}{3} r \cos\theta$. Therefore the distance of the centre of mass of the whole sector from O is

$$\frac{\lim_{\delta\theta \to 0} \sum_{\theta=-\alpha}^{+\alpha} \sigma \cdot \frac{1}{2} r^2 \delta\theta \cdot \frac{2}{3} r \cos\theta}{\lim_{\delta\theta \to 0} \sum_{\theta=-\alpha}^{+\alpha} \sigma \cdot \frac{1}{2} r^2 \delta\theta} = \frac{\int_{-\alpha}^{+\alpha} \frac{1}{3} \sigma r^3 \cos\theta \, d\theta}{\int_{-\alpha}^{+\alpha} \frac{1}{2} \sigma r^2 \, d\theta}$$

$$= \frac{\frac{2}{3} r \left[\sin\theta \right]_{-\alpha}^{+\alpha}}{\left[\theta \right]_{-\alpha}^{+\alpha}} = \frac{2 r \sin\alpha}{3\alpha}.$$

The centre of mass is on the radius of symmetry distant $\dfrac{2 r \sin\alpha}{3\alpha}$ from the centre.

A Thin Uniform Wire in the Shape of a Circular Arc

The arc AB of Fig. 90 is now taken to represent a thin uniform wire. If λ is the line density of the wire, the mass of PQ is $\lambda r \delta\theta$ and the distance of the centre of mass of PQ from the line through O perpendicular to OM is approximately $r \cos\theta$.

The centre of mass of the wire lies in OM, and if $\bar{x}$ is its distance from O,

$$\bar{x} = \frac{\lim_{\delta\theta \to 0} \sum_{\theta=-\alpha}^{+\alpha} \lambda r \delta\theta \cdot r \cos\theta}{\lim_{\delta\theta \to 0} \sum_{\theta=-\alpha}^{+\alpha} \lambda r \delta\theta} = \frac{r \int_{-\alpha}^{+\alpha} \cos\theta \, d\theta}{\int_{-\alpha}^{+\alpha} d\theta} = \frac{r \sin\alpha}{\alpha}.$$

The centre of mass is on the radius of symmetry distant $\dfrac{r \sin\alpha}{\alpha}$ from the centre.

This is an example in which the centre of mass of a rigid body is a point outside the body itself.

MISCELLANEOUS EXERCISES. VII

1. Three uniform rods AB, BC, CD, each of mass 40 lb and length 6 ft, are rigidly joined together so as to form three sides of a square framework $ABCD$. Find the distances of the centre of gravity of the framework from AB and BC. If the framework is free to rotate about a smooth fixed hinge at B and hangs in equilibrium under gravity, find, correct to the nearest degree, the inclination of BC to the downward vertical.

The framework is still hinged at B but a load of mass 100 lb is now hung from A. Equilibrium is maintained with BD vertical and D below B, by a horizontal force P lb wt. applied at C. Calculate P. Calculate also, in magnitude and direction, the resultant force exerted on the hinge. (Give your answers correct to the nearest lb wt. and nearest degree respectively.)   (N.)

2. A uniform wire AOB consists of two straight portions AO and OB, which are at right angles and are of lengths 1 ft and 2 ft respectively. Find the distances of the centre of gravity of the wire from AO and OB.

If the wire is suspended freely from A, find the angle of inclination of AO to the vertical.   (N.)

3. A uniform thin wire of mass 14 gm is bent so as to form three sides AB, BC, CD of a rectangle $ABCD$ where $AB = CD = 8$ cm and $BC = 12$ cm.

(i) Find the distance of the centre of gravity of the wire from BC.

(ii) The wire is freely suspended from B. Calculate the load which should be attached at A to bring BD vertical in the position of equilibrium.   (L.)

4. A uniform gate is supported by two hinges in a vertical line at a distance 3 ft apart. The breadth of the gate is 5 ft and its mass 100 lb. The upper hinge exerts a horizontal force only and will yield when this force exceeds 250 lb wt. If a boy of mass 140 lb stands on the gate without the hinge yielding, what is the greatest possible distance of his centre of gravity from the line of the hinges?   (O.C.)

5. A rectangular sheet of paper $ABCD$ has $AB = 30$ in., $AD = 20$ in., and E is a point in AB such that $AE = AD$. The triangle AED is folded about ED so that DA lies along DC. Find the distances from BC and DC of the centre of gravity of the folded sheet.   (L.)

6. ABC is an equilateral triangle. P is a point in AB such that $AP = 2PB$. Q and S are points in BC such that $BQ = QS = SC$. R is a point in AC such that $AR = 2RC$. Find the centre of mass of the pentagonal lamina $APQSR$.   (L.)

7. Find the position of the centre of gravity of a uniform solid right circular cone. A frustum of such a cone is made by cutting off one-third of the axis (measured from the vertex). Prove that the frustum will rest with a generator on a horizontal plane if

$$\tan^2 \alpha < \frac{17}{13}$$

where α is the semi-vertical angle of the cone.   (L.)

8. A uniform heavy plate has the form of a rectangle $ABCD$ with the sides AB, BC of lengths 8 ft and 6 ft respectively. By means of a cut along the line joining the mid-points M, N of the sides AB, AD the corner AMN is removed. Find the distances of the centre of gravity of $MBCDN$ from the sides BC and CD.

A particle of mass m lb is now attached to the mid-point of MN and it is found that the centre of gravity of the particle and the plate $MBCDN$ lies on the line BD. If the mass of the whole plate $ABCD$ is 100 lb, find m. (N.)

9. Find the semi-vertical angle of a right circular cone which is such that the centres of gravity of its *total* surface area and of its volume are coincident.   (L.)

10. A cylindrical vessel, made of sheet metal and open at the top, is of height h and radius r. It is suspended by a point on the rim. Show that the angle which the axis of symmetry of the vessel makes with the vertical is given by

$$\tan \alpha = \frac{r\,(2\,h + r)}{h\,(h + r)}.\qquad \text{(L.)}$$

11. A line AOB is a diameter of the base of a uniform solid hemisphere of radius a, O being the centre of the base. A conical portion of height $a/2$ is removed, OA being a diameter of the base of the cone. A hemispherical portion of radius $a/2$ is also removed, OB being a diameter of the base of this portion. Taking OA as the x-axis and a line through O perpendicular to the base as the y-axis, find the coordinates of the centre of gravity of the solid which remains.
(L.)

12. A uniform lamina is in the shape of an equilateral triangle ABC, where $BC = 2a$. A part CDE, where DE is parallel to AB and of length $2x$, is cut off. Prove that the distance of the centre of gravity of $ABED$ from DE is

$$\frac{(a - x)\,(2\,a + x)}{(a + x)\,\sqrt 3}.$$

Deduce that EB will be horizontal when the lamina is freely suspended from E if $x = \tfrac12 a(\sqrt 5 - 1)$.
(O.C.)

13. A uniform wire of mass $4M$ is bent so as to form four sides AB, BC, CD and DE of a regular hexagon, each side being of length $2a$; particles of masses $\tfrac12 M$ and M_1 are attached at A and D respectively. The wire is suspended by a string attached at C and is at rest with BC horizontal; prove that $M_1 = 4\,M$.

Find also the distance of the centre of gravity of the system from BC. (O.C.)

14. A uniform rod of length l with its cross-section a circle is sharpened at one end, like a pencil, to a conical point without shortening the axis of the cylinder. If the height of this cone is h, find the distance by which the centre of gravity has been displaced by the sharpening.
(L.)

15. $ABCD$ is a uniform quadrilateral lamina, in which BC is parallel to AD. The length of BC is a and the length of AD is b. Prove that the centre of gravity of the lamina coincides with that of masses placed at D, A, B, C, proportional to b, $a + b$, a, $a + b$ respectively.
(O.C.)

16. A light triangular frame ABC has weights attached to the corners, so that when the frame is suspended from B the side AC is horizontal and when suspended from C the side AB is horizontal. Prove that when it is suspended from A the side BC is horizontal.
(O.C.)

17. C is the centre of a sphere of uniform material and of radius 10 in. which contains two spherical cavities, whose centres are A, B and whose radii are 1 in. and 2 in., so situated that $CA = CB = 7{\cdot}5$ in. and $AB = 9$ in. Show that, when the sphere rests on a horizontal plane, the line AB makes an angle $\tan^{-1}(12/7)$ with the vertical.
(O.C.)

18. Prove that if, from a uniform solid hemisphere of radius a, a concentric hemispherical portion of radius $ka\,(k < 1)$ is removed, the centre of gravity of the remaining solid is at a distance

$$\frac{3\,a\,k^3}{8\,(1 + k + k^2)}$$

from that of the original hemisphere.
(L.)

19. A hemispherical shell of radius a is fitted with a plane base. A cylindrical can, of height $3a$, open at one end and with a base of radius a, is attached to the hemispherical shell so that the bases are in contact and the centres of the two bases coincide. Find the distance from the centre of the open end of the can of the centre of gravity of the body so formed, assuming that all parts are of the same uniform thin material.   (N.)

20. A plane lamina is formed by a uniform square of side $2a$ and a uniform semi-circle of radius a joined together, without overlap, so that an edge of the square coincides with the diameter of the semi-circle. If the lamina can rest vertically in equilibrium with any point of its curved edge in contact with a smooth horizontal plane, find the ratio of the surface densities of the square and semi-circular portions of the lamina.   (L.)

*21. (i) The coordinates of the vertices of a uniform triangular lamina are $(0, 2)$, $(3, 4)$ and (a, b); if the coordinates of the centre of gravity of the lamina are $(5, -6)$, find the values of a and b.

(ii) A uniform square board $ABCD$ is of side 3 ft and O is the intersection of the diagonals. Prove that the centre of gravity of the lamina when the triangle OBC is cut away is at a distance of 4 in. from O.

If the lamina is of mass 30 lb and is in equilibrium with AB horizontal when hung from a point H in AB and with bodies of masses 20 lb and 10 lb hung from C and D respectively, find the distance AH.   (O.C.)

*22. A lamina consists of a semicircle of radius $a + b$ from which semicircles of radii a and b have been cut away, all the semicircles having their diameters in the same line. Prove that the centre of gravity of the lamina is at a distance $2(a + b)/\pi$ from the line of the diameters.   (L.)

*23. A lamina in the form of an isosceles triangle ABC, in which the angle C is a right angle, can turn freely in a vertical plane about the point A which is fixed. The lamina is held in equilibrium by a vertical string attached at B, the vertex C being downwards, and B being below the level of A. Prove that the tension in the string is
$$\tfrac{1}{2} W(1 - \tfrac{1}{3}\tan\theta),$$
where W is the weight of the lamina, and θ the acute angle which AB makes with the horizontal.   (N.)

*24. A uniform solid sphere of radius a is divided into two parts by a plane distant c from its centre. Show that the distance between the centres of gravity of the two parts is
$$\frac{3a^3}{4a^2 - c^2}.$$ (L.)

*25. Prove by integration that the centre of gravity of a uniform semicircular lamina of radius a is at a distance $4a/3\pi$ from the centre.

ACB is such a lamina with diameter AOB, and OC is the radius perpendicular to AB. A square portion $OPQR$ is cut out of the lamina, P being on OB and OP having length $\tfrac{1}{2}a$. Find the distances from OA and OC of the centre of gravity of the remaining portion.

Hence show that, if the remaining portion is suspended from A and hangs in equilibrium, the tangent of the angle made by AB with the vertical is just less than $\tfrac{1}{2}$.   (C.)

*26. A box in the form of a cube of edge $2a$ has a lid hinged to it along an upper edge; it is made of thin uniform sheet material and stands on a horizontal table. If the lid is closed initially, find the horizontal and vertical displacements of the centre of gravity of the box when the lid is raised through an angle θ.

Prove that, as the lid is raised, the centre of gravity of the box describes an arc of a circle of radius $\frac{1}{6}a$.   (L.)

*27. A uniform wire is in the form of a semicircular arc ACB; $AB = 2a$ and O is the mid-point of AB. Prove that the distance of the centre of mass of the wire from O is $2a/\pi$.

Hence, or otherwise, prove that the centre of mass of a uniform semicircular lamina, bounded by ACB and AB, is at a distance $4a/(3\pi)$ from O.

A uniform wire, of mass M, is welded to the curved rim of the lamina whose mass is $3M$. The system is suspended from B and is at rest. Find the tangent of the angle which AB makes with the vertical.   (O.C.)

*28. State the coordinates of the centre of gravity of two particles of masses m_1 and m_2 situated at the points (x_1, y_1) and (x_2, y_2) respectively.

A cylindrical vessel, which has a base but no top, is made of uniform thin material of mass $0 \cdot 5$ gm/cm². The radius of the base of the vessel is 5 cm and its height is 10 cm. Find the distance of its centre of gravity from the base.

The vessel rests with its base on a horizontal table and water is slowly poured into it. Prove that the centre of gravity G of the water and vessel together is lowest when the height of the water is such that G lies in the water surface. Find the height of the water when this condition is satisfied.   (N.)

*29. A uniform hemispherical shell of radius 2 ft and mass 300 lb has a heavy uniform rim of mass 50 lb. It is hinged at one point of the rim and forms the lid of a cylindrical container. The lid is raised by a chain attached at the point of the rim opposite to the hinge. Find the tension in the chain, supposed vertical, when the plane of the rim makes an angle of 30° with the horizontal. (L.)

*30. (i) $OACB$ is a square formed of four uniform wires, each of length $2a$ and weight w. Particles of weights w, $2w$ and $3w$ are attached at A, C and B respectively. Find the coordinates of the centre of gravity of the system with respect to $\overrightarrow{OA}$ and $\overrightarrow{OB}$ taken as x- and y-axes.

The system is hung by a string attached at O and when a further particle, of weight W, is attached at A, the diagonal OC is vertical. Find the value of W in terms of w.

(ii) ABC is a uniform triangular board, of weight W, in which $BC = a$, $CA = b$, $AB = c$ and $\angle ABC$ is obtuse. The board is placed with its plane vertical and the side BC on a horizontal plane, and a weight w is suspended from A. If the system is in equilibrium, prove that

$$a^2 \geqq \frac{(W + 3w)\,(b^2 - c^2)}{3\,(W + w)}.$$ (O.C.)

*31. Prove that the centre of gravity of a thin uniform hemispherical shell is situated at a distance from the base equal to one-half the radius.

A particle of mass equal to twice that of the shell is fixed to a point of the rim, and the shell is allowed to come to rest with its curved surface in contact with a horizontal plane. Find to the nearest degree the angle that the plane of the base makes with the horizontal.   (L.)

*32. The diagonals AC, BD of a uniform lamina in the form of a quadrilateral $ABCD$ intersect at E. On AC the point F is taken such that $AE = CF$. Prove that the centre of gravity of the given quadrilateral coincides with the centre of gravity of the triangle BDF.

If the triangles ABC, ADC are of equal area and $AE : EC = 2 : 1$, prove that the centre of gravity divides AC in the ratio $5 : 4$.   (N.)

*33. A rectangular sheet $ABCD$ of metal of uniform thickness has $AB = 4a$ and $BC = 3a$. A point X of the sheet is taken such that $XB = XC$ and a piece of the sheet in the form of the isosceles triangle XBC is removed. The remainder is then suspended from B and it is found that BX is vertical. Prove that the area of the triangle XBC is $3(3 - \sqrt{3})a^2$.   (C.)

*34. A uniform solid right circular cone is suspended by a light inelastic string which has one end tied to the vertex and the other to a point on the circumference of the base and passes through two small smooth rings fixed at a distance a apart in a horizontal line. The altitude of the cone is $h\,(h > a)$ and the radius of the base is r. Prove that, if the cone hangs with its axis horizontal, the length of the string is,

$$a + \frac{(h - a)\,\sqrt{(h^2 + 4r^2)}}{h}\,.$$ (L.)

*35. Find the position of the centre of mass of a hollow right circular cone, of slant height l and vertical angle 2α, made of uniform thin metal and closed at the base.

Such a cone is cut by a plane parallel to the base and bisecting the vertical height. If the upper portion is removed, prove that the distance, from the base, of the centre of mass of the lower portion is

$$2l \cos \alpha/(9 + 12 \sin \alpha)\,.$$ (N.)

*36. The diagonals of a quadrilateral $ABCD$ intersect at O; $AO < OC$, $BO < OD$. From CO cut off CM equal to OA and from DO cut off DN equal to OB. Prove that the centres of gravity of each of the triangles ACN, BDM, and of the quadrilateral coincide with the centre of gravity of the triangle OMN.   (O.C.)

*37. A rigid body is in equilibrium under the action of three coplanar forces. Show that the lines of action of the forces are either concurrent or parallel.

A uniform solid has the shape formed by a complete revolution, about the axis of x, of the area in the first quadrant bounded by the curve $ay^2 = x^3$ and the lines $y = 0$, $x = a$. Show that the centre of gravity of the solid is distant $\frac{1}{5}a$ from its plane base.

The solid is placed with its plane base against a smooth vertical wall and is supported by a light string attached to its vertex and to a point of the wall above the solid. Show that the inclination of the string to the vertical must lie between $\tan^{-1}(4/5)$ and $\frac{1}{4}\pi$.   (N.)

*38. Prove that the centre of gravity of a uniform solid hemisphere of radius a is at a distance $3a/8$ from the centre.

The above hemisphere rests in equilibrium with its curved surface in contact with a smooth fixed horizontal table and with a light inextensible string of length $2a/5$ joining a point of its rim to a point of the table. Find the tension in the string and show that the ratio of the reaction of the table to the weight of the hemisphere is $41:32$. (L.)

39. Show that the centre of mass of a uniform semicircular lamina of radius r is distant $4r/(3\pi)$ from its bounding diameter.

A uniform solid is formed by rotating about the x-axis through π radians the area in the first quadrant bounded by the parabola $y^2 = 4ax$, the line $x = a$, and the x-axis. Find the distances of the centre of mass of this solid from its plane faces.

If a string is attached to one end of the straight edge of the solid, and the solid hangs freely under gravity with the string vertical, show that the straight edge of the solid is inclined to the vertical at an angle

$$\tan^{-1} \frac{\sqrt{(25\pi^2 + 1024)}}{30\pi}.$$ (L.)

40. Show that the centre of mass of a uniform solid hemisphere of radius a is at a distance $3a/8$ from its plane face.

The hemisphere is joined to a uniform solid right circular cylinder, of the same material and of radius a and height $\frac{1}{3}a$, so that the plane face of the hemisphere coincides with one end of the cylinder. Show that the centre of mass of the compound solid S thus formed is at a distance $19a/36$ from the plane base of S.

The solid S hangs in equilibrium under gravity, freely suspended from a point on the circumference of its plane face. Find, correct to the nearest degree, the inclination of the axis of the solid to the vertical. (N.)

41. A piece of thin uniform wire is bent into the shape of a triangle ABC. Prove that its mass-centre is at the in-centre of the triangle whose vertices are at the middle points of the sides of the triangle ABC. (N.)

CHAPTER VIII

THE DYNAMICS OF A PARTICLE

8.1. Newton's Laws of Motion

In Chapter I we discussed Newton's laws of motion, which we restate here.

1. A body remains in a state of rest or of uniform motion in a straight line unless it is acted upon by an external force.

2. The rate of change of the momentum of a body is proportional to the impressed force and takes place in the direction of that force.

3. To every action there is an equal and opposite reaction.

From these laws we deduced the fundamental equation of motion $P = mf$, and the associated absolute units of force:

1 *poundal* (pdl), the force which gives to a mass of 1 lb an acceleration of 1 ft/sec².

1 *dyne* (dyn), the force which gives to a mass of 1 gm an acceleration of 1 cm/sec².

The *gravitational* units of force are:

1 *pound weight*, the force which gives to a mass of 1 lb an acceleration equal to the acceleration due to gravity.

1 *gramme weight*, the force which gives to a mass of 1 gm an acceleration equal to the acceleration due to gravity.

Units and Notation

In addition to the units defined above, 1 newton (N) is the force required to give to a mass of 1 kgm an acceleration of 1 m/sec².

The variations in the value of g not only from place to place on the earth's surface, but also, more importantly now, variations which arise from differences of altitude, or even variations from one planet to another, all mean that it is now necessary to define and to *use* units of force which are constants independent of the local gravitational force. The kilogram force (kgmf) and the pound force (lbf) are the forces required to give to masses 1 kgm and 1 lb respectively the *standard acceleration* defined to be exactly 980·665 cm/sec². These

195

units are now recognized by the International Organization for Standardization and by the British Standards Institute which also defines analogously the ozf and the tonf.

A previous attempt to establish a system of units which would be independent of the value of the local gravitational force resulted in the definition of the unit of mass called the slug $(980 \cdot 665/30 \cdot 48)$ lb and thus 1 lbf corresponds to 1 slug ft/sec².

Examples. (i) A particle of mass m lb lies on a horizontal platform which is being accelerated upwards with an acceleration of f ft/sec². Calculate the force exerted by the platform on the particle.

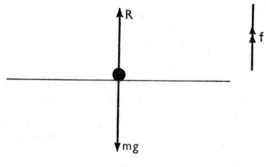

FIG. 91.

Figure 91 shows the forces acting *on the particle* (single arrow) and the acceleration *of the particle* (double arrow). Here, the forces are measured in absolute units. *It is essential that the forces should be measured in absolute units when the relation $P = mf$ of* (1 : 1) *is used.*

The *equation of motion* of the particle is

$$R - mg = mf,$$

$$\therefore R = mg + mf.$$

The upward force exerted by the platform on the particle is $(mg + mf)$ pdl, i.e. $(m + mf/g)$ lb wt.

(ii) A cyclist, whose mass together with that of his cycle is 168 lb, free-wheels down an incline of 1 in 14. The total resistance to the motion of the cycle due to friction, air resistance, etc., is 7 lb wt. Calculate the time taken by the cyclist to travel 70 yd from rest down the slope.

In such problems as this an approximation to the result is obtained by treating the moving body as a particle of mass equal to that of the body and located at the centre of mass of the body. When the moving body is a rigid body, moving without rotation, the assumption is a correct one, but when, as in this case, some parts of the body move relative to the other parts, the mathematical model which involves the assumption gives only an approximation to the correct result.

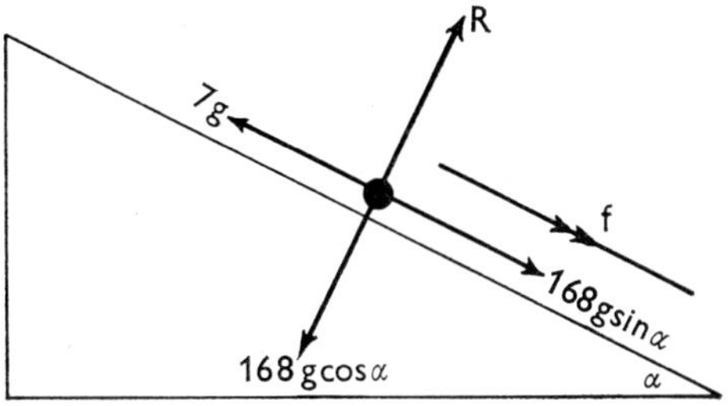

FIG. 92.

Figure 92 shows the components of the forces acting on the cyclist and his machine in the directions parallel and perpendicular to the inclined plane and the acceleration in the direction of motion. The sine of the angle of inclination is 1/14. (Conventionally in such problems we assume, "an incline of 1 in l" to mean an incline of $\sin^{-1}\left(\dfrac{1}{l}\right)$ with the horizontal. For small angles the difference between $\sin^{-1}\left(\dfrac{1}{l}\right)$ and $\tan^{-1}\left(\dfrac{1}{l}\right)$ is very small.)

The equation of motion for the cyclist and his machine is

$$168g \cdot \frac{1}{14} - 7g = 168f.$$

$$\therefore f = \frac{5g}{168} = \frac{20}{21}.$$

The cyclist accelerates down the incline at $\dfrac{20}{21}$ ft/sec².

Therefore the time taken to cover 70 yd, i.e. 210 ft, from rest, is given by ($s = \frac{1}{2}ft^2$)

$$210 = \frac{10}{21} t^2,$$

i.e. $$t = 21.$$

The cyclist travels 70 yd from rest down the incline in 21 sec.

(iii) A body of mass $(M + m)$ gm is being accelerated at f cm/sec² in a straight line on a smooth horizontal plane by means of an attached string. After a time t_1 sec from the beginning of the motion, the body breaks into two portions of M gm and m gm respectively, the string remains attached to the portion of mass M gm and the tension in the string is unchanged. Calculate the distance between the two portions of the body after a further t_2 sec and show that this distance is independent of t_1.

For the first part of the motion, if T dyn is the tension in the string,

$$T = (M + m)\,f.$$

Hence, when the body separates, if f_1 cm/sec² is the subsequent acceleration of the portion of mass M gm,

$$(M + m)\,f = M f_1.$$

$$\therefore f_1 = \frac{M + m}{M}\,f.$$

After the body separates, there is no force acting on the portion of mass m gm and it moves with uniform speed in its original direction. The body of mass M gm is therefore moving, *relative to the body of mass m gm*, with uniform acceleration $\dfrac{M + m}{M}\,f$ cm/sec². The velocity of the first body relative to the second body at the instant of separation is zero. Therefore the displacement s cm of the first body relative to the second after time t_2 sec from the instant of separation is given by

$$s = \frac{1}{2}\,\frac{M + m}{M}\,f t_2^2,$$

and this is independent of t_1.

(iii) Given that the tensile strength of a sample of steel is 30 tons wt./in² at London and that the acceleration due to gravity on Mars is $\frac{3}{4}$ of the acceleration due to gravity at London, express the tensile strength of steel on Mars in tons wt./in². Take the acceleration due to gravity in London as 981·33 and show that the tensile strength of the steel is about 30·02 tonf/in² everywhere.

$$\frac{\text{Tensile strength on Mars in tons wt./in}^2}{\text{Tensile strength in London in tons wt./in}^2} = \frac{\text{Acceleration due to gravity in London}}{\text{Acceleration due to gravity on Mars.}}$$

tensile strength on Mars is $\dfrac{4}{3} \times 30$ tons wt./in² = 40 tons wt./in².

$$\text{Tensile strength} = \frac{30 \times 981\cdot33}{980\cdot665}\ \text{tonf/in}^2 \ \doteqdot 30\cdot02\ \text{tonf/in}^2.$$

EXERCISES 8.1.

1. (i) Express 1 gm wt. in poundals at a point where $g = 980$ cm/sec².

(ii) Express 1 gm wt. at a point where $g = 980$ cm/sec² in gmf units. (Take 1 kgm as 2·21 lb, 1 in. as 2·54 cm.)

2. A 3-ton boat is moving at 5 m.p.h. What force will be needed to stop the boat in (a) 20 sec, (b) 20 ft? Give your answers in lb wt. (N.)

3. A mass of 7 lb is pulled along a smooth plane inclined at 30° to the horizontal by a force of 9 lb wt. acting along the plane. Find the acceleration up the plane and the force exerted by the mass on the plane. (N.)

4. A mass of 3 lb rests at the bottom of a smooth inclined plane whose inclination θ to the horizontal is given by $\tan\theta = \frac{5}{12}$. A force of 2 lb wt. up the plane now begins to act. Find the acceleration produced, the force exerted by the mass on the plane, and how long the mass will take to go 10 ft up the plane. (N.)

5. A train travelling uniformly on the level at the rate of 48 m.p.h. begins an ascent of 1 in 75. The tractive force that the engine exerts during the ascent is constant and equal to $2\frac{1}{2}$ tons wt., the resistance (due to friction, &c.) is constant and equal to 30 cwt wt., and the weight of the whole train is 225 tons Show that the train will come to a standstill after climbing for 1·65 miles. (O.C.)

6. Calculate the constant force P lb wt. required to pull a mass of 20 lb up a track inclined at 30° to the horizontal with an acceleration of 4 ft/sec² against a constant frictional resistance of 5 lb wt. If the mass starts from rest and the force P lb wt. acts for 1 min and then ceases to act, after how many more seconds will the mass come to rest? (L.)

7. A train of total mass 300 tons is being drawn up a slope of 1 in 150 by an engine which is exerting constant tractive force. If the frictional resistances amount to 10 lb wt./ton mass, and the train acquires a speed of 30 m.p.h. from rest as it travels 2 miles up the slope, calculate the tractive force of the engine in lb wt. (C.)

8. Two bodies, of mass respectively 1 oz and 1000 lb, are moving with velocities of 1000 ft/sec and 1 ft/sec. Equal constant retarding forces are applied to the bodies simultaneously. Prove that if the lighter body is brought to rest in 1 sec, the heavier body will be brought to rest in 16 sec, and find the distances described by the two bodies before coming to rest.

Find the time that elapses after retardation begins before the bodies have equal velocities. (O.C.)

9. A man of mass 10 stone stands in a lift. Find the force, in lb wt., between the man's feet and the floor of the lift when

(a) the lift is ascending with an acceleration of 2 ft/sec².

(b) the lift is descending at a uniform speed of 12 ft/sec. (N.)

10. A body is hung from a spring-balance suspended from the roof of a lift. When the lift is descending with uniform acceleration 3 ft/sec² the balance indicates a weight of $14\frac{1}{2}$ lb wt. When the lift is ascending with uniform acceleration x ft/sec² the reading is 18 lb wt. Find the value of x. (O.C.)

11. A train is travelling over level ground at 45 m.p.h.; with steam shut off it is brought to rest in 220 yd by a constant retarding force f per unit mass. Find f, stating the units that you employ.

The train subsequently travels down a slope of 1 in 15 at 35 m.p.h. with steam shut off; the same constant retarding force is then applied. Prove that the train comes to rest in 44 sec. (O.C.)

12. A load of 1500 lb is being raised from rest with uniform acceleration by a cable. The cable is allowed to become slack, and the load comes to rest 160 ft above its original position. The total time from rest to rest is 5 sec. Prove that the tension at the lower end of the cable when it is tight is 2500 lb wt. (O.C.)

13. An object of mass 150 gm hangs from the ceiling of a lift by a light spring of natural length 50 cm, which is such that a force of 35,000 dyn extends it by 5 cm. Calculate the length of the spring when

    (i) the lift is ascending with acceleration 70 cm/sec^2,

    (ii) when the lift is descending with acceleration 70 cm/sec^2.   (L.)

14. A particle of mass m lb which is subject to a constant retarding force is observed to cover s_1 and s_n feet respectively in the 1st and nth seconds of its motion. Find an expression in terms of s_1 and s_n for the magnitude of the retarding force in lb wt.

8.2. The Motion of Connected Particles

In the following examples we consider some cases of the motion of two or more connected masses. In these examples it is important

    (i) to draw a clear diagram,

    (ii) to mark all the forces acting on each mass separately, and

    (iii) to mark the component accelerations of each mass separately.

Examples. (i) Two particles of masses m_1 and m_2 $(m_1 > m_2)$ are connected by a light string passing over a small smooth fixed pulley of negligible mass. Calculate the tension in the string and the accelerations of the particles. Prove that the centre of mass of the particles descends with acceleration $\left(\dfrac{m_1 - m_2}{m_1 + m_2} \right)^2 g$.

Because the pulley is smooth and of negligible mass, the tension T of the string will be the same throughout its length, and the forces, in absolute units, acting on each of the particles will be those shown in Fig. 93. Because the string remains tight throughout the motion, the magnitude of the acceleration downwards of the mass m_1 will be equal in magnitude to the acceleration upwards of the mass m_2.

The equation of motion,

    (1) for the particle m_1, is $m_1 g - T = m_1 f,$

(2) for the particle m_2, is $T - m_2 g = m_2 f.$

$$\therefore f = \frac{m_1 - m_2}{m_1 + m_2} g,$$

$$T = \frac{2 m_1 m_2 g}{m_1 + m_2}.$$

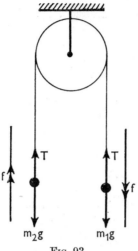

FIG. 93.

When the distances of the particles from the centre of the pulley are x_1 and x_2 and $\bar{x}$ is the distance of their centre of mass from the same point,

$$\bar{x} = \frac{m_1 x_1 + m_2 x_2}{m_1 + m_2},$$

$$\therefore \frac{d\bar{x}}{dt} = \frac{m_1 \dfrac{dx_1}{dt} + m_2 \dfrac{dx_2}{dt}}{m_1 + m_2}$$

and

$$\frac{d^2 \bar{x}}{dt^2} = \frac{m_1 \dfrac{d^2 x_1}{dt^2} + m_2 \dfrac{d^2 x_2}{dt^2}}{m_1 + m_2}.$$

But

$$\frac{d^2 x_1}{dt^2} = - \frac{d^2 x_2}{dt^2} = f = \frac{m_1 - m_2}{m_1 + m_2} g.$$

Therefore the acceleration of the centre of mass is

$$\frac{d^2 \bar{x}}{dt^2} = \frac{m_1 - m_2}{m_1 + m_2} f = \left(\frac{m_1 - m_2}{m_1 + m_2} \right)^2 g.$$

14*

(ii) A mass of m lb lies on the smooth inclined face of a wedge. The face is inclined at an angle α with the horizontal. An inextensible string lies along the line of greatest slope of the wedge, passes over a small smooth pulley at the top edge of the wedge and carries at its other end a mass of nm lb which hangs vertically [Fig. 94(i)].

(a) Show that if $n > \sin\alpha$ the mass on the inclined face moves up the face of the wedge and find the value of $\sin\alpha$ for the case in which this mass is pulled up the face of the wedge with acceleration

$$\frac{ng}{k(1+n)}, \ (k > 1).$$

(b) Calculate the force exerted on the pulley in terms of n, m and α.

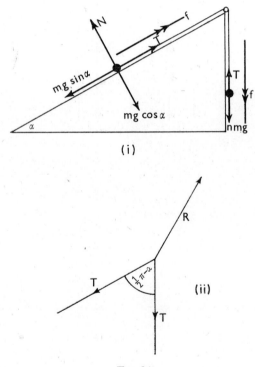

(i)

(ii)

Fig. 94.

(a) Figure 94(i) shows the forces acting on each of the particles and the acceleration of each of the particles.

The equation of motion,

(1) for the particle on the sloping face of the wedge is

$$T - mg \sin \alpha = mf,$$

(2) for the hanging particle, is

$$nmg - T = nmf.$$

Hence, $\qquad f = g(n - \sin \alpha)/(1 + n).$

This expression for f is positive if $n > \sin \alpha$ and therefore, if this condition is fulfilled, the particle accelerates up the inclined face of the wedge.

When

$$f = \frac{ng}{k(1+n)}$$

$$\frac{ng}{k(1+n)} = \frac{g(n - \sin \alpha)}{1 + n},$$

i.e. $\qquad \sin \alpha = \dfrac{k-1}{k} n.$

Note that the particle on the inclined plane has no component of acceleration perpendicular to the plane and so the equation of motion perpendicular to this plane gives

$$N - mg \cos \alpha = 0.$$

(b) The *small* portion of string in contact with the pulley is acted on by the forces shown in Fig. 94 (ii), where R is the force exerted by the pulley on the string. Since the mass of the string is so small as to be negligible the resultant force acting on the string is also so small as to be negligible. (This follows from the equation of motion for a small portion of the string.)

$$\therefore \; R = 2T \cos(\tfrac{1}{4}\pi - \tfrac{1}{2}\alpha).$$

From the equations of motion of the two masses,

$$T = nmg(1 + \sin \alpha)/(n + 1).$$

$$\therefore \; R = \{2nmg(1 + \sin \alpha) \cos(\tfrac{1}{4}\pi - \tfrac{1}{2}\alpha)\}/(n + 1).$$

The force exerted on the pulley is equal and opposite to R, i.e.,

$$\frac{2nmg(1 + \sin \alpha) \cos(\tfrac{1}{4}\pi - \tfrac{1}{2}\alpha)}{(n + 1)}$$

in a downward direction bisecting the angle between the inclined face
of the wedge and the vertical.

(iii) Figure 95 shows a system of two small fixed smooth pulleys A
and B and a movable smooth pulley C of mass $2m$. A continuous
inextensible string passes round the pulleys and the parts of the string
not in contact with the pulleys are vertical. The string carries a mass
of $4m$ at one end P and a mass of $2m$ at the other end Q. Calculate
the acceleration of the movable pulley and the accelerations of the
masses at P and Q.

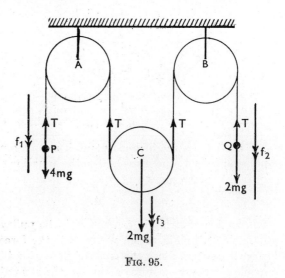

FIG. 95.

Figure 95 shows the forces acting on the movable pulley and those
acting on each of the masses at P and Q. The acceleration of each of
these bodies is also shown in the figure. Since the pulleys are smooth,
the tension, T, in the string is constant throughout its length.

The equation of motion,

(1) for the mass at P, is $4\,mg - T = 4mf_1$,

(2) for the mass at Q, is $2mg - T = 2mf_2$,

(3) for the movable pulley is $2mg - 2T = 2mf_3$.

The equation which interprets the geometrical constraints of the
system is

(4) $$f_3 = -\tfrac{1}{2}(f_1 + f_2),$$

for if the masses at P and Q descend distances x_1 and x_2 respectively, the movable pulley descends a distance x_3 given by $x_3 = -\frac{1}{2}(x_1 + x_2)$. Hence

$$f_3 = \frac{d^2(x_3)}{dt^2} = -\frac{1}{2}\left(\frac{d^2 x_1}{dt^2} + \frac{d^2 x_2}{dt^2}\right) = -\frac{1}{2}(f_1 + f_2).$$

Then, from equations (1) and (2),

$$2f_1 - f_2 = g,$$

and from equations (1) and (3),

$$4f_1 - f_3 = 3g.$$
$$\therefore\ 4f_1 + \tfrac{1}{2}(f_1 + f_2) = 3g,$$
$$\therefore\ 9f_1 + f_2 = 6g.$$
$$\therefore\ f_1 = \frac{7g}{11}, \quad f_2 = \frac{3g}{11}, \quad f_3 = -\frac{5g}{11}.$$

(iv) Figure 96 shows a fixed pulley A over which hangs a light inextensible string which carries a mass m_1 at one end and a small movable pulley B of negligible mass at the other. Pulley B carries a light inextensible string with a mass of m_2 at one end and a mass of m_3 at the other end. Find an expression for the acceleration of the mass m_1.

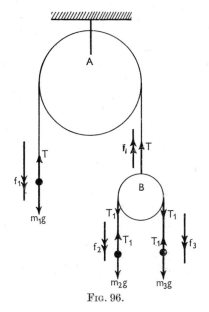

FIG. 96.

The forces acting on each part of the system and the acceleration of each part are shown in Fig. 96. Because pulley B is accelerating, the acceleration downwards of m_2 is not equal in magnitude to the acceleration upwards of m_3. The acceleration downwards *relative to the pulley B* of the mass m_2 is equal to the acceleration upwards *relative to the pulley B* of the mass m_3, i.e.

$$f_2 + f_1 = -(f_3 + f_1).$$
$$\therefore\ f_2 + 2f_1 + f_3 = 0. \tag{1}$$

The equation of motion,

(2) for the mass m_1, is $m_1 g - T = m_1 f_1$,

(3) for the mass m_2, is $m_2 g - T_1 = m_2 f_2$,

(4) for the mass m_3, is $m_3 g - T_1 = m_3 f_3$,

(5) for the pulley B, (since its mass is negligible), is $T = 2T_1$.

From equations (2), (3) and (5),

$$m_1 f_1 - 2m_2 f_2 = m_1 g - 2m_2 g, \tag{6}$$

and from equations (2), (4) and (5),

$$m_1 f_1 - 2m_3 f_3 = m_1 g - 2m_3 g.$$

Therefore using equation (1)

$$m_1 f_1 + 2m_3(f_2 + 2f_1) = m_1 g - 2m_3 g.$$
$$\therefore\ (m_1 + 4m_3)\, f_1 + 2m_3 f_2 = m_1 g - 2m_3 g. \tag{7}$$

Solution of equations (6) and (7) gives

$$f_1(m_1 m_3 + m_1 m_2 + 4m_3 m_2) = m_1 m_3 g - 4m_2 m_3 g + m_1 m_2 g.$$
$$\therefore\ f_1 = \frac{m_1 m_3 - 4m_2 m_3 + m_1 m_2}{m_1 m_3 + 4m_2 m_3 + m_1 m_2}\, g.$$

(v) A particle of mass m can slide down the smooth inclined face of a wedge of mass nm and angle α, [Fig. 97 (i)]. The wedge stands on a smooth horizontal plane over which it is free to move. A horizontal force of kmg acting through its centre of mass is applied to the wedge in the plane of a line of greatest slope. Find the acceleration of the wedge and show that the condition that the particle does not accelerate *relative to the wedge* during the subsequent motion is

$$k = (n + 1)\tan\alpha.$$

Figure 97 (i) shows the forces acting on the wedge. R is the action of the particle on the wedge and N is the action of the horizontal plane on the wedge. F is the acceleration of the wedge and f is the

acceleration of the particle *relative* to the wedge. Figure 97 (ii) shows
the forces acting on the particle and its accelerations.

The equation of motion,

(1) for the wedge in a horizontal direction, is

$$kmg - R\sin\alpha = nmF,$$

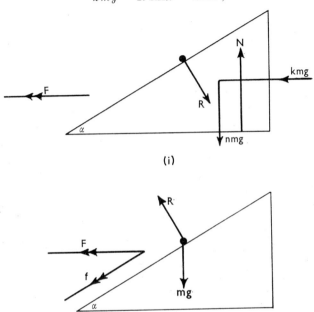

(i)

(ii)

FIG. 97.

(2) for the particle in the direction parallel to the plane, is

$$mg\sin\alpha = mF\cos\alpha + mf,$$

(3) for the particle in the direction perpendicular to the plane, is

$$R - mg\cos\alpha = mF\sin\alpha.$$

The geometrical constraint of the system, that the particle remains
in contact with the inclined face of the wedge, is expressed by the
choice of component accelerations of the particle. Had we represented
these component accelerations as, for example, two components at
right angles unrelated to the acceleration of the wedge, it would
have been necessary to include an equation expressing the fact that

the component accelerations of the wedge and the particle in the direction *perpendicular to the face of the wedge* are equal.

From equations (1) and (3),

$$kmg - (mg\cos\alpha + mF\sin\alpha)\sin\alpha = nmF.$$

$$\therefore F = \frac{g\,(k - \sin\alpha\cos\alpha)}{n + \sin^2\alpha}.$$

Therefore, from equation (2),

$$g\sin\alpha = \frac{g\,(k - \sin\alpha\cos\alpha)\cos\alpha}{n + \sin^2\alpha} + f.$$

$$\therefore f = \frac{g}{n + \sin^2\alpha}\,(n\sin\alpha + \sin^3\alpha - k\cos\alpha + \sin\alpha\cos^2\alpha)$$

$$= \frac{g}{n + \sin^2\alpha}\,(n\sin\alpha + \sin\alpha - k\cos\alpha).$$

Hence $f = 0$, so that the particle does not accelerate relative to the wedge, when

$$n\sin\alpha + \sin\alpha - k\cos\alpha = 0,$$

i.e. when

$$\tan\alpha = k/(n + 1).$$

EXERCISES 8.2.

1. A particle of mass 9 lb is connected to a particle of mass 7 lb by a light string passing over a smooth fixed light pulley. The system is released from rest with the string taut. Find

(i) the acceleration, in ft/sec², of either particle,

(ii) the tension, in lb wt., of the string,

(iii) the force, in lb wt., supporting the pulley.   (N.)

2. Masses of 2 lb and 3 lb are attached to the ends A and C respectively of a light string, part of which rests on a smooth horizontal table. At opposite edges of the table the string passes over small smooth pulleys and the masses at A and C hang vertically. A mass of 3 lb is attached at a point B of that part of the string which lies on the table. The system is released from rest with the string taut and ABC in a vertical plane. Show that the acceleration of each mass is 4 ft/sec² and find in lb wt. the tension in each portion of the string.

If the string BC breaks one second after the start of the motion, show that the string AB comes to instantaneous rest when B is $2\frac{5}{8}$ ft from its starting point.   (N.)

3. A particle of mass 4 lb slides down the smooth face of a wedge inclined at 27° to the horizontal. The wedge, which rests with its horizontal face on a smooth horizontal plane, is held at rest by a horizontal force P lb wt. Calculate the value of P and also the acceleration, in ft/sec², of the particle. (Give your answers correct to three significant figures.)   (N.)

4. Two particles are connected by a light string. One particle A of mass m lb is placed on a smooth horizontal table at a distance 3 ft from the edge E of the table. The string, after passing over a small smooth pulley at E, supports the other particle B of mass 2 lb which hangs vertically. The system starts from rest with the string taut and in a plane at right angles to the edge of the table. If the particle A reaches E after $\frac{3}{4}$ sec, find m. Find also, in lb wt., the tension in the string. (N.)

5. A mass P of 4 lb carries a detachable rider R of mass 2 lb; P and R are attached to one end of a light inextensible string which passes over a small smooth peg and carries a mass Q of 5 lb at its other end. If the system begins to move, find (i) the acceleration, (ii) the tension in the string.

The rider R can be removed by means of a fixed ring through which P can pass freely. The system is released from rest when P, carrying R, is at a point 2 ft 9 in. above the ring. Prove that P, after leaving the rider on the ring, comes to instantaneous rest at a point distant 2 ft 3 in. below the ring. (N.)

6. Two particles, A and B, of masses $3m$ and m respectively, are connected by a light inextensible string of length l; A is held at rest on a smooth horizontal table so that the string is taut and at right angles to the edge of the table with B just hanging over the edge of the table. The particle A is released and when it has travelled a distance $\frac{1}{2}l$ on the table, the string breaks. Neglecting friction at the edge, prove that, when A reaches the edge of the table, B is at a distance $3l/2$ below the edge, and that the velocity of B is then $\frac{3}{2}\sqrt{(gl)}$. (N.)

7. A light inextensible string passes across a smooth horizontal table and is in a vertical plane, perpendicular to a pair of opposite edges. The ends of the string hang downwards; to one end is attached a mass of 5 lb and to the other a mass of 1 lb, and to the horizontal portion is fastened a mass of 10 lb. If the system is released from rest, find (i) the tension in each part of the string, (ii) the speed acquired by any one of the masses in moving through 1 ft. (N.)

8. A smooth wedge of mass M is placed on a smooth horizontal table. A particle of mass m moves from rest down the face of the wedge which is inclined at an angle α to the horizontal. Show that the acceleration of the wedge is

$$\frac{mg\sin 2\alpha}{2(M + m\sin^2\alpha)}. \qquad \text{(N.)}$$

9. A smooth, fixed inclined plane slopes at $30°$ to the horizontal. At the top of the plane is a smooth fixed pulley over which passes a string connecting a mass of 8 lb which hangs freely and a mass of 12 lb which rests on the plane. If the system is released from rest, find
(i) the acceleration of either mass in ft/sec^2,
(ii) the tension in the string in lb wt.,
(iii) the reaction in lb wt. between the plane and the 12 lb mass. (L.)

10. An inextensible string passes over a fixed smooth pulley and carries particles of mass m, m' $(m > m')$ at its ends, the parts of the string not in contact with the pulley being vertical. Prove that the acceleration of the particles is

$$\frac{m - m'}{m + m'}\,g.$$

Find the acceleration of the string relative to the pulley when the pulley is made to descend with a constant acceleration α, less than g.

Find the value of α in order that the mass m' may be stationary, and state the corresponding acceleration of the mass m. (O.C.)

*11. A light inextensible string passes over a smooth fixed peg and carries at one end a particle A of mass $5m$ and at the other a light smooth pulley;

over the latter passes a second light inextensible string carrying particles of mass $2m$ and $3m$ at its ends. Find the acceleration of A when the particles move vertically under gravity.

Find by how much the mass of A must be reduced in order that A can remain at rest while the other two particles are in motion.

*12. A, B are masses of 6 oz and 3 oz respectively resting on two smooth tables, placed with their edges parallel. They are connected by a fine string, which hangs between the tables with its hanging parts vertical and carries in its loop a smooth pulley C of mass 4 oz. The string lies in a vertical plane and crosses the edges of the tables at right angles to the edges.

Find the tension in the string (1) when A and B are held fast, (2) when B is held but A moves, (3) when A and B both move; and show that in the three cases the tensions are in the ratio $21 : 18 : 14$.　　　(O.C.)

8.3. Impulse and Momentum

If a *constant* force P pdl acts for time t sec on a particle of mass m lb it gives to the particle an acceleration P/m ft/sec^2 and changes its component velocity in the direction of the line of action of the force from its initial value u to a value v given by the equation

$$v = u + \frac{P}{m} t,$$

i.e.　　　　　　　　$$Pt = mv - mu. \tag{8.1}$$

The quantity, mass $\times$ velocity, has been defined in Chapter I, § 1.2 as a property of the motion of a body called its *momentum*. The quantity, force $\times$ time (force constant), is called the *impulse* of the force over the time interval concerned. Both momentum and impulse are vector quantities and the dimensions of each of them are lb ft/sec. We shall refer to the absolute units of momentum and the absolute units of impulse as lb ft/sec. The corresponding gravitational units are lb wt. ft/sec. In the metric system of units the corresponding units are gm cm/sec and gm wt. cm/sec. Equation (8.1) expresses a general principle of dynamics which is stated as:

The impulse of a force = the change in momentum it produces.

The Time Integral of the Equation of Motion

The equation of motion of a particle moving along a straight line, $P = mf$, where P acts along the line and is not constant but is a function of the time t, may be integrated to give

$$\int_{t_1}^{t_2} P \, dt = \int_{t=t_1}^{t=t_2} m \frac{dv}{dt} \, dt = \left[mv \right]_{v_1}^{v_2} = mv_2 - mv_1,$$

if m is constant, $v = v_1$ at time $t = t_1$ and $v = v_2$ at time $t = t_2$.

$\int_{t_1}^{t_2} P\,dt$ is defined as the impulse of the force P over the interval $t = t_1$ to $t = t_2$ and, with this definition, we have, once more the impulse of a force = the change in momentum it produces.

In general, the concept of impulse is used only in problems concerning sudden changes of motion produced by a large, variable force acting for a very short time. In such cases it is not usually possible to consider the variation of force with time but it is possible to measure the impulse of a force by measuring the change in momentum produced by the force. We therefore extend the definition of impulse and *define* the impulse of a force as

the measure of the change in momentum produced by the force.

Examples. (i) A bullet of mass m gm is fired with velocity v cm/sec into a fixed block of wood from which it emerges, t sec after striking it, with a velocity kv cm/sec. Calculate the resistance of the block, supposed constant, to the motion of the bullet.

Change in momentum of bullet is $m(v - kv)$ gm cm/sec. Therefore the impulse of the resisting force on the bullet is $m(v - kv)$ gm cm/sec. Therefore resisting force is

$$m(v - kv)/t \text{ dyn} = m(v - kv)/gt \text{ gm wt.}$$

(ii) A particle is moving in a straight line under the action of a force directed towards a point O in the line and of magnitude $k\cos\omega t$ pdl where k and ω are constant and t sec is the time that has elapsed since the beginning of the motion. Calculate the impulse of the force for the interval $t = 0$ to $t = \pi/2\omega$.

$$\text{Impulse} = \int_0^{\frac{\pi}{2\omega}} k\cos\omega t\,dt \text{ lb ft/sec}$$

$$= \left[\frac{k}{\omega}\sin\omega t\right]_0^{\frac{\pi}{2\omega}} \text{ lb ft/sec} = \frac{k}{\omega} \text{ lb ft/sec.}$$

(iii) A particle of mass m slides from rest a distance l ft down a smooth inclined plane of inclination $30°$. At the bottom of this plane it strikes a smooth horizontal plane and rebounds a horizontal distance $\frac{1}{2}l$ ft before striking the horizontal plane again. Calculate the impulse of the horizontal plane on the particle at the first instant of striking.

The component of force acting on the particle in the direction down the inclined plane is $mg \sin 30° = \frac{1}{2}mg$ and therefore the acceleration of the particle in this direction is $\frac{1}{2}g$ and its velocity in this direction at the instant of striking the horizontal plane is $\sqrt{(gl)}$.

Since the horizontal plane is smooth, the action of this plane on the particle is vertical and the change in momentum as the result of the impact is a vertical one. The horizontal component of velocity of the particle therefore remains unchanged as $\sqrt{(g\,l)} \cos 30 = \sqrt{(3gl/4)}$.

The time of flight, t, of the particle in its parabola of rebound is given by
$$0 = vt - \tfrac{1}{2}gt^2,$$

where v is the vertical component of the velocity of the particle just after striking the horizontal plane.

$$\therefore t = \frac{2v}{g}.$$

Therefore the range of the rebound is $\dfrac{2v}{g}\sqrt{\left(\dfrac{3gl}{4}\right)}$.

$$\therefore \frac{2v}{g}\sqrt{\left(\frac{3gl}{4}\right)} = \frac{l}{2},$$

i.e.
$$v = \frac{1}{2}\sqrt{\left(\frac{gl}{3}\right)}.$$

Hence the change in momentum of the particle at first impact with the horizontal plane is

$$m\left\{\frac{1}{2}\sqrt{(gl)} + \frac{1}{2}\sqrt{\left(\frac{gl}{3}\right)}\right\} = \frac{1}{6}(3 + \sqrt{3})\,m\,\sqrt{(gl)}$$

in the upward vertical direction. Therefore the impulse of the horizontal plane on the particle at first instant of striking is $\frac{1}{6}(3 + \sqrt{3})\,m\sqrt{(gl)}$ in the upward vertical direction.

(iv) A particle of mass 2 lb moving with velocity 4 ft/sec towards the N. is given an impulse of 4 lb ft/sec towards the NW. Calculate the initial velocity of the particle after the impulse.

Figure 98 is a vector diagram for the momentum of the particle immediately after the impulse. The particle has its initial momentum

8 lb ft/sec towards the north together with the momentum 4 lb ft/sec towards the NW. given to it by the impulse.

The resultant velocity of the particle is, therefore,

$$\frac{1}{2}\sqrt{\{(8 + 2\sqrt{2})^2 + (2\sqrt{2})^2\}} \text{ ft/sec in a direction } \tan^{-1}\left(\frac{\sqrt{2}}{4 + \sqrt{2}}\right) \text{ W. of N.,}$$

i.e. approximately 5·60 ft/sec in a direction $14\frac{1}{2}°$ W. of N.

It is important to remember that the *impulse* determines the *initial* velocity of the particle only. Subsequent motion is determined by the *forces* acting on the system.

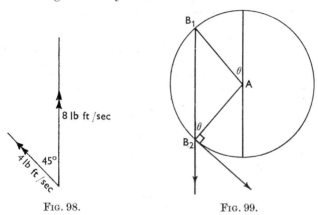

FIG. 98.   FIG. 99.

(v) A particle of mass m lb is attached to the end B of an inextensible string AB of length l ft. The string is fixed at A and is held taut in a vertical plane so that it makes an angle θ with the upward vertical. The particle is released, and it falls vertically until the string tightens, after which the particle immediately begins to move in a vertical circle. Find an expression for the impulse exerted by the string at the instant when the string tightens.

The velocity acquired by the particle in falling freely under gravity from B_1 to B_2 is $2\sqrt{(gl\cos\theta)}$ ft/sec (Fig. 99).

Therefore the component of momentum destroyed by the impulse in the string at the instant when the string tightens, i.e. the component in the direction AB_2, is $2m\cos\theta\sqrt{(gl\cos\theta)}$ lb ft/sec.

Therefore the impulse exerted by the string at this instant is $2m\cos\theta\sqrt{(gl\cos\theta)}$ lb ft/sec.

This impulse, exerted by a string which suddenly tightens, is sometimes called the *impulsive tension* in the string. It is important to remember that it is not a force (or tension) in the conventional sense of that word, but *an impulse* and that it can be measured or calculated *only by measuring or calculating the change in momentum which it produces.*

EXERCISES 8.3.

1. A particle of mass m lb falls freely from a height h_1 ft and strikes a smooth horizontal floor, rebounding to a height of h_2 ft. Find expressions for the impulse of the floor on the particle (a) in pdl sec, (b) in lb wt. sec.

2. A machine gun fires 800 rounds a minute horizontally with a muzzle velocity of 1800 ft/sec. Each bullet has a mass of 1 oz. Find the horizontal force necessary to keep the gun steady. (N.)

3. A bullet of mass 30 gm is fired into a fixed block of wood with a velocity of 294 m/sec and is brought to rest in $\frac{1}{150}$ sec. Find in dynes, and in grams weight, the resistance exerted by the wood, supposing it to be uniform. (O.C.)

4. A small metal sphere of mass m lb falls vertically through a height h ft and strikes a smooth plane inclined at an angle α with the horizontal. The sphere rebounds from the plane horizontally. Calculate the impulse of the plane on the sphere.

5. A jet of water issues from a circular pipe of 3 in. diameter at a speed of 12 ft/sec and impinges directly on a plane, its momentum being wholly destroyed by the impact. Calculate, in lb wt., the force, assumed constant, exerted by the jet on the plane. (Take the mass of 1 ft³ of water as $62\frac{1}{2}$ lb.)

6. A ball, mass 4 oz, is released when at relative rest from a position 6 ft above the floor of a lift, which is descending with a uniform acceleration of 4 ft/sec². Prove that, if the ball rises to the same position after striking the floor, the impulse on the floor at impact is nearly 9·2 foot-pound-second units, and find the times of descent and ascent of the ball relative to the lift. (O.C.)

In exercises 7–12 a force P which is given as a function of the time t is applied to a particle of mass m.

7. $P = at$: find an expression for the impulse of the force over the interval $t = 0$ to $t = 1$.

8. $P = ma\omega^2 \sin\omega t$: find an expression for the velocity of the particle at time t_1 given that $v = a\omega$ when $t = 0$.

9. $P = 3 + 4t$: the units of P are poundals and the units of t are seconds. Calculate the impulse of P over the interval $t = 0$ to $t = 1$, and, given that the mass of the particle is 2 lb, calculate the increase of the velocity of the particle in the direction of P in this interval.

10. $P = 8 - 2t^2 [t \leq 2]$; the units of P are gm wt., the units of t are sec, and the mass of the particle is 10 gm. Calculate in gm wt. sec the impulse of P over the interval $t = 0$ to $t = 2$ and, given that the particle was at rest at time $t = 0$, calculate the velocity of the particle at time $t = 2$.

11. An equation of motion of the particle is $v = u + \varphi(t)$; write down an expression for the impulse over the interval $t = 0$ to $t = t_1$.

12. An equation of motion of the particle is $f = 3t$; calculate the impulse of P over the interval $t = 0$ to $t = 2$ sec if $m = 2$ gm.

13. A particle of mass m gm is moving towards the W. with velocity v cm/sec, when it receives an impulse of I gm cm/sec in a direction towards the N. Obtain an expression for the initial velocity of the particle after the impulse.

14. A particle of mass 4 lb is moving towards the west with a velocity of 2 ft/sec. Calculate the magnitude of the impulse towards the north required to change its velocity to a direction N. 60° W.

15. A particle of mass 4 lb is attached to one end B of an inextensible string AB of length 2 ft the other end of which is fixed at A. The particle is held at A, is released, and falls vertically. Calculate the impulse exerted by the string on the particle when the string tightens.

16. A particle of mass m lb is attached to one end B of an inextensible string AB of length l ft. The system lies on a smooth horizontal table with the string taut and with A attached to a fixed point of the plane. The particle is now given an impulse I lb ft/sec in a direction making an angle of 45° with BA so that the string slackens initially. Calculate the impulse exerted by the string on the particle at the instant when the string tightens again.

8.4. Conservation of Momentum

If two particles A and B collide, then, by Newton's third law, the action of A on B is equal and opposite to the action of B on A. The period of contact is the same for particle A as for particle B and therefore the impulse of A on B is equal in magnitude and opposite in direction to the impulse of B on A. It follows that the change in momentum of particle A is equal in magnitude and opposite in direction to the change in momentum of particle B and that, therefore, the total change in momentum, during the collision, for this particular, simple system is zero.

It can be shown that this principle is true also of a set of any number of particles. It is stated in the form:

"The vector sum of the momenta of any set of particles remains constant, provided that no external forces act on the set." This result is called "the *Principle of Conservation of Momentum*".

It is a corollary of this result that, provided no external forces act, the sum of the component momenta of particles of the set in any one direction remains constant.

Examples. (i) A particle of mass m_1 moving with velocity v_1 collides with, and coalesces with, a particle of mass m_2 moving in the same direction with velocity v_2. Calculate the velocity of the combined particle after the collision.

Momentum sum in direction of motion before impact = momentum sum in direction of motion after impact.

$$\therefore\ m_1 v_1 + m_2 v_2 = (m_1 + m_2)\ V,$$

where V is the magnitude of the velocity after impact.

$$\therefore\ V = \frac{m_1 v_1 + m_2 v_2}{m_1 + m_2}.$$

(ii) A particle of mass $2m$ moving in a direction N. 15° E. with speed V collided with, and coalesced with, a particle of mass m and speed $3V/2$. After the collision the combined particle moved in a direction N. 15° W. Calculate the possible directions of motion of the second particle immediately before the collision, and the corresponding speeds of the combined particle immediately after the collision.

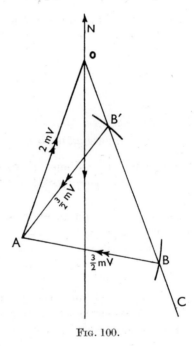

Fig. 100.

Figure 100 shows the two possible triangles of vectors which express the fact that the vector sum of the momenta of the particles before collision is equal to the vector sum of their momenta after collision. (In diagrams illustrating problems of *initial motions*, impulses and momenta are marked throughout the book with a double arrow and velocities are marked with a single arrow.)

The equations of motion are,

(1) for the mass on the table, $T = nmf$,

(2) for the hanging mass, $mg - T = mf$.

$$\therefore f = g/(n + 1).$$

At any subsequent stage of the problem, the acceleration of the system consisting of n particles of mass m, tautly connected, on the table with a mass m hanging over the edge is given by this formula.

(b) In the first stage of the motion the hanging particle and the first particle on the table each move with acceleration $\frac{1}{2}g$ for a distance l, each acquiring a speed of $\sqrt{(gl)}$.

(c) The string connecting the first two particles on the table suddenly becomes taut and there is an *impulse* in *each* of the light strings.

Figure 101 (ii) is a diagram showing the initial momenta of the particles (double arrows), the impulses in the strings (double arrows) and the initial velocities of the particles immediately after the jerk (single arrows). *Impulse-momentum* equations for each of the three particles are,

$$m \sqrt{(gl)} - I_1 = mv_1,$$

$$I_1 + m \sqrt{(gl)} - I_2 = mv_1,$$

$$I_2 = mv_1.$$

Hence, by addition,

$$3mv_1 = 2m \sqrt{(gl)}.$$

$$\therefore v_1 = \tfrac{2}{3} \sqrt{(gl)}.$$

The student should observe that this result could have been reached from the assumption that the total momentum *in the direction of motion of the tight string* remains constant. This assumption is a correct one. The system of pulley and strings acts as a machine designed to produce motion in one direction as the result of induced motion in a different direction. *It is wrong, however, to assume that the application of this assumption is a direct application of the conservation of momentum law, since to do so would be to ignore the vector nature of momentum.*

(d) The system continues in motion with an acceleration, for each of its components, of $\frac{1}{3}g$. Before the last string tightens the system acquires a velocity v given by,

$$v^2 = \frac{4}{9}gl + \frac{2g}{3}l.$$

$$\therefore v = \sqrt{\left(\frac{10}{9}gl\right)}.$$

(e) The last string becomes taut [Fig. 101 (iii)]. The impulse–momentum equations for the particles are

$$m\sqrt{\left(\frac{10}{9}gl\right)} - J_1 = mv_2,$$

$$J_1 + m\sqrt{\left(\frac{10}{9}gl\right)} - J_2 = mv_2,$$

$$J_2 + m\sqrt{\left(\frac{10}{9}gl\right)} - J_3 = mv_2,$$

$$J_3 = mv_2.$$

By addition (or by using the principle quoted above)

$$v_2 = \frac{3}{4}\sqrt{\left(\frac{10}{9}gl\right)}.$$

$$\therefore J_1 = \frac{m}{4}\sqrt{\left(\frac{10}{9}gl\right)},$$

$$J_2 = \frac{m}{2}\sqrt{\left(\frac{10}{9}gl\right)},$$

$$J_3 = \frac{3m}{4}\sqrt{\left(\frac{10}{9}gl\right)}.$$

$$\therefore J_1 : J_2 : J_3 = 1 : 2 : 3.$$

(v) Two particles of mass $2m$ and m are attached to the end of a string of length $4h$ which passes over a small smooth pulley fixed at a height $3h$ above an inelastic table. The system is released from rest with each particle at a height h above the table. Prove that when the heavier particle reaches the table for the first time it will remain there for a time $2\sqrt{\left(\frac{2h}{3g}\right)}$ before it is jerked into motion again. Prove also that the time between the first and second jerk is $\frac{8}{3}\sqrt{\left(\frac{2h}{3g}\right)}$

and that the system will be permanently at rest after a time $9\sqrt{\left(\dfrac{2h}{3g}\right)}$ measured from the instant of release.   (N.)

Figure 102 shows the pulley with the particles in their initial positions. The forces and accelerations are as shown in the figure and, from the equations of motion for the particles, $f = \frac{1}{3}g$.

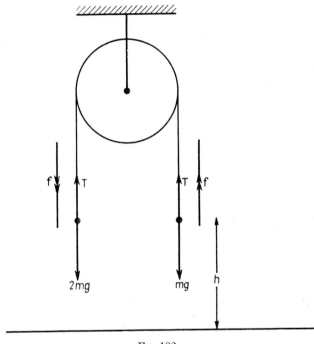

2mg   mg   h

FIG. 102.

(a) The heavier particle reaches the table in time t_1 given by

$$h = \frac{1}{2}\left(\frac{g}{3}\right)t_1^2, \quad \text{i.e.} \quad t_1 = \sqrt{\left(\frac{6h}{g}\right)},$$

acquiring a velocity v_1 given by

$$v_1^2 = \frac{2gh}{3}, \quad \text{i.e.} \quad v_1 = \sqrt{\left(\frac{2gh}{3}\right)}.$$

(b) Since the table is inelastic, the heavy particle does not rebound and so the lighter particle now moves freely under gravity with initial velocity $\sqrt{\left(\dfrac{2gh}{3}\right)}$ upwards, and returns to the point at which the string tightens again in time t_2 given by

$$0 = t_2\sqrt{\left(\frac{2gh}{3}\right)} - \frac{1}{2}gt_2^2, \quad \text{i.e.} \quad t_2 = 2\sqrt{\left(\frac{2h}{3g}\right)},$$

and with velocity $\sqrt{\left(\dfrac{2gh}{3}\right)}$ downwards. The heavier particle therefore remains on the table for a time $2\sqrt{\left(\dfrac{2h}{3g}\right)}$, and the string now tightens and the heavier particle is picked up off the table.

(c) From the impulse–momentum principle [as in example (iv)] when the particle is picked up off the table (first jerk) the speed of each particle becomes $\dfrac{1}{3}\sqrt{\left(\dfrac{2gh}{3}\right)}$.

(d) The acceleration of the system is now once more $\frac{1}{3}g$ in the downward direction for the particle of mass $2m$. With this acceleration and with initial velocity $\dfrac{1}{3}\sqrt{\left(\dfrac{2gh}{3}\right)}$ the particle will once more return to the table in time t_3 given by

$$0 = t_3 \cdot \frac{1}{3}\sqrt{\left(\frac{2gh}{3}\right)} - \frac{1}{6}gt_3^2, \quad \text{i.e.} \quad t_3 = 2\sqrt{\left(\frac{2h}{3g}\right)}.$$

and with velocity $\dfrac{1}{3}\sqrt{\left(\dfrac{2gh}{3}\right)}$.

(e) The lighter particle moves freely under gravity with initial upward velocity $\dfrac{1}{3}\sqrt{\left(\dfrac{2gh}{3}\right)}$ and returns to the position with the string taut in time t_4 given by

$$0 = t_4 \cdot \frac{1}{3}\sqrt{\left(\frac{2gh}{3}\right)} - \frac{1}{2}gt_4^2, \quad \text{i.e.} \quad t_4 = \frac{2}{3}\sqrt{\left(\frac{2gh}{3}\right)}.$$

(f) The second jerk now takes place, and therefore the time between the first and second jerks is $2\sqrt{\left(\dfrac{2h}{3g}\right)} + \dfrac{2}{3}\sqrt{\left(\dfrac{2h}{3g}\right)} = \dfrac{8}{3}\sqrt{\left(\dfrac{2h}{3g}\right)}$.

(g) The time between any successive pair of jerks can be shown by a calculation similar to the one above to be $\frac{1}{3}$ of the time between the immediately preceeding pair of jerks. The total time for the motion is therefore:

$$\sqrt{\left(\frac{6h}{g}\right)} + 2\sqrt{\left(\frac{2h}{3g}\right)} + \left\{\frac{8}{3}\sqrt{\left(\frac{2h}{3g}\right)} + \frac{8}{9}\sqrt{\left(\frac{2h}{3g}\right)} + \frac{8}{27}\sqrt{\left(\frac{2h}{3g}\right)} + \cdots\right\}$$

$$= \sqrt{\left(\frac{6h}{g}\right)} + 2\sqrt{\left(\frac{2h}{3g}\right)} + \frac{8}{3}\sqrt{\left(\frac{2h}{3g}\right)}\Big/\left(1 - \frac{1}{3}\right).$$

$$= 3\sqrt{\left(\frac{2h}{3g}\right)} + 2\sqrt{\left(\frac{2h}{3g}\right)} + 4\sqrt{\left(\frac{2h}{3g}\right)}$$

$$= 9\sqrt{\left(\frac{2h}{3g}\right)}.$$

(vi) A shell of mass m lb is fired horizontally by a gun of mass M lb which is free to recoil and which is on horizontal ground. Show that the initial speeds of the gun and the shell are in the inverse ratio of their masses.

This *very much simplified* mathematical model represents a situation in which the explosive gases exert equal and opposite *impulses* on the gun and the shell; the total momentum of the gun and the shell in the direction of firing, therefore, remains zero. Hence, if V and v are the velocities of the gun and the shell in the direction of firing, immediately after the explosion,

$$M V + m v = 0.$$

$$\therefore \quad \frac{V}{v} = -\frac{m}{M}.$$

$$\therefore \quad \frac{\text{speed of gun}}{\text{speed of shell}} = \left|\frac{V}{v}\right| = \frac{m}{M},$$

i.e. the initial speeds of gun and shell are in the inverse ratio of their masses.

(vii) A shot of mass m lb is fired from a gun of mass nm lb which is placed on a smooth horizontal plane at an elevation α. If V is the muzzle velocity of the shot (i.e. the velocity in space) at an elevation θ, show that $\tan\theta = (1 + 1/n)\tan\alpha$.

If the range on the plane is $\sqrt{3}\,V^2/(2g)$ and n is 20, find the two possible values of $\tan\alpha$.   (L.)

PQ represents the gun barrel, of finite length (Fig. 103). If u is the horizontal velocity of recoil of the gun, and V, at an angle θ with the horizontal, is the velocity in space with which the shot leaves the gun, then V is the resultant of the velocity of the shot relative to the barrel and u.

(a) The *horizontal* momentum of the shot is equal in magnitude and opposite in direction to the *horizontal* momentum of the gun.

$$\therefore \ n m u = m V \cos\theta.$$

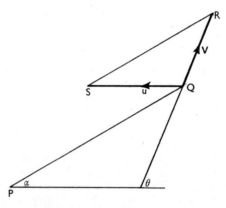

FIG. 103.

(b) In the triangle of velocities QSR, SR is parallel to PQ.

$$\therefore \ \angle SRQ = \theta - \alpha \quad \text{and} \quad \angle RSQ = \alpha.$$

$$\therefore \ \frac{u}{\sin SRQ} = \frac{V}{\sin RSQ},$$

i.e.
$$\frac{u}{\sin(\theta - \alpha)} = \frac{V}{\sin\alpha}.$$

From (a) and (b)

$$n m u \frac{\sin(\theta - \alpha)}{u} = m V \cos\theta \frac{\sin\alpha}{V}.$$

$$\therefore \ n \sin\theta \cos\alpha - n \cos\theta \sin\alpha = \cos\theta \sin\alpha.$$

$$\therefore \ (n + 1) \cos\theta \sin\alpha = n \sin\theta \cos\alpha.$$

$$\therefore \ \left(1 + \frac{1}{n}\right) \tan\alpha = \tan\theta.$$

The range on the plane is $\dfrac{V^2 \sin 2\theta}{g}$ (neglecting the height of Q above the plane).

$$\therefore \frac{V^2 \sin 2\theta}{g} = \frac{V^2 \sqrt{3}}{2g}.$$

$$\therefore \sin 2\theta = \tfrac{1}{2}\sqrt{3}, \quad \theta = 30° \quad \text{or} \quad 60°.$$

$$\therefore \frac{21}{20} \tan \alpha = \frac{1}{\sqrt{3}} \quad \text{or} \quad \frac{21}{20} \tan \alpha = \sqrt{3}.$$

$$\therefore \tan \alpha = \frac{20\sqrt{3}}{63}, \quad \text{or} \quad \frac{20\sqrt{3}}{21}.$$

EXERCISES 8.4.

1. Two masses P and Q move in the same direction along a straight line starting 12 ft apart at the same time; P starts from rest and moves with acceleration 1 ft per sec^2 and Q moves with constant velocity of 5 ft/sec. Find where they meet, and if they then coalesce find their common velocity if the mass of P is double the mass of Q.   (N.)

2. A particle of mass 5 lb is connected to a particle of mass 3 lb by a light string passing over a smooth pulley. The system is released from rest with the string taut. Find the acceleration of either particle and the tension in the string.

After two seconds the ascending particle picks up a stationary particle of mass 4 lb. Find the velocities of the particles immediately afterwards and show that they come to instantaneous rest 4 sec after the start of the motion.   (N.)

3. A shell of mass 200 lb is fired horizontally with a speed of 840 ft/sec from a gun of mass 5 tons. Find the initial speed of recoil of the gun, which is assumed to be on horizontal ground.

Find in tons weight the force that must be applied to the gun (after the shell has left it) in order to bring it to rest in 1 sec.   (N.)

4. Three small bodies of mass 4, 5, 6 oz respectively lie in order in a straight line on a large smooth table, the distance between consecutive bodies being 6 in. Two slack strings, each 2 ft in length, connect the first with the second and the second with the third. The third body is projected with a speed of 15 ft/sec directly away from the other two. Find the time which elapses before the first begins to move and the speed with which it starts.   (O.C.)

5. Two masses of 3 oz and 5 oz are connected by a light inextensible string passing over a smooth peg. Calculate the acceleration of the system. After moving for 2 sec, the 5 oz mass strikes the ground and does not rebound. Calculate:

(i) the time for which the 5 oz mass remains on the ground,
(ii) its speed immediately it leaves the ground.   (L.)

6. A target of mass M, sliding freely along a smooth horizontal plane with speed U, is struck directly by bullets each of mass m and moving with speed u in the opposite direction. Assuming that each bullet embeds itself in the target, find the speed of the target when it has been hit by (i) one bullet. (ii) n bullets.

If, alternatively, the target is struck by the bullets in rapid succession, so that a constant mass σ enters the target per unit of time, show that the speed of the target at time t after the firing begins is

$$\frac{M U - \sigma u t}{M + \sigma t}.$$ (N.)

7. Two masses A and B, of 6 oz and 10 oz respectively, are connected by a string 38 in. long and are placed on a smooth horizontal table. A is placed at the edge of the table and B at a distance of 11 in. from the edge so that the line AB is at right angles to the edge. If A is pushed gently over the edge of the table find

    (i) the speed with which B begins to move;

    (ii) the common acceleration of A and B after the string becomes taut;

    (iii) the common speed of A and B when B reaches the edge of the table.   (L.)

8. Bodies of masses m, $5m$ are connected by a fine string which passes over a smooth pulley. After the lighter body has ascended through one foot it picks up a rider of mass $2m$ which was at rest and after rising another foot it picks up another rider also of mass $2m$ and at rest. Find the final velocity of the bodies.

(O.C.)

9. Two particles A and B of mass 3 lb and 5 lb respectively are attached one to each end of a light inextensible string which passes over a fixed smooth pulley with the masses hanging vertically. The system is released from rest with the string taut and with B at a height of 1 ft above a horizontal inelastic plane. Show that, after B hits the plane, A will rise a further distance of 3 in.

Show also that, when A has fallen again to the position which makes the string taut, the speed of both particles just after the jerk is 1·5 ft/sec.   (N.)

10. A light inelastic string passes over a smooth light pulley and masses of 3 lb and 5 lb are attached to its ends. The masses are released from rest with the 5 lb mass 4 ft above an inelastic horizontal table. Find the time which elapses from the instant when the masses are first released until the 5 lb mass hits the table for the second time, assuming that the 3 lb mass hits neither the table nor the pulley.   (C.)

11. Two particles A and B, of equal mass, are connected by a light inextensible string, of length 1 ft, and lie in contact on a table. The particle A is projected vertically upwards with velocity 24 ft/sec. Calculate:

    (i) the velocity with which B starts to move;

    (ii) the time which elapses before B strikes the table;

    (iii) the velocity with which A strikes the table.   (N.)

12. Two particles, of masses m lb and $2m$ lb respectively, are attached to the ends of an inextensible string of length 4 ft. The string passes over a small smooth pulley fixed at the ridge of two smooth planes, each inclined at 30° to the horizontal. The particles are held close to the pulley and released at the same instant so that one moves down each plane. Find the impulse in the string when it becomes taut, and the speed of the particles immediately after.

Find also the time, from the instant that the string becomes taut, for the particle of mass m lb to reach the pulley, and the speed of the particles just before this happens.   (L.)

13. Two particles A, B of masses m, m' are moving with velocities u, v in directions inclined at an angle α. If the two particles collide and coalesce, find the velocity of the resultant particle and the angle that its direction makes with the initial direction of motion of A.   (O.C.)

*14. A particle is projected with a velocity whose horizontal and vertical components are U and V respectively. Prove that its range up a plane of inclination β is

$$\frac{2\,U\,(V\cos\beta - U\sin\beta)}{g\cos^2\beta}.$$

A gun of mass M, which is free to recoil on a horizontal plane, projects a shell of mass m with muzzle velocity u (that is, the velocity relative to the gun); the elevation of the gun is $60°$. Find the velocity with which the gun recoils and the range of the shell up a plane of inclination $30°$.   (O.C.)

*15. A man of mass M, standing at rest upon a smooth floor, throws a ball of mass m which is caught by a dog of mass M', also standing at rest upon the floor. When the ball leaves the man its velocity relative to the man is of magnitude V and in a direction inclined at an angle θ to the horizontal. Show that the dog acquires a velocity

$$\frac{m\,M\,V\cos\theta}{(m + M)(m + M')}.$$ (O.C.)

8.5. Work and Energy

If a *constant* force P pdl acts on a particle of mass m lb so that it moves the particle through a distance s ft in the line of action of the force, it gives to the particle an acceleration (P/m) ft/sec and increases the component velocity of the particle in the line of action of the force from its initial value u to a value v given by the equation

$$v^2 = u^2 + \frac{2P}{m}\,s,$$

i.e. $$Ps = \tfrac{1}{2}mv^2 - \tfrac{1}{2}mu^2. \tag{8.2}$$

The quantity $\tfrac{1}{2}mV^2$ is defined as the *kinetic energy* of a particle of mass m moving with speed V, and the quantity, force $\times$ distance (force constant), is called the work done by the force over the space interval concerned. Equation (8.2) expresses algebraically the general principle of dynamics which is stated as:

Work done by a force = change in kinetic energy produced by the force.
In general terms, the kinetic energy of a body measures the distance through which, because of its mass and velocity, it can overcome a given resisting force.

The absolute unit of work, and therefore of kinetic energy, in the FPS system of units is

1 foot poundal

and the corresponding unit in the metric system is

$$1 \text{ erg, which is equal to } 1 \text{ dyn cm.}$$

The latter unit is small for most practical purposes and the larger unit

$$1 \text{ Joule} = 10^7 \text{ ergs}$$

is frequently used.

Corresponding gravitational units are the ft lb wt. and the cm gm wt. Both work and energy are scalar quantities.

The Space–Integral of the Equation of Motion

The equation of motion $P = mf$, where P acts in a fixed direction and is not constant, but is a function of the displacement s of a particle of mass m from a fixed point, may be integrated to give

$$\int_0^{s_1} P \, \mathrm{d}s = \int_{s=0}^{s=s_1} mv \frac{\mathrm{d}v}{\mathrm{d}s} \, \mathrm{d}s,$$

and, if $v = v_1$ when $s = 0$, $v = v_2$ when $s = s_1$,

$$\int_0^{s_1} P \, \mathrm{d}s = \int_{v_1}^{v_2} mv \, \mathrm{d}v.$$

$$\therefore \int_0^{s_1} P \, \mathrm{d}s = \tfrac{1}{2} m v_2^2 - \tfrac{1}{2} m v_1^2.$$

$\int_0^{s_1} P \, \mathrm{d}s$ is defined as the work done by the force P over the space-interval $s = 0$ to $s = s_1$ and, with this definition, we have, once more,

Work done by a force = change in kinetic energy produced by the force.

Example. Find an expression for the work done by a vertically upward force P on a particle of mass m which is lifted vertically from rest to a height h above its starting point and given a velocity v.

The resultant force acting on the particle is $P - mg$. The increase of kinetic energy of the particle is $\tfrac{1}{2} m v^2$.

$$\therefore (P - mg)h = \tfrac{1}{2} m v^2.$$

$$\therefore Ph = \tfrac{1}{2} m v^2 + mgh.$$

The work done by the force P is therefore $\tfrac{1}{2} m v^2 + mgh$. Conventionally the work done by gravity on the particle in this motion is regarded as "negative work", in this case $(-mgh)$, the acceleration of the particle having been in a direction opposite to that of gravity.

Gravitational Potential Energy

If a particle of mass m at a height z above a horizontal plane is allowed to fall freely until it reaches the plane, the work done by gravity on the particle is equal to the kinetic energy gained by the particle, i.e.

$$\tfrac{1}{2} m v^2 = \tfrac{1}{2} m (2gz) = mgz,$$

where v is the speed with which the particle reaches the plane. We *define* the quantity mgz as the gravitational *potential energy* of the particle referred to the level of the plane as origin. Potential energy, as thus defined, has no absolute value, but the difference between the potential energies of a particle in two different positions can be stated absolutely. It can be shown that the work done by a force in raising a particle of mass m from rest at the origin to a height z above the origin is independent of the path of the particle and is equal to mgz. An alternative definition of the gravitational potential energy of a body is thus: *the work done on a body in raising it from a chosen level as origin to its existing level.*

The Potential Energy of a Stretched Elastic Spring

If an elastic spring, of natural length l and modulus λ, is stretched or compressed to a length $l \pm x$, the tension in the spring, by Hooke's Law, is $\dfrac{\lambda x}{l}$. In a further extension or compression by a small distance δx, the work done on the spring is approximately equal to $\dfrac{\lambda x}{l}\,\delta x$. Therefore the total work done on the spring in extending it from its natural length l to length $l + y$ is

$$\lim_{\delta x \to 0} \sum_{x=0}^{x=y} \frac{\lambda x}{l}\,\delta x = \int_0^y \frac{\lambda x}{l}\,dx = \frac{\lambda y^2}{2l}.$$

This quantity $\dfrac{\lambda y^2}{2l}$ is the potential energy of the stretched or compressed string, being equal to the amount of work which could be done on a particle by the return of the spring to its natural length.

An elastic *string* may be stretched, but not compressed. The elastic potential energy of an elastic string which is stretched to a total length $l + y$ from its natural length l is $\dfrac{\lambda y^2}{2l}$, where λ is its elastic modulus.

Examples. (i) Particles of mass m lie on a straight line on a smooth horizontal table. The first particle is projected towards the second with velocity u; it collides with and coalesces with the second particle and the combined particle then collides with and coalesces with the third particle. This process continues throughout the chain of particles. Find how many collisions are necessary before 99 per cent of the initial kinetic energy of the system is lost.

After r impacts, i.e. when the total mass of the moving particle is $(r + 1)m$, the velocity of the moving particle is v_r where, by conservation of linear momentum,

$$(r + 1)mv_r = mu.$$

$$\therefore\ v_r = \frac{u}{r + 1}.$$

The initial kinetic energy is $\frac{1}{2}mu^2$ and the kinetic energy after the rth collision is

$$\frac{1}{2}(r + 1)m\left\{\frac{u}{(r + 1)}\right\}^2 = \frac{mu^2}{2(r + 1)}.$$

Therefore the kinetic energy lost after the rth collision is

$$\frac{mu^2}{2} - \frac{mu^2}{2(r + 1)} = \frac{1}{2}mu^2\frac{r}{(r + 1)}.$$

At least 99 per cent of the original kinetic energy has been lost when

$$\frac{r}{r + 1} \geqq \frac{99}{100},$$

i.e. when
$$100\,r \geqq 99\,r + 99,$$

i.e. when
$$r \geqq 99.$$

After 99 collisions, 99 per cent of the original kinetic energy has been lost.

(ii) Calculate the work done in raising the water contained by a full rectangular tank a ft long, b ft wide and c ft deep to a uniform height of h ft above the horizontal base of the tank.

(Take the mass of 1 ft³ of water as 62·5 lb.)

The centre of gravity of the water in the tank is at a height $\frac{1}{2}c$ ft above the base. In raising the water, therefore, a resultant force of 62·5 abc lb wt. has to be overcome through a distance of $(h - \frac{1}{2}c)$ ft.

$$\therefore \text{ work done} = 62{\cdot}5\, abc\, (h - \tfrac{1}{2}c) \text{ ft lb wt.}$$

(iii) A particle of mass m is attracted towards a fixed point O by a force P which is inversely proportional to the square of the distance of the particle from O. Obtain an expression in terms of the constant of variation, for the work done by the force P in moving the particle (in a straight line) from displacement r_1 to displacement r_2 from O.

$$\text{Work done} = \int_{r_1}^{r_2} P\, ds = \int_{r_1}^{r_2} \frac{k}{r^2}\, dr = k\left(\frac{1}{r_1} - \frac{1}{r_2}\right),$$

where k is a constant.

In this case it can also be shown that the work done by the force is independent of the path of the particle.

(iv) A pile-driver of mass M tons falls from a height h ft onto a pile of mass m tons, driving the pile s ft into the ground and remaining in contact with the pile. Find an expression, in tons wt., for the resistance of the ground, assumed to be constant.

The velocity of the pile-driver immediately before impact is $\sqrt{(2gh)}$ ft/sec downward.

Therefore, by conservation of momentum, if V ft/sec is the velocity of the combined pile and driver immediately after impact.

$$(M + m)\,V = M \sqrt{(2gh)}.$$

$$\therefore\ V = \frac{M}{M + m}\, \sqrt{(2gh)}.$$

The kinetic energy of the pile and driver immediately after impact is

$$\frac{1}{2}(2240)(M + m)\left(\frac{M}{M + m}\right)^2 2gh \text{ ft pdl}$$

$$= 2240\,\frac{M^2}{M + m}\, gh \text{ ft pdl}.$$

This kinetic energy is destroyed in a distance s ft by a resultant force $2240\,\{R - (M + m)\}\,g$ pdl, where R tons wt. is the resistance of the ground.

$$\therefore\ 2240g\,\{R - (M + m)\}\,s = 2240\,\frac{M^2}{M + m}\, gh.$$

$$\therefore\ R = \frac{1}{s}\left\{\frac{M^2}{M + m}\, h + (M + m)s\right\}.$$

(v) A hammerhead of mass m_1, moving horizontally with velocity v, strikes a nail of mass m_2 and there is no rebound, the hammer remaining in contact with the nail in the subsequent motion. Immediately after the contact the nail begins to penetrate horizontally a block of mass m_3 which is free to move on a smooth horizontal plane, penetration being resisted by a constant force R. Prove that the nail will penetrate the block for a distance

$$\frac{m_1^2 m_3 v^2}{2R(m_1 + m_2)(m_1 + m_2 + m_3)}$$

during a time

$$\frac{m_1 m_3 v}{(m_1 + m_2 + m_3)R}.$$

(a) Velocity of hammer and nail after impact (conservation of momentum) is $m_1 v/(m_1 + m_2)$.

(b) Suppose the final velocity of the system to be v_3. Then, again from conservation of momentum,

$$(m_1 + m_2 + m_3)v_3 = m_1 v, \quad \therefore \ v_3 = m_1 v/(m_1 + m_2 + m_3).$$

(c) The initial kinetic energy, just after the impact but before penetration, is

$$\frac{\frac{1}{2}(m_1 + m_2)m_1^2 v^2}{(m_1 + m_2)^2} = \frac{m_1^2 v^2}{2(m_1 + m_2)}.$$

The final kinetic energy, after penetration ceases, is

$$\frac{\frac{1}{2}(m_1 + m_2 + m_3)m_1^2 v^2}{(m_1 + m_2 + m_3)^2} = \frac{m_1^2 v^2}{2(m_1 + m_2 + m_3)}.$$

(d) The work–energy equation is

$$\frac{m_1^2 v^2}{2(m_1 + m_2)} = \frac{m_1^2 v^2}{2(m_1 + m_2 + m_3)} + Rx,$$

where x is the distance which the nail penetrates the block.

$$\therefore x = \frac{m_1^2 v^2}{2R}\left(\frac{1}{m_1 + m_2} - \frac{1}{m_1 + m_2 + m_3}\right)$$

$$= \frac{m_1^2 m_3 v^2}{2R(m_1 + m_2)(m_1 + m_2 + m_3)}.$$

(e) The impulse–momentum equation is

$Rt =$ loss of momentum of nail and hammer during penetration.

$$\therefore t = \frac{(m_1 + m_2)}{R}\left(\frac{m_1 v}{m_1 + m_2} - \frac{m_1 v}{m_1 + m_2 + m_3}\right) = \frac{m_1 m_3 v}{(m_1 + m_2 + m_3)R}.$$

EXERCISES 8.5.

1. Given that 1 in. = 2·54 cm and 1 kgm = 2·205 lb, determine the force in dynes required to impart an acceleration of 5 in./sec² to a mass of 2 oz.

If the above mass is raised vertically through a distance of 1 yd, calculate the work done against gravity in ergs. (L.)

2. (i) A mass of 1 kgm is raised vertically through a distance of 1 m. Calculate the work done against gravity in foot poundals,

(ii) Express a pressure of 1 atm., i.e. 14·7 lb wt./in.², in dyn/cm².

(Take 1 kgm = 2·205 lb; 1 in. = 2·54 cm.) (L.)

3. A force equal to the weight of 5 lb acts on a mass of 30 lb, originally at rest, for 10 sec. Find, in feet, the distance travelled by the mass, and in ft lb wt. the kinetic energy generated in it. (O.C.)

4. A pebble, of mass 0·1 lb, is moving with a velocity of 80 ft/sec. Find its kinetic energy in ft lb wt.

Find in lb wt. the force required to bring the pebble to rest in a distance of 5 ft. (N.)

5. A car of mass 1½ tons moves along a level road at a speed of 30 m.p.h. The brakes are applied and the car is brought to rest in 3 sec. If the frictional resistance opposing the motion during the braking period is constant, show that it is of magnitude $\frac{11}{16}$ ton wt. Find, in yards, the distance in which the car may be brought to rest from a speed of 75 m.p.h. by this same frictional resistance. (N.)

6. A ship of mass 5000 tons is moving at 20 ft/sec. A shell, whose mass is ½ ton, is moving at such a speed that its kinetic energy is equal to that of the ship.

(i) Calculate the kinetic energy of the shell in ft tons wt. and its speed in ft/sec.

(ii) If the shell were to hit the ship head on horizontally and come to rest in the ship without exploding, calculate, in ft/sec correct to the nearest tenth, by how much the speed of the ship would be reduced. (L.)

7. A bullet of mass m enters a fixed block of wood with speed u and is brought to rest in a distance c. Find the resistance to penetration, assuming this resistance to be a constant force.

If the bullet, moving with speed u, enters a fixed block of thickness $\frac{3}{4}c$ which offers the same resistance as the first block, find the speed with which the bullet emerges. Find also the time taken to pass through the block. (L.)

8. A nail of mass 1 oz is driven horizontally into a fixed block of wood by a hammer of mass 2 lb. Immediately before striking the nail the hammer is moving horizontally at 33 ft/sec. If the hammer does not rebound, calculate the common speed of the hammer and nail just after the blow. If the nail is driven 3 in. into the block of wood, calculate the average resistance in lb wt. of the wood. (L.)

9. A ball of mass 4 oz and moving at the rate of 20 ft/sec is struck by a bat and rebounds with a velocity of 44f t/sec. Find in ft lb wt. the work done on the ball, and in lb. wt. the average force exerted by the bat on the ball, assuming the bat and the ball to be in contact for 0·1 sec. (O.C.)

16*

10. A projectile of mass 4 oz leaves the muzzle of a gun of mass 120 lb with a horizontal velocity of 1440 ft/sec. Assuming that the gun is free to move horizontally find its momentum and kinetic energy when the projectile leaves it, stating clearly the units employed.

If a gun can fire 240 such projectiles in a minute, find the average force, in lb wt., needed to keep it at rest. (C.)

11. A body of mass 50 lb falls from a height of 25 ft on to a pile of mass 75 lb and drives it 6 in. into the ground. Find the resistance of the ground, supposed constant, and the time during which the pile is moving, assuming the body to remain in contact with the pile during the penetration. Find also the kinetic energy lost at the impact, in ft lb wt.

What would the initial velocity of the pile have been if the body had rebounded to a height of 3 in.? (N.)

12. A body of 20 lb mass falls 10 ft from rest and is brought to rest again by penetrating 1 ft into sand. Find, in lb wt., the resistance exerted by the sand, assuming that the resistance is uniform. (N.)

13. A load of coal of mass m lb is raised from rest to rest, from the bottom to the top of a mine of depth h ft, by an engine which exerts a constant vertical force of $3m$ lb wt. for the first part of the time, after which the power is shut off. Prove that the velocity of the load at the instant when the power is shut off is $2\sqrt{(gh/3)}$ ft/sec. (N.)

*14. A number n of uniform wooden planks, each of weight W, thickness t and width a, lie in a pile of height nt on horizontal ground. The planks are taken from the pile and placed one on top of another to form a vertical wall of height na. Find the work done against gravity. (N.)

*15. Two particles, of masses m and $3m$, are connected by a light inelastic string of length $2l$ which passes over a small smooth fixed peg. The particles are held in contact with the peg and then allowed, at the same instant, to fall under gravity from rest, one on either side of the peg. Prove that

   (i) the speed of each particle just after the string tightens is $\sqrt{(gl/2)}$,

  (ii) the sudden tightening of the string causes a loss of energy equal to $3mgl$,

 (iii) the lighter particle reaches the peg again after a total time $\sqrt{(6l/g)}$. (N.)

*16. The base of a frustum of a right pyramid is a square of side $2a$, the height of the frustum is h, and its top face is a square of side a. Show that its centre of gravity is at a height $11h/28$ above the base.

If the frustum is lying with one of its trapezoidal faces on horizontal ground, find the work done against gravity in raising it so that it stands on its base and show that this work is positive if $a < 11h/\sqrt{476}$. (L.)

In each of questions 17–20 calculate the work done by the force P defined, in the usual notation and in FPS absolute units, by the equation(s) given.

17. $P = 2s + 3$: from $s = 0$ to $s = 4$.

18. $P = \cos 3s$: from $s = 0$ to $s = \pi/6$.

19. $P = kt,\ s = t^3$: from $t = 1$ to $t = 2$.

20. $P = k/v,\ s = v^3 - 1$: from $s = 0$ to $s = 7$.

MISCELLANEOUS EXERCISES. VIII

1. Two particles are connected by a light string. One particle, of mass 3 oz, is placed on a smooth plane inclined at an angle of 30° to the horizontal; the string, after passing over a small smooth pulley at the top of the plane, supports the other particle, of mass 1 oz, which hangs vertically. The system starts from rest with the string taut. Find the acceleration of either particle and show that the tension in the string is $2\frac{1}{4}$ pdl. Calculate the magnitude of the force exerted on the pulley.   (N.)

2. Two trucks A and B, of masses 5 tons and 8 tons respectively, are moving with speeds 3 ft/sec and 2 ft/sec respectively in the same direction on the same set of horizontal rails, so that A overtakes B. After collision B moves off with speed $2\frac{5}{8}$ ft/sec; find the corresponding speed and direction of motion of A.

Find, in ft lb wt. the kinetic energy lost through impact.   (N.)

3. Masses of 200 gm and 300 gm are joined by a light inextensible string which passes over a smooth fixed peg. If the system is released from rest, so that the masses move vertically, find the tension in the string in grams weight.
                                                                        (N.)

4. A light inextensible string, passing over a small smooth fixed pulley, carries at one end a mass of 4 oz and at the other two masses, each of 3 oz. If the system is allowed to move, find the acceleration with which the mass of 4 oz ascends.

If one of the 3 oz masses falls off after the 4 oz mass has ascended a distance of $2\frac{1}{2}$ in., how much further will the 4 oz mass ascend?   (O.C.)

5. A bullet of mass $\frac{1}{5}$ lb is fired horizontally with velocity 1002 ft/sec into a block of wood, of mass 100 lb, which can slide freely on a smooth table. If the bullet is embedded in the block, find, in ft lb wt., the kinetic energy lost owing to impact.   (O.C.)

6. A railway truck of mass 12 tons starts from rest at the top of a slope of length 324 ft and of inclination α, where $\sin \alpha = \frac{1}{256}$. Neglecting frictional resistances, show, by the use of the principle of conservation of energy, or otherwise, that, when the truck reaches the bottom of the slope, its speed is 9 ft/sec.

Just after reaching the bottom of the slope the truck collides with a stationary truck of mass 6 tons. If the trucks move on together after the impact find their common velocity. Find also the loss of kinetic energy in ft lb wt. due to the impact.   (N.)

7. A light string hangs over a fixed smooth pulley and carries a mass m at each of its ends, A and B. A mass m/n is detached from B, and when A has fallen through 1 foot a mass $2m/n$ is detached from A. Determine how much farther A will fall, and prove that the velocity of A when it has risen to its original position is given by

$$v^2 = \frac{8(n-1)}{(2n-1)(2n-3)} g.$$ (O.C.)

8. A bucket of mass 5 cwt is raised by a crane. If the maximum safe tension in the rope is 6 cwt, find the greatest distance from rest through which the bucket can be raised in 10 sec, and the shortest time in which it can be raised through 60 ft from rest to rest. (L.)

9. A light string passes over a light smooth pulley fixed to the ceiling of a lift, and carries masses of 6 lb and 7 lb at its ends. The 7 lb mass is held in contact with the pulley and the 6 lb mass is hanging with the string vertical. If the 7 lb mass is now released, find the tension in the string while motion occurs, and the time that elapses before the 7 lb mass is 3 ft below the pulley,

(i) when the lift remains at rest,

(ii) when the lift is rising vertically with constant acceleration $\frac{1}{8}g$. (L.)

10. A railway truck of mass 10 tons moving along a level track with a speed of 4 ft/sec is overtaken by a truck of mass 5 tons moving with a speed of 6 ft/sec along the same track. After the collision the 10-ton truck has a speed of 5 ft/sec Calculate the velocity of the 5-ton truck just after the collision and find the total loss of kinetic energy in ft tons wt.

Find the uniform force, in tons wt., required to bring the 5-ton truck to rest after the collision in a distance of $2\frac{1}{2}$ ft. (N.)

11. Two trucks, of mass respectively 5 tons and 3 tons, are standing on the same level set of rails. If the heavier truck impinges on the lighter, which is at rest, with a speed of 5 ft/sec, and the velocity of the lighter relative to the heavier after they separate is 3 ft/sec, find the actual speeds of the two trucks after they separate, and calculate the number of ft lb wt. of kinetic energy lost by the impact. (O.C.)

12. Two masses of $1\frac{3}{4}$ lb and $2\frac{1}{4}$ lb are connected by a light inextensible string passing over a smooth peg. Initially the masses are at rest and level, 12 ft from the ground. They are then released and, at the end of 2 sec, the string breaks just above the $2\frac{1}{4}$ lb mass. Calculate the speed of this mass at that moment and how long, from then, it will take to reach the ground. (L.)

13. A gun of mass 3 tons fires a shell of mass 14 lb. horizontally with a speed of 2400 ft/sec. Find the velocity of recoil of the gun and the kinetic energy in ft tons wt. generated by the explosion. Calculate the uniform force in tons wt. required to bring the gun to rest after a recoil of $18\frac{3}{4}$ in. (N.)

14. A ball-bearing of mass 3 gm is dropped from a height of 60 cm on to a steel plate. It rebounds to a height of 50 cm. Find the change in momentum, and the loss of kinetic energy, owing to the impact.

If the time of contact between the bearing and the plate is 0·01 sec, show that the average force between the bearing and the plate is about 200 gm wt. (N.)

15. A truck of mass 11 cwt and moving at 20 ft/sec crashes into a 7 cwt truck moving at 2 ft/sec in the opposite direction; after the crash they move along together. Find their common speed and show that nearly 47 per cent of the kinetic energy is lost owing to the collision. (N.)

16. A truck, of mass 6 tons, travelling on a straight level track at 6 ft/sec, overtakes a truck, of mass 4 tons, travelling in the same direction at 1 ft/sec; at the moment of impact the trucks are coupled together and they then travel 105 ft before coming to rest. Find the resistance per ton (assumed uniform) in lb wt.

What percentage of the initial kinetic energy of the trucks is lost on impact? (O.C.)

17. A railway truck of mass 10 tons is moving at 6 ft/sec when it collides with another truck of mass 15 tons moving in the same direction at 3 ft/sec. After collision the relative speed of the trucks is 1 ft/sec. Find

(i) the speed of each truck after the collision,

(ii) the loss of kinetic energy in ft tons wt. due to the collision,

(iii) the distance travelled by the 10 ton truck after the collision, if it is retarded by a braking force of 140 lb wt. (L.)

18. An inelastic pile of mass 0·25 ton is driven 1 ft into the ground by a blow of a hammer of mass 2 tons and falling 9 ft. Determine in ft tons wt. the kinetic energy of the pile and hammer immediately after the blow and find the resistance of the ground, assuming it to be uniform. (L.)

19. A bullet of mass 3 oz strikes horizontally a block of wood of mass 25 lb, which rests on the top of a wall 10 ft high. If the block, with the bullet in it, strikes the ground 3 ft from the wall, find the speed of the bullet just before it struck the block. Friction, and any resistance due to the movement of the block on the wall, may be neglected. (L.)

20. (a) A particle S of mass 8 lb, moving with a speed of 15 ft/sec on a smooth horizontal table, strikes a stationary particle T of mass 12 lb which is free to move on the table. If S is brought to rest by the impact, calculate the loss of kinetic energy in ft lb wt.

(b) A particle of mass 12 oz is moving at 16 ft/sec in a direction due E. when it is struck by a second equal particle moving at 32 ft/sec in a direction N. 30° W. and the two particles coalesce. Show that the combined particle starts to move after the impact in a direction due N. and find the speed with which it starts to move. (N.)

21. A pile-driver of mass 6 cwt falls freely from a height of 9 ft upon a pile of mass 18 cwt. Assuming that the pile-driver does not rebound, show that the common speed of the pile and pile-driver immediately after the impact is 6 ft/sec. Find what fraction of the energy is dissipated by the blow.

The resistance of the ground to penetration, assumed to be constant, is $3\frac{3}{5}$ tons wt. If the pile-driver remains in contact with the pile during penetration, show that the pile is driven into the ground a distance $3\frac{3}{8}$ in. (N.)

*22. A smooth wedge, of mass M and triangular cross-section ABC, is placed with the face through AB on a horizontal plane; the angles CAB and ABC are α and $\pi/2$ respectively. A particle of mass m is placed on the inclined face, directly above the centre of gravity G of the wedge. A constant horizontal thrust P is then applied perpendicular to the vertical face and towards G. If the wedge has acceleration F in the direction of the thrust, show that

$$P = mg \sin\alpha \cos\alpha + (M + m \sin^2\alpha)F,$$

and that the reaction of the horizontal plane on the wedge is

$$(M + m \cos^2\alpha)g + mF \sin\alpha \cos\alpha. \qquad \text{(N.)}$$

23. A block of metal of mass M rests on a smooth table. At one point of its base is attached a small smooth pulley, around which passes a smooth string carrying at its ends masses m_1 and m_2 ($m_1 > m_2$). These two masses hang over the edge of the table and the horizontal portions of the string lie side by side and perpendicular to the smooth edge. If the system is released so that m_1 and m_2 descend vertically and M moves without rotating, find the tension in the string and the accelerations of M and m_1.   (L.)

24. A 100-ton tug, moving ahead at 7 ft/sec, suddenly takes in tow a 200-ton barge moving ahead along the same course at 4 ft/sec. Calculate the common speed of the two vessels when the hawser connecting them becomes taut. Calculate also, in ft tons wt., the total loss of kinetic energy.

If the resistance, assumed uniform, to the motion of each vessel is $2\frac{1}{2}$ lb wt./ton, calculate the time after the hawser becomes taut before the vessels come to rest. Calculate also, in ft, the distance covered by the vessels in this time. (N.)

25. A bullet of mass m lb, fired horizontally with velocity u ft/sec, enters a block A of mass M lb which is free to move on a smooth horizontal table. If the bullet leaves A with velocity $\frac{1}{2}u$ ft/sec with its direction unaltered, find the velocity imparted to A and the amount of energy (in ft lb wt.) lost owing to the passage of the bullet through the block.

After leaving A the bullet enters a fixed block B and is brought to rest after penetrating to a distance of 6 in. Find the force, assumed uniform, exerted by B on the bullet.   (O.C.)

26. Two particles, of masses m and $3m$, are connected by a light inelastic string of length $2l$ which passes over a small smooth fixed peg. The particles are held in contact with the peg and then allowed, at the same instant, to fall under gravity from rest, one on either side of the peg. Prove that

  (i) the speed of each particle just after the string tightens is $\sqrt{(gl/2)}$,

  (ii) the sudden tightening of the string causes a loss of energy equal to $3\,mgl$,
                                                                (N.)

27. A locomotive of mass 75 tons is being coupled to a train of mass 325 tons. The locomotive backs on to the train at 2 ft/sec and, after impact, the whole train (including the locomotive) moves backwards unbraked. Find the speed with which it moves immediately after the collision.

If the whole train it subject to a frictional resistance of $3\frac{3}{4}$ tons wt. calculate how long it will take to come to rest after the impact.   (L.)

***28.** A light inextensible string hangs over a smooth fixed pulley. It carries at one end a particle of mass $3m$, and at the other end a small smooth pulley whose weight may be neglected. Over this pulley hangs a second string carrying at its ends particles of masses m and $2m$. Prove (i) that the tension of the first string is twice the tension of the second string, (ii) that the acceleration of the particle $3\ m$ is $g/17$.

Find the acceleration of the second string relative to the small pulley. (O.C.)

29. A train travelling on the level at 30 m.p.h. is brought to rest in 12 sec by the application of a constant braking force. Express the force exerted by the brakes as a fraction of the weight of the train and determine the distance travelled before coming to rest.

Work the corresponding problem for a train running down a slope of 1 in 144.   (L.)

***30.** A smooth wedge of mass M and angle α rests on a fixed smooth inclined plane also of angle α, so that one face of the wedge is horizontal. A particle of mass m is placee at a point on the horizontal face of the wedge at a horizontal distance d from the inclined plane, and the system is released from rest. Find the acceleration of the wedge down the plane, and show that the particle reaches the plane after a time

$$\left(\frac{2d}{g}\right)^{1/2}\left[\frac{M + m \sin^2\alpha}{(M + m) \sin\alpha \cos\alpha}\right]^{1/2}.$$ 　　(L.)

*31. A shot of mass m fired from a gun of mass M, which is elevated at an angle α to the horizon and is movable on a horizontal plane, leaves at an angle θ with the horizontal. Shew that

$$\tan\theta = (1 + m/M)\tan\alpha,$$

and that the gun begins to recoil with velocity V, where

$$(M + m)(M + m \sin^2\alpha)\, V^2 = 2 m E \cos^2\alpha,$$

E being the kinetic energy imparted to gun and shot by the explosion.　　(C.)

*32. A gun of mass M lb discharges a bullet of mass m lb horizontally. The recoil of the gun is opposed by a constant force F lb wt. which brings it to rest in t sec. Find the velocity of the bullet, and show that the energy of the explosion is $g F^2 t^2 (M + m)/2\, M m$ ft lb.　　(O.C.)

*33. A particle of mass m is moving in a straight line with velocity v when it explodes into two parts each of mass $\frac{1}{2}m$ and travelling in the same straight line as before. If the explosion increases the energy of the system by $\frac{1}{2}mu^2$, find the velocities of the particles immediately after the explosion.　　(O.C.)

34. The driving weight of a pile-driver is of mass 1 ton. The weight falls from rest through 3 ft on to a pile, of mass 2 tons, driving it 6 in. into the ground. Assuming the resistance of the ground is constant, find its value in tons wt. The weight is then raised and again allowed to fall from rest, driving the pile a further 7 in. into the ground. Assuming the resistance of the ground remains unaltered, find the distance in feet through which the weight is raised before the second blow.　　(L.)

35. A small body of mass M lying at rest on a smooth horizontal table is given a velocity u by a blow applied in a horizontal direction. A second horizontal blow of equal magnitude is then applied in such a direction that there is no change in the kinetic energy of the body. Find the angle between the directions of the two blows.　　(L.)

36. Particles of masses $2m$ and $3m$ are connected by a light inextensible string passing round a light pulley and both the pulley and the particles lie on a smooth horizontal table. A second string has one end attached to the axle of the pulley and at the other end it carries a particle of mass m. Initially the two portions of the first string are taut and perpendicular to one edge of the table; the particle of mass m is held just off this edge of the table, with the second string slack and with the line joining the particle to the axle of the pulley parallel to each portion of the first string. This particle is then released, and after it has fallen freely a distance h, the particles on the table are jerked into motion. Find the impulses in the two strings when the jerk occurs and show that the loss of kinetic energy due to the jerk is $\frac{24}{29}mgh$.　　(N.)

*37. A smooth wedge, of mass M, rests on a horizontal table, the normal cross section of the wedge, which is an equilateral triangle, being vertical. A light string connects two particles, of masses m_1 amd m_2, which are placed one on each inclined face. The system is released from rest when the string is taut and in the plane of a normal cross section of the wedge. Prove that, if $m_1 > m_2$, the acceleration of the wedge is

$$(m_1 - m_2)g\sqrt{3}/(3m_1 + 3m_2 + 4M).$$ (L.)

*38. During the operation of a pile-driver, a mass, M lb, after falling vertically through a height h ft from rest, hits a pile of mass m lb and does not rebound. If the resistance of the ground to the motion of the pile is assumed to be constant and to be such that the addition of a mass μ lb ($> M$) would just cause the pile to sink in when the mass M is not resting upon it, show that the pile is driven by the impact a distance

$$\frac{M^2 h}{(M + m)(\mu - M)}\,\text{ft}.$$ (L.)

*39. Two particles of masses m_1 and m_2 are moving in the same straight line under their mutual action only, which is equal to P. Prove that their relative acceleration F is given by $P = MF$, where $M = m_1 m_2/(m_1 + m_2)$.

Show also that the kinetic energy is equal to $\frac{1}{2}M V^2 + \frac{1}{2}\dfrac{Q^2}{m_1 + m_2}$, where V is the relative velocity and Q is the constant momentum of the system.   (L.)

CHAPTER IX

FRICTION

9.1. The Nature of Friction

In Chapter II, § 2.6, friction was defined as the component parallel to the reacting surface of the action of one body on another in contact with it. In conformity with Newton's third law, there is an equal and opposite component of reaction of the second body on the first. If there is no friction between two surfaces in contact, an ideal concept which cannot be realised in the physical world, the surfaces in contact are said to be *smooth*. The amount of friction between two surfaces is related to the "roughness" of the surfaces and to the normal reaction between them. The quality of "roughness" between two surfaces is too imprecise to permit of accurate mathematical definition and the normal reaction between two surfaces can be increased to a point at which the nature of the surfaces in contact is changed by the pressure between them. It is not possible, therefore, to construct a mathematical model of this physical phenomenon in action which is both accurate and comprehensive. Experimental data, however, suggest a set of rules, to which the force of friction approximately conforms, which we adopt as the mathematical definition of the force and which gives an approximation to observed experimental results in cases where the normal reaction between the surfaces is not abnormally great.

9.2. The Laws of Friction

(a) Friction is a variable force between surfaces in contact which, subject to an upper limit on its magnitude, is of such a magnitude and acts in such a direction as to prevent the motion of one surface over the other. So long as there is no relative motion between the surfaces, the direction of friction is thus opposite to that direction in which the surface of the body on which it acts would move if there were no friction, and its line of action is the line of action of the equilibrant of the forces acting on the body. If there is relative

241

motion between the surfaces, the friction acting on the body is in a direction opposite to the direction of that relative motion.

(It is assumed here that forces acting on the body, not in the plane of the surfaces in contact, are in equilibrium. The law also assumes the possibility of a "frictional couple" in the case of a rigid body which can rotate in contact with another body.)

(b) The upper limit of the magnitude of the friction between two surfaces is called *limiting friction* and it is related to the normal reaction between the surfaces by the law:

$$\frac{\text{limiting friction}}{\text{normal reaction}} = \text{a constant for the surfaces.}$$

The constant of this law is called "the coefficient of friction between the two surfaces"; it is usually denoted by μ, and the law is usually written $F/N = \mu$. *It is most important to remember that in this statement of the law, F denotes limiting friction only.*

Limiting friction between two surfaces, the nature of each of which is considered to be homogeneous over a finite area, is thus stated to be independent of the extent of the surfaces in contact.

Experimental evidence shows that the limiting friction between two surfaces in contact, when there is relative motion, is slightly less than it would be if there were no relative motion. We shall not include this slight variation within the stated laws which provide our mathematical model of friction.

9.3. The Angle of Friction

The resultant of the normal force and the friction with which one surface acts upon another surface in contact with it is called the *resultant action* (or reaction) of the one surface on the other. *When the friction is limiting*, the angle between the normal action and the resultant action of the one surface on the other is called the *angle of friction* (Fig. 104). The angle of friction is usually denoted by λ and, clearly,

$$\tan \lambda = \frac{\text{limiting friction}}{\text{normal reaction}} = \mu.$$

9.4. The Equilibrium of a Particle on an Inclined Plane

Figure 105 shows the forces acting on a particle of weight W in limiting equilibrium on a plane inclined at an angle θ with the horizontal. The coefficient of friction between the particle and the plane is μ.

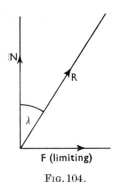

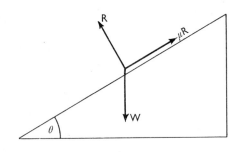

FIG. 104.   FIG. 105.

Equations of equilibrium for the forces acting on the particle are
(1) the sum of the components parallel to the plane is zero.

$$\therefore \ \mu R = W \sin\theta,$$

(2) the sum of the components perpendicular to the plane is zero,

$$\therefore \ R = W \cos\theta.$$

$$\therefore \ \tan\theta = \mu.$$

$$\therefore \ \theta = \lambda,$$

where λ is the angle of friction between the particle and the plane.

This example suggests an experimental method by means of which the coefficient of friction between two surfaces can be found approximately. The angle of inclination of the plane at which one surface just begins to move relatively to the other is the angle of friction between the surfaces.

Figure 106 (i) shows the forces acting on a particle of weight W, held in equilibrium on a plane inclined at an angle φ to the horizontal by a force P acting in a direction making an anticlockwise angle α with the upward direction of the plane. We consider only the case in which all the forces act in a vertical plane through a line of greatest slope of the inclined plane. The force system in a diagram is constructed on the assumption that the sum of the components parallel to the plane of the forces of the system other than friction is an upward force. If this sum is a downward force, then the direction of friction is reversed as in Fig. 106 (ii).

For the case illustrated in Fig. 106 (i) the equations of equilibrium for the particle are,

(1) the sum of components parallel to the plane is zero,

$$F + W \sin\varphi - P \cos\alpha = 0,$$

(2) the sum of components perpendicular to the plane is zero,

$$R - W \cos\varphi + P \sin\alpha = 0.$$

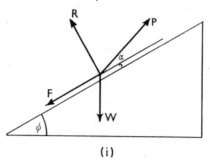

(i)

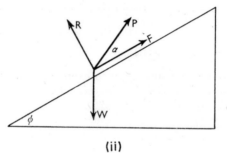

(ii)

Fig. 106.

P is not determined by these two equations. Until friction becomes limiting, F can take any value between $R \tan\lambda$ down the plane and $R \tan\lambda$ up the plane. The first equation shows that P increases with F and, therefore,

$$P \cos\alpha \leqq R \tan\lambda + W \sin\varphi.$$

$$\therefore \ P \cos\alpha \leqq (W \cos\varphi - P \sin\alpha) \tan\lambda + W \sin\varphi.$$

$$\therefore \ P(\cos\alpha \cos\lambda + \sin\alpha \sin\lambda) \leqq W(\cos\varphi \sin\lambda + \sin\varphi \cos\lambda).$$

$$\therefore \ P \leqq W \frac{\sin(\varphi + \lambda)}{\cos(\alpha - \lambda)}.$$

It follows that, if α varies, the minimum value of P required just to pull the particle up the plane is $W \sin(\varphi + \lambda)$ in a direction making an anticlockwise angle λ with the upward direction of the plane.

If the sum of the force-components parallel to the plane for the forces other than friction is down the plane, the forces are as marked in Fig. 106 (ii). The equations of equilibrium for the particle are

$$F + P \cos\alpha - W \sin\varphi = 0,$$
$$R + P \sin\alpha - W \cos\varphi = 0,$$

whence

$$P \cos\alpha \geqq W \sin\varphi - R \tan\lambda,$$

i.e. $\qquad P \cos\alpha \geqq W \sin\varphi - (W \cos\varphi - P \sin\alpha) \tan\lambda,$

i.e. $\quad P(\cos\alpha \cos\lambda - \sin\alpha \sin\lambda) \geqq W(\sin\varphi \cos\lambda - \cos\varphi \sin\lambda),$

i.e. $$P \geqq \frac{W \sin(\varphi - \lambda)}{\cos(\alpha + \lambda)}.$$

It follows that, if α varies, the minimum value of P required to prevent the particle from slipping down the plane is $W \sin(\varphi - \lambda)$ at a *clockwise* angle λ with the upward direction of the plane. If, in this case, α is limited to the range $0 \leqq \alpha \leqq 90°$, the least value of P is $\dfrac{W \sin(\varphi - \lambda)}{\cos\lambda}$ upwards and parallel to the plane.

9.5. Examples Involving Friction

The examples and the miscellaneous exercises which follow illustrate problems *already considered in this book but which include friction as an additional factor. It is important*

(a) *to discriminate carefully between problems in which friction is limiting and problems in which friction is not limiting,*

(b) *to use an inequality sign in cases in which the statement "friction is less than limiting" is involved, and in which the maximum or minimum value of some other variable factor is required.*

Miscellaneous Exercises IX are chosen so as to provide a revision set of exercises covering most of the contents of the book up to this point.

Examples. (i) Two small rings each of mass m are threaded on a fixed rough horizontal wire and are connected by a light inextensible string of length $2a$. To the middle point of the string is attached a particle of mass $6m/5$. Show that, if the coefficient of friction between each ring and the wire is $\frac{1}{2}$, the depth of the particle below the wire in the position of limiting equilibrium is $3a/5$. (L.)

Friction is Limiting. The forces acting on each ring, and the forces acting on the particle *in the position of limiting equilibrium* are shown in Fig. 107. The system is symmetrical (mechanically as well as geometrically) about a vertical line through the mid-point of the string and so the components of reaction at A are equal, respectively, to the components of reaction at B and the tension in the string

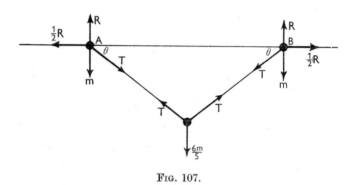

Fig. 107.

is the same in each of its parts. The weights of the particle and the rings are in gravitational units. Equations of equilibrium are,

(a) for the particle, $2T \sin\theta = \dfrac{6m}{5}$,

(b) for either ring, $R = m + T \sin\theta$,

$$\tfrac{1}{2}R = T \cos\theta.$$

$$\therefore\ 2T \cos\theta = m + T \sin\theta.$$

$$\therefore\ 2T \cos\theta = \frac{5T}{3}\sin\theta + T \sin\theta.$$

$$\therefore\ \tan\theta = \tfrac{3}{4}.$$

Therefore the depth of the particle below the wire is

$$a \sin\theta = \tfrac{3}{5}a.$$

(ii) A bullet of mass 2 oz is fired horizontally with velocity 900 ft/sec into a wooden block of mass 10 lb which is initially at rest on a rough horizontal surface. The coefficient of friction between the block and the surface on which it rests is 5/8. Assuming that the bullet becomes embedded in the block, that the time taken by the passage of the bullet into the block is negligible, and that the block subsequently slides without rotation along the surface, calculate (a) the velocity with which the block is set in motion, and (b) the distance the block will move before it comes to rest.   (C.)

Friction is limiting. The momentum of the bullet immediately before striking the block is

$$\tfrac{1}{8} \times 900 \text{ lb ft/sec}.$$

Therefore the velocity of bullet and block immediately after impact is

$$\left(\tfrac{900}{8}\big/\tfrac{81}{8}\right) \text{ft/sec} = \tfrac{100}{9} \text{ft/sec}.$$

Therefore the initial kinetic energy of bullet and block is

$$\tfrac{1}{2} \times \tfrac{81}{8} \times \left(\tfrac{100}{9}\right)^2 \text{ft pdl}.$$

The force of friction between the block and the plane is

$$\tfrac{5}{8} \times \tfrac{81}{8} g \text{ pdl}.$$

The work done by friction on the block = kinetic energy destroyed.

$$\therefore \ \tfrac{5}{8} \times \tfrac{81}{8} \times 32 y = \tfrac{1}{2} \times \tfrac{81}{8} \times \left(\tfrac{100}{9}\right)^2,$$

where y ft is the distance moved by the block before coming to rest.

$$\therefore \ y \doteqdot 3{\cdot}1.$$

The block moves about 3 ft 1 in before coming to rest.

(iii) Two particles A and B, of masses m_1 and m_2, connected by a light string of length a, are placed on a rough horizontal table with the string just taut. The coefficients of friction between the table and A and B are μ_1 and μ_2 respectively. The particles are both given an initial velocity V in the direction from B to A. If $\mu_1 < \mu_2$, find the distance described by each particle before it comes to rest. If $\mu_1 > \mu_2$, prove that the particles will come to rest without a collision, provided that

$$V^2(\mu_1 - \mu_2) < 2\mu_1\mu_2 g a. \tag{N.}$$

Friction is Limiting. If $\mu_1 < \mu_2$, the string remains taut throughout the motion and the forces acting on the system of particles are as shown in Fig. 108. Since there is no motion in the direction perpen-

T.M.S.F.I.   17

dicular to the table, $R = m_1 g$, $S = m_2 g$ and the equation of motion
for the whole system in the direction of the string is

$$-\mu_1 m_1 g - \mu_2 m_2 g = (m_1 + m_2) f.$$

$$f = -\left(\frac{\mu_1 m_1 + \mu_2 m_2}{m_1 + m_2}\right) g$$

and so each particle describes a distance

$$\frac{V^2 (m_1 + m_2)}{2 (\mu_1 m_1 + \mu_2 m_2) g}$$

before coming to rest.

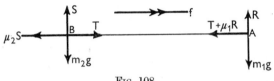

FIG. 108.

If $\mu_1 > \mu_2$, the string will instantly become slack after the initial
impulse and the accelerations of A and B respectively in the direction
BA are $-\mu_1 g$ and $-\mu_2 g$. Therefore the distance covered by A before
coming to rest is $\dfrac{V^2}{2\mu_1 g}$, and the distance covered by B before coming
to rest is $\dfrac{V^2}{2\mu_2 g}$. Also, since the particles start with the same velocity
and the retardation of A exceeds the retardation of B, the distance
between the two particles decreases continuously until motion stops
or there is a collision. Therefore there is no collision if

$$a + \frac{V^2}{2\mu_1 g} - \frac{V^2}{2\mu_2 g} > 0,$$

i.e. if
$$V^2(\mu_1 - \mu_2) < 2\mu_1\mu_2 g a.$$

(iv) To the end A of a uniform rod AB is attached one end of
a light inelastic string, whose length is equal to that of the rod.
The other end of the string is fixed to a point in a rough vertical
wall, and the rod is in equilibrium with the end B in contact with
the wall. Prove that the inclination of the rod to the wall cannot
be less than $\cot^{-1}(\mu/3)$, where μ is the coefficient of friction.

Show also that the tension in the string is less when equilibrium
is limiting than when it is not limiting.   (O.C.)

Equilibrium is Not Necessarily Limiting. Let the inclination of the rod to the wall in a position of equilibrium be θ. The forces acting on the rod are as shown in Fig. 109. The equations of equilibrium for the rod are,

(1) the sum of horizontal components of forces is zero,

$$R = T \sin\theta,$$

(2) the sum of vertical components of forces is zero,

$$F + T \cos\theta = W,$$

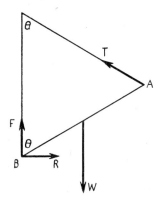

FIG. 109.

(3) the sum of moments of forces about B is zero,

$$W a \sin\theta = T \, 2a \sin 2\theta,$$

where $2a$ is the length of the rod.

$$\therefore \ T = \frac{W}{4 \cos\theta}, \quad F = \frac{3W}{4}, \quad R = \frac{W \sin\theta}{4 \cos\theta}.$$

But

$$\frac{F}{R} \leqq \mu.$$

$\therefore \ 3 \cot\theta \leqq \mu, \quad \cot\theta \leqq \mu/3.$

$\therefore \ \theta \geqq \cot^{-1}(\mu/3)$ since $\cot\theta$ decreases with θ for $0 < \theta \leqq \frac{1}{2}\pi$.

When equilibrium is limiting, $F = \mu R$, θ has its minimum value $\cot^{-1}(\mu/3)$ and $T = W/(4 \cos\theta)$.

T is therefore least when $\cos\theta$ is greatest for $0 < \theta < \frac{1}{2}\pi$. It follows that T is least when θ is least, i.e. when equilibrium is limiting.

17*

(v) A heavy uniform wire is bent into the form of an equilateral triangle ABC and rests with BC horizontal and supported by a rough peg at its middle point, the vertex A being below BC. A gradually increasing horizontal force is applied at A in the plane of the wire. Show that, as long as the wire does not slip on the peg, when BC is inclined at an angle θ to the horizontal the ratio of the frictional force to the normal reaction at the peg is

$$\frac{2 \tan\theta}{3 + \tan^2\theta}.$$

Deduce that the wire never slips if the coefficient of friction between the wire and the peg exceeds $1/\sqrt{3}$.　　　　　　　　(L.)

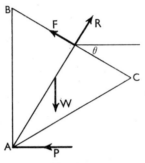

FIG. 110.

Let the weight of the wire triangle be W. The centre of mass of the wire is at the centroid of the triangle.

In the displaced position the forces acting are shown in Fig. 110. The equations of equilibrium of the triangle are,

(1) the sum of the horizontal components of forces is zero,

$$P = -F\cos\theta + R\sin\theta,$$

(2) the sum of the vertical components of forces is zero,

$$R\cos\theta + F\sin\theta = W,$$

(3) the sum of the moments of the forces about the peg is zero,

$$\tfrac{1}{3}\sqrt{3}\,aW\sin\theta = \sqrt{3}\,aP\cos\theta,$$

where $2a$ is the length of a side of the triangle.

$$\therefore\ P = \tfrac{1}{3}W\tan\theta.$$

Therefore, from equation (2),

$$R \cos\theta + F \sin\theta = 3P \cot\theta,$$

and from equation (1),

$$R \cos\theta + F \sin\theta = (-F \cos\theta + R \sin\theta) 3 \cot\theta.$$

$$\therefore \; 2R \cos\theta = F\left(\sin\theta + \frac{3 \cos^2\theta}{\sin\theta}\right).$$

$$\therefore \; \frac{F}{R} = \frac{2 \sin\theta \cos\theta}{\sin^2\theta + 3 \cos^2\theta} = \frac{2 \tan\theta}{3 + \tan^2\theta}.$$

Therefore the rod does not slip if

$$\frac{2 \tan\theta}{3 + \tan^2\theta} \leqq \mu,$$

i.e. if $\qquad \mu \tan^2\theta - 2 \tan\theta + 3\mu \geqq 0.$

This is true for all values of θ (since μ is positive) if

$$4 \leqq 12\mu^2,$$

i.e. if $\qquad\qquad \mu \geqq \dfrac{1}{\sqrt{3}}.$

(vi) A uniform rod of length a is in limiting equilibrium inside a fixed rough spherical surface of radius a, with one end at the lowest point of the surface. Prove that the coefficient of friction is $\sqrt{15 - 2\sqrt{3}}$.

(O.C.)

This is an example in the solution of which the *angle of friction* and the *resultant reaction are used*.

Figure 111 represents the rod AB in equilibrium under the action of *three forces only*, the resultant actions R and S at A and B respectively and the weight W of the rod acting vertically downwards through its mid-point. These three forces must act at a point. Let the lines of action of R and S intersect on the line of action of W at T.

Friction is Limiting. If the sphere were smooth, the rod would slip in the direction in which M, its centre of gravity, would be lowered. Friction is therefore upwards at B and horizontally towards B at A. The resultant reactions R and S make angles, each equal to the angle of friction λ between the rod and the surface, with OA and OB respectively in the directions shown.

Then, since OA is vertical, TM is parallel to OA.

Hence, from the triangle ATB in which $\angle TAB = 60° - \lambda$, $\angle TBA = 60° + \lambda$, $\angle ATM = \lambda$, $\angle MTB = 60° - \lambda$ and $\angle TMB = 60°$,

$$2 \cot 60° = \cot \lambda - \cot(60 - \lambda).$$

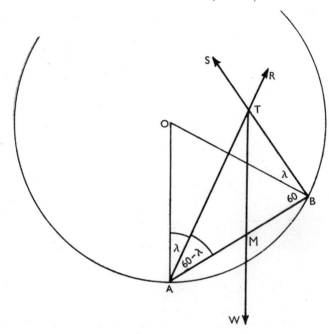

Fig. 111.

Therefore, if $\tan \lambda = \mu =$ coefficient of friction between rod and spherical surface,

$$\frac{2}{\sqrt{3}} = \frac{1}{\mu} - \frac{1 + \mu\sqrt{3}}{\sqrt{3} - \mu}.$$

This equation reduces to

$$\mu^2 + \mu 4\sqrt{3} - 3 = 0$$

and therefore, since μ is positive,

$$\mu = \sqrt{15} - 2\sqrt{3}.$$

(vii) Two small rough rings A and B, of masses $2m$ and m respectively, can slide on a fixed rough horizontal rod, the coefficient

of friction between each ring and the rod being μ. A smooth ring M
of mass m is supported by a string of length $2a$ connecting A and B.
Show that, in any position of equilibrium, the friction at A cannot
be limiting, and that the greatest possible distance apart of A and B is

$$\frac{6a\mu}{\sqrt{(1+9\mu^2)}}. \tag{L.}$$

The forces acting on each of the elements of the system are shown
in Fig. 112. Because the middle ring is smooth, the two parts of the
string are equally inclined to the vertical.

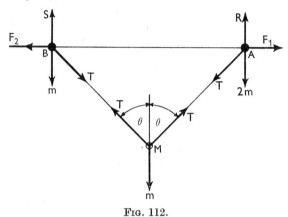

FIG. 112.

Equations of equilibrium *for the whole system* are, using gravitational
units throughout,

(1) the sum of the horizontal components of the forces is zero,

$$F_1 = F_2 = F \text{ (say)},$$

(2) the sum of the vertical components of the forces is zero,

$$R + S = 4m,$$

(3) the sum of the moments of the forces about B is zero.

$$2R = 2 \times 2m + 1 \times m.$$

$$\therefore R = \frac{5m}{2}, \quad S = \frac{3m}{2}.$$

$$\therefore \frac{F}{S} > \frac{F}{R}.$$

But $\dfrac{F}{S} \leqq \mu$ in all positions of equilibrium.

$$\therefore \dfrac{F}{R} < \mu \text{ in all positions of equilibrium.}$$

∴ friction cannot be limiting at A.

(4) A condition of equilibrium for the smooth ring M is $2\,T\cos\theta = m$.

(5) Conditions of equilibrium for the ring at B are

$$F = T\sin\theta, \quad S = T\cos\theta + m.$$

Therefore from above $F = \dfrac{1}{2}\,m\tan\theta$ and $S = \dfrac{3\,m}{2}$.

But $$\dfrac{F}{S} \leqq \mu, \quad \therefore \tan\theta \leqq 3\,\mu.$$

$$\therefore AB = 2a\sin\theta \leqq \dfrac{6a\,\mu}{\sqrt{(1 + 9\,\mu^2)}}.$$

(viii) A triangular prism is placed with a rectangular face of breadth $2c$ on a rough horizontal plane, the coefficient of friction being μ. The prism is a uniform right prism and its two inclined faces are equal rectangles whose common edge is at a height h above the horizontal face. If the plane is rotated slowly about a line which is parallel to the three parallel edges, prove that the prism will topple or slide according as $\mu \gtrless 3c/h$.   (N.)

Figure 113 shows a vertical section through the centre of gravity of the prism. Equilibrium is possible only if the vertical through the centre of gravity G falls inside the base BC, otherwise, unless

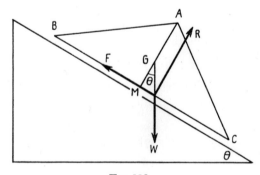

FIG. 113.

friction is limiting, the prism will topple (§ 7.6). Hence the prism topples before it slides if $GM \tan\theta > MC$,

i.e. if $$\tan\theta > \frac{3c}{h},$$

and $$\frac{F}{R} < \mu, \quad \text{i.e.} \quad \mu > \tan\theta.$$

Therefore the prism topples before it slides if $\mu > 3c/h$.

The prism slides before it topples if the combined conditions $\tan\theta < 3c/h$ and $\mu < \tan\theta$ obtain, i.e. if $\mu < 3c/h$.

(ix) A uniform solid cube, of weight W and edge $2a$, rests in equilibrium with one face in contact with a fixed rough plane inclined at an angle α to the horizontal. One pair of opposite faces is vertical. If the coefficient of friction is μ, prove that $\tan\alpha$ must not be greater than the smaller of the two numbers 1 and μ.

A downward force P, parallel to the lines of greatest slope of the plane and of gradually increasing magnitude, is now applied at the centre of one of the faces of the cube which is perpendicular to the force. If $\mu < 1$, show that, when equilibrium is broken, the cube begins to slide down the plane, and that the magnitude of P is then

$$W \cos\alpha(\mu - \tan\alpha).$$

As the magnitude of P increases from zero to this critical value, show that the distance from the centre of the cube to the line of action of the normal reaction increases from $a\tan a$ to $a\mu$. (N.)

(a) Figure 114(i) shows a vertical section through the centre of gravity G of the cube and the forces acting on the cube.

Equilibrium conditions for the cube are,

(1) $F = W \sin\alpha$,

(2) $N = W \cos\alpha$,

(3) $\dfrac{F}{N} \leqq \mu$, (ensures no sliding),

(4) $MT \leqq MB$, i.e. $a \tan\alpha \leqq a$, (ensures no toppling). Hence, from (1) and (2), $\dfrac{F}{N} = \tan\alpha$ and therefore from (3), $\tan\alpha \leqq \mu$ and from (4), $\tan\alpha \leqq 1$. Therefore, for equilibrium, $\tan\alpha$ must not be greater than the smaller of 1 and μ.

Figure 114(ii) shows the same section of the cube, and the forces acting when the force P is introduced.

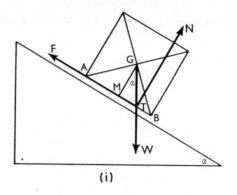

(i)

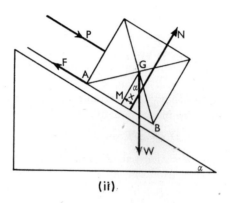

(ii)

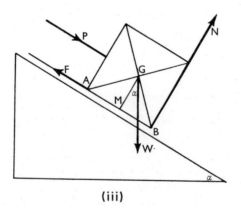

(iii)

FIG. 114.

Equilibrium is broken by sliding when P attains the value for which

$$P + W \sin\alpha = F,$$
$$W \cos\alpha = N,$$

and
$$F = \mu N;$$

i.e. when
$$P = W \cos\alpha (\mu - \tan\alpha)$$

provided that equilibrium is not broken by toppling before P reaches this value.

Equilibrium would be broken by toppling when P attains the value for which N acts through B [Fig. 114 (iii)], and taking moments about B

$$Pa = W\sqrt{2}a \cos(45 + \alpha) = Wa(\cos\alpha - \sin\alpha),$$

i.e.
$$P = W \cos\alpha (1 - \tan\alpha).$$

If $\mu < 1$,
$$\mu - \tan\alpha < 1 - \tan\alpha$$

and therefore equilibrium is broken by sliding when

$$P = W \cos\alpha (\mu - \tan\alpha).$$

When $P = 0$ and there is equilibrium [Fig. 114 (i)] the sum of the moments of the forces about M is zero.

$$\therefore xN = aW \sin\alpha,$$

where x is the distance of the force N from the centre of the cube.

$$\therefore xW \cos\alpha = aW \sin\alpha.$$

$$\therefore x = a \tan\alpha.$$

For other values of P up to the critical value, Fig. 114 (ii),

$$aP + aW \sin\alpha = xN,$$

$$\therefore x = \frac{Pa + Wa \sin\alpha}{W \cos\alpha}.$$

x therefore increases as P increases up to the critical value when

$$x = \frac{aW \cos\alpha (\mu - \tan\alpha) + aW \sin\alpha}{W \cos\alpha} = a\mu.$$

(x) Two particles are resting on a rough inclined plane of inclination α and are connected by a taut string which makes an angle of 45° with the line of greatest slope. The weight of the lower particle is twice that of the upper, and the coefficient of limiting friction between the upper particle and the plane is twice that between the lower particle and the plane. If both particles are on the point of slipping, show that the coefficient of limiting friction for the lower particle is $\sqrt{\frac{5}{8}}\tan\alpha$, and find the tension in the string.   (N.)

The *direction of friction* in this example is not immediately evident. Fig. 115 shows the forces in the plane of imminent motion acting on each of the particles, and shows friction making an anticlockwise angle θ with the upward direction of a line of greatest slope for the lower particle and a clockwise angle φ with a line of greatest slope for the upper particle; μ is the coefficient of friction for the lower particle.

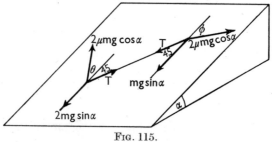

FIG. 115.

Then, equations of equilibrium for each of the particles are,
(1) for the upper particle

$$T\sin 45° = 2\mu mg\cos\alpha\sin\varphi,$$

$$mg\sin\alpha = 2\mu mg\cos\alpha\cos\varphi - T\cos 45°,$$

(2) for the lower particle

$$T\sin 45° = 2\mu mg\cos\alpha\sin\theta,$$

$$2mg\sin\alpha = 2\mu mg\cos\alpha\cos\theta + T\cos 45°.$$

Hence $\theta = \varphi$, and

$$3mg\sin\alpha = 4\mu mg\cos\alpha\cos\theta.$$

$$\therefore\ \mu = \frac{3\tan\alpha}{4\cos\theta}.$$

Also

$$mg\sin\alpha = 2T\cos 45°.$$

$$\therefore\ T = \frac{1}{\sqrt{2}}mg\sin\alpha.$$

$$\therefore\ \tfrac{1}{2}mg\sin\alpha = 2\mu mg\cos\alpha\sin\theta.$$

$$\therefore\ \mu\sin\theta = \tfrac{1}{4}\tan\alpha.$$

But
$$\mu \cos\theta = \tfrac{3}{4}\tan\alpha,$$
$$\therefore\ \mu^2 = \tfrac{10}{16}\tan^2\alpha,$$
$$\mu = \sqrt{(\tfrac{5}{8})}\,\tan\alpha.$$

MISCELLANEOUS EXERCISES. IX

1. A block of stone of mass 100 lb is pulled along a rough horizontal plane by a force P lb wt. inclined at 30° to the horizontal. If the angle of friction between the block and the plane is 30°, find the least value of P. (N.)

2. A uniform beam LM of mass 36 lb rests with the end L on a rough horizontal plane and the end M against a smooth vertical wall. The beam makes an angle of 30° with the wall. Find, in magnitude and direction, the forces exerted on the beam by the wall and by the plane. (N.)

3. Two particles are connected by a light string. One of the particles, of mass 13 oz, is placed on a rough plane inclined at an angle of 30° to the horizontal. The string, after passing over a small smooth pulley at the top of the plane, supports the other particle of mass x oz which hangs vertically. If the first particle is on the point of slipping up the plane and if the angle of friction between this particle and the plane is 30°, find x. (N.)

4. A boat of mass 400 lb can just be pulled down a slipway of inclination α, where $\sin\alpha = 7/25$, by a force of 16 lb wt. acting parallel to the slipway. Show that the coefficient of friction between the boat and the slipway is $\tfrac{1}{3}$. Find also the least force, acting parallel to the slipway, required to pull the boat up the slipway. (N.)

5. A block of mass 120 lb is just prevented from slipping down a rough inclined plane of inclination 45° by a force of x lb wt. acting up the plane. If the coefficient of friction between the block and the plane is $\tfrac{1}{3}$, find x. (N.)

6. A uniform beam AB of mass 100 lb rests in limiting equilibrium with A against a rough vertical wall and B on rough horizontal ground; the coefficient of friction at each end of the beam is $\tfrac{1}{3}$. Show that the vertical component of the reaction at B is 90 lb wt. and find the inclination of the beam, to the vertical. (N.)

7. A mass of 6 lb rests on a rough horizontal plane. When it is pulled by a force of 5 lb wt. acting at 30° with the horizontal, it is just about to slide. Find μ, the coefficient of friction.

If the 5 lb wt. force is now increased to 6 lb wt., μ remaining the same, show that the mass will start to move with an acceleration of 8 ft/sec² approx. (N.)

8. A sledge of mass 60 lb is pulled along ice, coefficient of friction 0·1, by a horizontal force of 9 lb wt. What acceleration will be produced, and how far will the sledge go in 3 sec if it starts with a velocity of 5 ft/sec? (N.)

9. Two particles are connected by a light string. One particle A of mass 15 lb is placed on the smooth part of a horizontal table; the string, after passing over a small smooth pulley at the edge of the table, supports the other particle B of mass 3 lb which hangs vertically. The system starts from rest with the string taut. Find the acceleration of either particle and show that the tension in the string is $2\tfrac{1}{2}$ lb wt.

One second after the commencement of the motion A comes to a rough part of the table; the coefficient of friction between A and the table is $\frac{1}{2}$. Show that the particles come to rest after a further $\frac{2}{3}$ sec.   (N.)

10. A block of mass 6 lb rests on a smooth horizontal table and is attached by a light string to a particle of mass $\frac{1}{2}$ lb hanging over the edge of the table. From this particle is suspended another particle of mass $1\frac{1}{2}$ lb by a second string. The system is released from rest with the strings taut. Find the acceleration of the block, in ft/sec^2, and the tension, in lb wt., in each of the strings when the system is moving freely.

When this system is released from a similar position with the block on a rough horizontal table the acceleration of the block is found to be 4 ft/sec^2. Calculate the coefficient of friction between the block and this table.   (N.)

11. A horizontal force of 15 lb wt. is just sufficient to move a mass of 40 lb lying on a horizontal plank. Find the coefficient of limiting friction. If the plank is tilted until its inclination to the horizontal is 48°, and if the coefficient of friction is taken to have the same value throughout the question, calculate:

(i) the force, parallel to the plank, required just to move the mass up the plank,

(ii) the force, parallel to the plank, required to move the mass up the plank with an acceleration of 4 ft/sec.   (L.)

12. A body is supported on a rough inclined plane by a force acting along the plane. If the least force required to maintain equilibrium when the plane is inclined at the angle α to the horizontal is equal to the greatest force for which equilibrium can be maintained when the plane is inclined at the angle β, prove that the angle of friction is $\frac{1}{2}(\alpha - \beta)$.   (N.)

13. A body is placed on a rough plane inclined at an angle α to the horizontal. Find, in magnitude and direction, the least force that will move it up the plane if the coefficient of friction is μ.

A particle is placed inside a rough hollow sphere of radius a which is fixed in position. If the coefficient of friction is 0·6, show that the particle cannot rest in equilibrium at a height greater than about 0·14a above the lowest point of the sphere.   (N.)

14. Prove that a particle placed on a rough plane will slip when the angle of inclination of the plane to the horizontal is greater than the angle of friction.

A particle of weight W is held in equilibrium on a rough plane inclined at angle α to the horizontal by a horizontal force in the same vertical plane as the line of greatest slope through the particle. If λ is the angle of friction and α is greater than λ, prove that when the particle is about to slip down the plane the force is $W \tan(\alpha - \lambda)$.   (N.)

15. A heavy ladder whose centre of gravity divides its length (measured from its foot) in the ratio 1:3 rests with its upper end against a rough vertical wall and with its lower end on a smooth horizontal floor. The ladder is in a vertical plane at right angles to the wall and makes an angle of 45° with the horizontal. It is just kept from slipping down by a horizontal force in this plane applied at its foot. Find the magnitude of this force in terms of W, the weight of the ladder, and μ, the coefficient of friction between the ladder and the wall, and show that it is less than $\frac{1}{3} W$.

FRICTION 261

Show that, if the force exerted at the foot of the ladder is $\frac{1}{2}W$, the foot of the ladder will slide towards the wall unless $\mu \geqq \frac{1}{2}$. (C.)

16. Two particles H and K are connected by a light inextensible string. The particle H, which is of mass m, is placed on a rough fixed plane inclined to the horizontal at an angle α. The string, after passing over a small smooth pulley P at the top of the plane, supports the particle K which is of mass $2m$ and hangs vertically. The coefficient of friction between the particle H and the plane is $\frac{1}{2}\tan\alpha$. The system is released from rest with the string taut and PH along a line of greatest slope of the plane. Find the acceleration of either particle and show that the tension in the string is $\frac{1}{3}mg(2 + 3\sin\alpha)$. Find also in magnitude and direction the force exerted by the string on the pulley. (N.)

17. A uniform ladder rests, with one end on the ground and the other end against a vertical wall, in a plane perpendicular to the line of intersection of wall and ground. The coefficients of friction between the ladder and the ground and between the ladder and the wall are both equal to tan 15°. Show that the inclination of the ladder to the ground cannot be less than 60°.

Show that the ladder can just rest at an inclination of 30°, if a weight $(\sqrt{3} + 1)/2$ of its own is attached to its lower end. (O.C.)

18. Two small rings A and B, each of weight W, are free to move on a rough horizontal rod, the coefficient of limiting friction being $\frac{1}{4}$. The rings are connected by a smooth light inextensible string, of length 10 ft, which passes through another small smooth ring of weight $2W$. Prove that, in a position of equilibrium of the system, the distance AB cannot exceed $2\sqrt{5}$ ft; and find the tension in the string when AB is $2\sqrt{5}$ ft. (L.)

19. A uniform rod AB of weight W and length $4a$ rests in a horizontal position on a rough peg P distant a from B, the coefficient of friction being $\frac{1}{2}$. The end A is supported by a string making an acute angle θ with BA produced. Show that equilibrium in this position is possible if θ is not less than 45°.

If the upper end of the string is attached to a small heavy ring threaded on a rough horizontal rod in the same vertical plane as AB, find the least possible weight of the ring consistent with equilibrium when $\theta = 45°$, the coefficient of friction between ring and rod being $\frac{1}{2}$. (N.)

20. A uniform rod AB of weight W rests with its end B in contact with a rough plane inclined at an angle α to the horizontal. The rod is supported in a horizontal position, in a vertical plane through a line of greatest slope of the inclined plane, by a string attached to A and parallel to the line of greatest slope through B. If the equilibrium is limiting, show that the angle of friction at B is $(\frac{1}{2}\pi - 2\alpha)$ and find the tension in the string. (L.)

21. A heavy uniform cube rests in limiting equilibrium having one edge in contact with a horizontal floor and another edge in contact with a vertical wall. The face of the cube containing these edges makes an angle θ ($< 45°$) with the floor. If the coefficient of friction at the floor is μ and that at the wall is μ', show that

$$\tan\theta = \frac{1 - \mu\mu'}{1 + \mu\mu' + 2\mu}.$$ (N.)

22. A uniform pole of mass 250 lb resting with its lower end on rough level ground is supported at an angle θ to the horizontal by a horizontal force of P lb wt. acting at its upper end. If the coefficient of friction between the pole and the ground is 0·65 and if the pole is on the point of slipping, *calculate* the values of P and θ.   (L.)

23. A uniform rod AD, 16 in. long, rests in a vertical plane with its foot A in contact with a rough horizontal floor and with a point C of the rod in contact with the smooth edge of a stool 12 in. from the floor. If the length AC is 13 in. and the equilibrium is limiting, prove that the coefficient of friction between the floor and the rod is approximately 0·24.   (C.)

24. A uniform rod OA of weight W is in equilibrium with the lower end O resting on a rough horizontal plane. The rod makes an angle 2α with the vertical and is held by a light string tied to the end A. The string passes over a smooth peg B vertically above O and supports a particle of weight w which hangs freely. If $OB = OA$ and H is the midpoint of AB, show that, in considering the equilibrium of the rod, OHB may be taken as a triangle of forces. Deduce that $W > w$, and that the angle of friction at O is greater than α.   (N.)

25. A ladder of length $2l$, with its centre of gravity at its middle point, is placed with its end A on a rough horizontal floor and with its end B resting against a smooth vertical wall. Prove that the height of B above the floor when the ladder is just about to slip is $2l/\sqrt{(1 + 4\mu^2)}$, where μ is the coefficient of limiting friction between the ladder and the floor.   (O.C.)

26. A uniform beam AB, of length $2a$, is supported by a rough peg, and the lower end A of the beam rests against a rough vertical wall. The beam is inclined at an angle of $45°$ to the vertical, and the vertical plane through AB is perpendicular to the wall; the coefficient of friction between the beam and the peg and between the beam and the wall is $\frac{1}{2}$. Prove that, if the lower end of the beam is on the point of slipping downwards, the distance of A from the peg is $7a/8$.   (O.C.)

27. A uniform rod of length $2a$ and weight W is placed at an inclination α to the horizontal so as to rest against the top of a smooth vertical wall of height h and have its lowest point on a rough horizontal plane, the vertical plane through the rod being at right angles to the wall . If $2a \sin \alpha > h > a \sin \alpha$, show that the coefficient of friction between the rod and the ground, if the rod is on the point of slipping, is

$$\frac{a \sin^2 \alpha \cos \alpha}{h - a \sin \alpha \cos^2 \alpha}.$$

Prove also that the pressure between the rod and the wall is $\dfrac{a}{h} W \sin \alpha \cos \alpha$.
      (O.C.)

28. A right circular cylinder of radius 4 in. whose axis is horizontal is fixed in contact with a horizontal plane. A uniform rod of length $6 \sqrt{3}$ in. rests with its lower end on the plane and a point of its length in contact with the cylinder, the vertical plane through the rod being perpendicular to the axis of the cylinder. If the rod is inclined at $60°$ to the horizontal and is about to slip at both points of contact, prove that, if the coefficient of friction between the rod and the cylinder is $1/\sqrt{3}$, that between the rod and the plane is $\sqrt{3}/5$.   (N.)

29. A particle of mass 1 oz is projected up a line of greatest slope, 10 ft long, of a rough plane of inclination $30°$. Assuming the coefficient of friction between the plane and the particle to be $1/5$, find (i) the speed of projection if the particle just reaches the top of the plane, (ii) the time then taken to reach the top.

Find also the kinetic energy lost by the time the particle has reached halfway up the plane. (L.)

30. A particle P, of mass 2 lb, is placed on a rough horizontal table at O; a string, attached to P, passes over a small smooth pulley A at the edge of the table and carries a particle Q of mass 4 lb hanging vertically. The system is released from rest when P is at a distance of 2 ft from A. If the coefficient of friction between P and the table is $\frac{1}{2}$, prove that P reaches A after $\frac{1}{2}$ sec.

Prove also that when the particles have been moving for $\frac{1}{4}$ sec the speed of their centre of mass is $4\sqrt{5}/3$ ft/sec. (O.C.)

31. A and B are two particles, of mass m and $2m$ respectively, lying on a rough horizontal table and connected by a taut light inextensible string; B is connected to a particle C, of mass $3m$, by a similar string which passes over a small fixed smooth pulley at the edge of the table; C hangs vertically and in the vertical plane through AB. If the coefficient of friction between the table and each of the particles A and B is $1/2$, prove that, when the system is released from rest, C descends a distance of 4 ft in the first second of its motion. (O.C.)

32. A particle A of mass m_1 and a particle B of mass m are connected by a light inextensible string. A second light inextensible string connects B to another particle C of mass $m_2 (< m_1)$. The particle B is placed on a rough horizontal table, the coefficient of friction between the particle B and the table being μ. The strings pass over opposite parallel edges of the table and the particles A and C hang freely. The system is released from rest with the particles A, B, C in a vertical plane perpendicular to the parallel edges of the table. Prove that the particles will move if $m_1 > m_2 + \mu m$;

and in this case find the acceleration of the system and the tensions of the two strings. (N.)

*33. A particle of mass m rests on a rough table and it is connected by a light inextensible string passing over a smooth pulley at the edge of table and attached at its other end to a smooth pulley of mass m. Over this pulley another string passes, carrying masses $11m$ and $\frac{1}{2}m$ respectively hanging freely. If, when the masses are released, the mass $\frac{1}{2}m$ remains at rest, find the coefficient of friction between the first mass and the table. (L.)

*34. A uniform cubical block of weight W lies on a rough horizontal floor. A gradually increasing force is applied in a central vertical plane at the middle point of a top edge, pulling upwards at a fixed *acute* angle θ with the top face. If the block begins to move by turning about a lower edge, show that the force of friction between the floor and the block at the instant when equilibrium is broken is

$$\frac{W}{2(1+\tan\theta)}.$$

Find also the normal reaction of the floor, and deduce that the block begins to tilt before it slides if $\tan\theta > \dfrac{1}{\mu} - 2$, where μ is the coefficient of friction. If $\mu = 0.6$, state how equilibrium is broken and find, in terms of W and θ, the corresponding magnitude of the applied force. (N.)

*35. A uniform cube of edge $4a$ and weight W stands on a rough horizontal plane. A gradually increasing force P is applied inwards at right angles to a face F of the cube at a point distant a vertically above the centre of that face.

Prove that equilibrium will be broken by sliding or by tilting according as the coefficient of friction between the cube and the plane is less than or greater than a certain value, and find this value.

If P has not reached a value for which equilibrium is broken, and $P = \frac{1}{2}W$, find how far from the face F of the cube the normal reaction acts. (C.)

*36. A cube rests on a rough plane, inclined to the horizontal at an angle α, $(\alpha < \frac{1}{4}\pi)$, with two of its upper and two of its lower edges horizontal. Show that it will not be possible to drag the cube up the plane without upsetting it, by means of a rope attached to the middle point of the uppermost edge of the cube and pulled parallel to the inclined plane, if the coefficient of friction between the plane and the cube exceeds $\frac{1}{2}(1 - \tan\alpha)$. (O.C.)

*37. A uniform rod AB lies on a rough horizontal ground. A cord, attached to the end B, passes over a small pulley fixed at a point D, vertically over a point C lying in the line AB produced beyond B. Prove that, if the cord is pulled with a gradually increasing force, the rod will begin to slide along the ground, if μ, the coefficient of friction between the rod and the ground, is less than $\cot DBC$; but that, otherwise, it will begin to turn about the extremity A, and the extremity A will not slip till $\mu(\tan\beta - 2\tan\alpha) = 1$, where α and β are the angles which AB and BD respectively then make with the horizontal. (O.C.)

*38. A uniform cube, whose edges are each 8 ft long, stands on a rough horizontal plane. A gradually increasing horizontal force is applied normally to one of its vertical faces at a height of 2 ft above the centre of that face. Determine how equilibrium will be broken:

(1) when the coefficient of friction between the plane and the cube is 0·5;

(2) when this coefficient is 0·7. (O.C.)

*39. A uniform beam, of weight W and length $2b$, rests in equilibrium with one end A against a smooth vertical wall and the other end B on a rough horizontal floor. The vertical plane through AB meets the line of intersection of the wall and the floor in the point O. The angle OAB is θ. The end B of the beam is connected to O by a spring of natural length b and modulus $\frac{1}{2}W$.

(i) Calculate the normal reactions at A and B.

(ii) Show that the frictional force at B is

$$\tfrac{1}{2}W(1 + \tan\theta - 2\sin\theta)$$

acting towards O.

(iii) If the beam is about to slip when $\tan\theta = 4/3$, find the coefficient of friction between the beam and the floor. (N.)

*40. A uniform beam AB, of length $2a$ and weight W, rests in equilibrium with one end A against a smooth vertical wall and the other end B on a rough horizontal floor. The vertical plane containing the beam is perpendicular to the plane of the wall. The inclination of the beam to the vertical is θ and the coefficient of friction between the beam and the floor is μ. Show that $\tan\theta \leqq 2\mu$.

A gradually increasing horizontal force P is applied at a point C of the beam where $BC = \frac{2}{3}a$. This force acts away from the wall and in the vertical plane through AB. Find, in terms of P, W and θ, the force of friction at B and the normal reaction at A whilst equilibrium persists. If $\mu = \frac{3}{4}$, $\theta = 45°$, show that equilibrium is broken by the beam slipping when P exceeds $3W/8$. (N.)

*41. A light rigid rod AB of length $7a$ rests in a horizontal position with the end A against a rough vertical wall. The rod is perpendicular to the wall and the coefficient of friction at A is $\frac{1}{4}$. The rod is kept in place by a light cord which joins a point C on the rod to a point D on the wall vertically above A, where $AC = 4a$ and $AD = 3a$. A heavy particle rests on the rod at a point X. Find AX in terms of a if the end A is about to slip downwards.

Find also the positions of the two points on the rod between which the particle may be placed without disturbing equilibrium. (N.)

*42. A particle of mass m rests on an inclined plane, being attached to a fixed point of the plane by a light elastic string which lies along a line of greatest slope. If the coefficient of friction between the particle and plane is 0·5, find limits between which the inclination α of the plane to the horizontal must lie
(i) if the particle can rest on the plane without the string being stretched,
(ii) if the particle can only rest on the plane with the string stretched.
If α has a value consistent with (ii) and the modulus of the string is λ, show that the distance between the extreme positions of equilibrium of the particle is

$$mga \cos\alpha/\lambda$$

where a is the natural length of the string. (N.)

*43. A particle P, of weight w, is attached to the rim of a uniform circular disc, centre O and weight W; the disc, of radius a, rests on a rough horizontal floor and against an equally rough vertical wall in a vertical plane perpendicular to the wall, and is about to slip when P is above the level of O and at a distance $a/2$ from the wall. If λ is the angle of friction concerned, prove that

$$\cos 2\lambda - \sin 2\lambda = W/(W + w).$$

Find the value of λ if $w = W(\sqrt{2} - 1)$. (O.C.)

*44. A homogeneous hemisphere rests in limiting equilibrium with its curved surface on a rough inclined plane. Its plane face is vertical and the horizontal diameter of this face is perpendicular to the line of greatest inclination of the plane. Show that the coefficient of friction is $3/\sqrt{55}$. (N.)

*45. A triangular framework ABC is formed of three equal uniform rods smoothly jointed at their ends. The framework rests in equilibrium with the rod BC in contact with a small rough peg, and with the corner A vertically beneath C. Show that the coefficient of friction between BC and the peg is at least $1/\sqrt{3}$, and find the ratio of the reactions between the rods at B and C. (L.)

*46. A particle is projected with a velocity of 40 ft/sec directly up a plane inclined at 30° to the horizontal. The surface of the plane is smooth for the first 18 ft, but after traversing this distance the particle reaches a part of the plane where friction increases the retardation of the particle by one third of its previous value. Find the time that elapses (i) before the particle travels 36 ft from the point of projection, (ii) before it first comes instantaneously to rest. (C.)

*47. A particle is projected up a line of greatest slope from the foot of a rough inclined plane of inclination 60° to the horizontal with speed 4 ft/sec. If the angle of friction is 30°, prove that the particle will return to its starting-point with speed $2\sqrt{2}$ ft/sec. (L.)

*48. Two particles, of the same weight, are connected by a string which passes over a small pulley at the edge of a rough horizontal table. The system is released from rest when one particle is hanging freely and the other is on

18*

the table at a distance of 2 ft from the pulley. If the coefficient of friction between the particle and the table is $\frac{3}{4}$, prove that the time taken by the particle on the table to reach the pulley is 1 sec. (N.)

*49. Two particles of mass 3 lb and 6 lb are connected by a taut inextensible string, and rest in equilibrium on a plane inclined at an angle 30° to the horizontal with the string along a line of greatest slope, the 3 lb particle being the higher. The contact between the 6 lb particle and the plane is smooth, that between the 3 lb particle and the plane is rough (coefficient of friction 3). Calculate the force of friction. Find also the greatest angle to which the plane can be tilted before the equilibrium is broken. (N.)

*50. The cross-section of a prism is a regular polygon of 24 sides, and the prism can be turned about its axis, which is horizontal. On the uppermost face, which is horizontal, is placed a block whose coefficient of friction is 0·5, and on each of the two adjacent faces are placed blocks whose coefficients of friction are 0·6. The prism is then turned slowly about its axis. Find which of the blocks is the first to slide. (O.C.)

*51. A wedge of mass M rests on a smooth horizontal table and a particle of mass m rests on the rough inclined face of the wedge. If μ is the coefficient of friction between the particle and this face (which makes an angle α with the horizontal) find the horizontal force which must be applied to the wedge if the particle is to be on the point of moving up the inclined face. (L.)

*52. A particle of weight w slides down the smooth slant face of a wedge of weight W which *rests* on a horizontal table. The angle of the wedge is 45° and the coefficient of friction between the wedge and the table is μ. If the force of friction between the wedge and the table is $\frac{1}{2}\mu R$, where R is the normal reaction of the table, prove that

$$\mu = \frac{2w}{2W + w} .$$

If the equilibrium of the wedge on the table is limiting when the weight of the particle is increased by w', prove that

$$w' = \frac{w}{1 - \mu} .$$

(O.C.)

CHAPTER X

CONSERVATION OF ENERGY

10.1. Energy in the Physical World

In Chapter VIII (§ 8.5) we defined the *kinetic energy* of a particle of mass m moving with velocity v as $\frac{1}{2}mv^2$, and we described kinetic energy as the measure of the *work* which a particle could do by virtue of its velocity. In § 8.5 we defined the *gravitational potential energy* of a particle of mass m at a height z above an arbitrary origin as mgz referred to that origin and we described gravitational potential energy as a measure of the work done on the particle in moving it from the origin to its displaced position. We stated that the work done in such a displacement could be shown to be independent of the path by which the particle reached its displaced position. In § 8.5 we established that the *potential energy of a compressed or extended spring* is $\frac{\lambda x^2}{2l}$, where λ is the modulus of the spring, l is the natural length and x the extension of the spring from its natural length; in fact we obtained the potential energy of such a spring by calculating the work which would be required to extend or compress the spring from its natural length to its new length.

If *energy* is described, loosely, as "capacity for doing work", there are many other kinds of energy in the physical world in addition to the kinds of *mechanical energy* described above; there are, for example, heat energy, the energy of an electric current and chemical energy. Such different kinds of energy are convertible one to another in various ways of which one very obvious one is the conversion of mechanical energy into heat energy when work is done against friction.

The principle of *Conservation of Energy* stated that the total amount of energy of all kinds in the universe remains constant. Because of modern research and modern achievement with the destruction of the atom, if for no other reasons, this statement of a principle must now be abandoned or widened to include a definition of the potential energy inherent in all matter by reason of the nature of atomic structure. Here we are concerned with the more limited principle concerning mechanical energy which we state in the next paragraph.

10.2. Conservation of Mechanical Energy

A *conservative system of forces* is one in which the work done in taking a particle from one point to another is independent of the particular route chosen. Thus a gravitational field *in which there is no friction or air resistance,* is a conservative field. There are other conservative forces besides gravity, and in general, any force, the magnitude of which is a function of its distance from a fixed point in the field and the direction of which is towards that point, is a conservative force.

The principle of *conservation of mechanical energy* is stated as follows:

For a system of bodies in motion under the action of a conservative system of forces, the sum of the kinetic energy and the potential energy of the system remains constant.

Three very simple cases of the application of this principle are:

(a) A particle of mass m falling freely from a height h above a horizontal plane has potential energy, referred to the plane as origin, $mg(h-x)$ and kinetic energy $\frac{1}{2}mv^2 = \frac{1}{2}m(2gx) = mgx$ at a point of its flight distance x below the point from which it has fallen. Thus the total of the kinetic energy and potential energy of the particle is constant and equal to mgh.

(b) A particle of mass m projected with velocity u at an angle θ to the horizontal in a medium whose resistance is negligible has component velocities $u\cos\theta$ and $\sqrt{(u^2\sin^2\theta - 2gh)}$ at height h above the point of projection.

Hence, the total mechanical energy of the particle at this height is

$$\underset{\text{kinetic energy}}{(\tfrac{1}{2}mu^2\cos^2\theta + \tfrac{1}{2}mu^2\sin^2\theta - mgh)} + \underset{\substack{\text{potential}\\ \text{energy}}}{mgh} = \tfrac{1}{2}mu^2,$$

which is constant for all values of h.

(c) A particle of mass m slides down a *smooth*, fixed plane inclined at an angle α to the horizontal. In this case the particle is *constrained* to move in a particular way by its contact with the smooth plane. Here neither the action of the plane on the particle nor the equal and opposite reaction of the particle on the plane do any work during the motion and the system of forces is a conservative one.

In general, if there are equal and opposite reactions at *smooth* contacts (but no impacts), or equal and opposite tensions in strings (which remain tight during the motion), a system of forces which is otherwise conservative remains a conservative one.

The velocity acquired by the particle in sliding a distance x down the plane with its acceleration $g \sin\alpha$ is given by $v^2 = 2gx \sin\alpha$, and the vertical distance of the particle below its starting point is then $x \sin\alpha$. Hence, if the potential energy of the particle is measured from its starting point as origin, the total mechanical energy of the particle, in its displaced position, is

$$\underset{\substack{\text{kinetic}\\\text{energy}}}{\tfrac{1}{2}m(2gx \sin\alpha)} - \underset{\substack{\text{potential}\\\text{energy}}}{mg\,x \sin\alpha} = 0.$$

Thus the total mechanical energy of the particle is constant for all values of x.

This last example also serves as an illustration of a conservative system of forces in operation. The total energy of the particle in any position is independent not only of x but also of α and, therefore, the total energy is independent of the *path* by which the particle has reached its new position provided that, if necessary, such a path is assumed to be the limiting case of the sum of a number of inclined planes.

Friction and External Forces

Where friction is involved, and where work is done by external forces on the system concerned, the principle of conservation of mechanical energy is extended to give the more general statement:

Increase in mechanical energy = work done by external forces — work done against friction.

Clearly, work may be done *against* external forces, in which case the appropriate term of the equation is a negative one and there is a corresponding decrease in mechanical energy.

The general statement of the principle of conservation of energy presupposes that there is no additional loss of mechanical energy because of impacts or sudden tightening of strings.

Collisions

Where collisions between two bodies occur, or where there is a sudden tightening of an inextensible string connecting the bodies, there is a stage during which there is a distortion of the shape of the bodies concerned, and a temporary loss of kinetic energy is to some extent stored in the distorted bodies as potential energy. As the bodies regain their shape, only part of the energy is recovered as kinetic energy, part is converted into heat energy, and part, perhaps, into other forms of energy. In all such cases, except the ideal one which is described as a *perfectly elastic* collision, mechanical energy is lost in the collision.

Examples. (i) A particle of mass m is connected by a tight inextensible string of length l to a point on the same horizontal level as the particle. The particle is allowed to fall freely from rest in this position; it describes a quadrant of a circle in a vertical plane and then collides with, and coalesces with, another particle of mass m, at the lowest point of its path. The new particle moves freely in an arc of the same vertical circle and, when it again reaches the lowest point, it collides with, and coalesces with, a third particle of mass m. This process isr epeated continuously. Prove that the angle made by the string with the vertical when the composite particle is at its highest point following its rth collision is $\cos^{-1}\left\{\dfrac{r(r+2)}{(r+1)^2}\right\}$.

If v is the velocity of the particle when it first reaches the lowest point of its path, then, by the principle of energy,

$$v^2 = 2gl.$$

Immediately after the first collision, if v_1 is the velocity of the new particle, then, by conservation of momentum,

$$v_1 = \tfrac{1}{2}\sqrt{(2gl)},$$

and, by the principle of energy, the new particle will rise to a height h_1 given by $2mgh_1 = \tfrac{1}{2}(2m)\dfrac{2gl}{4}$ so that

$$h_1 = \tfrac{1}{4}\,l.$$

The particle swings back to its lowest position, acquiring a velocity $\tfrac{1}{2}\sqrt{(2gl)}$ and, immediately after the second collision, its mass becomes $3m$ and its velocity becomes $\tfrac{1}{3}\sqrt{(2gl)}$.

After the rth collision the velocity of the particle becomes $\sqrt{(2gl)}/(r+1)$, and the height to which the particle rises is then given by:

$$(r+1)\,mg\,h_r = \frac{1}{2}(r+1)m\,\frac{2gl}{(r+1)^2}.$$

$$\therefore\ h_r = \frac{l}{(r+1)^2}.$$

Therefore the angle with the vertical made by the string when the particle is at its highest point following the rth collision, Fig. 116, is

$$\theta = \cos^{-1}\left(\frac{ON}{OB}\right) = \cos^{-1}\left(\frac{OA - NA}{OB}\right) = \cos^{-1}\left\{\frac{r(r+2)}{(r+1)^2}\right\}.$$

(ii) Figure 117 shows a smooth wire BAC in a vertical plane. The straight portions BA and AC of the wire are at right angles and AB is horizontal and higher than C. Smooth rings P and Q each

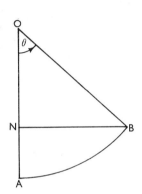

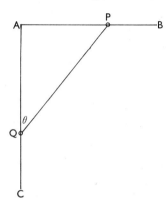

FIG. 116.   FIG. 117.

of mass m are threaded onto BA and AC respectively and connected by a tight inextensible string of length $5l$ ft. The system is released from rest with P at a distance $4l$ ft from A. Calculate the speed of Q when P is $3l$ ft from A.

Notation

Here we introduce the notation $\dot{x}$ and $\ddot{x}$ to mean $\dfrac{dx}{dt}$ and $\dfrac{d^2x}{dt^2}$ respectively. This notation is reserved, in theoretical mechanics, for differentiation with respect to time although, in pure mathematics, it is also used to indicate differentiation with respect to a parameter.

If potential energy is measured from the level of AB as origin, the energy equation is

$$\tfrac{1}{2}mv_P^2 + \tfrac{1}{2}mv_Q^2 - mg \cdot 5l\cos\theta = -mg \cdot 3l, \qquad (1)$$

where v_P and v_Q are the speeds of P and Q respectively.

The equation which expresses the geometrical constraint of the system is:
$$x^2 + y^2 = 5l^2, \quad \text{where} \quad AP = x, \qquad AQ = y.$$

$$\therefore \ 2x\dot{x} + 2y\dot{y} = 0. \tag{2}$$

$$\therefore \ \frac{\dot{x}}{\dot{y}} = -\frac{y}{x} = -\cot\theta \quad \text{where} \quad \angle\, AQP = \theta.$$

$$\therefore \ v_P/v_Q = \cot\theta. \tag{3}$$

(The negative sign for the ratio $\dot{x}/\dot{y}$ interprets the fact that AQ increases as AP decreases.)

Therefore, when $\theta = \sin^{-1}(\tfrac{3}{5})$, substitution from equation (3) in equation (1) gives

$$\tfrac{1}{2}m(\tfrac{4}{3}v_Q)^2 + \tfrac{1}{2}mv_Q^2 - 5mgl\tfrac{4}{5} = -3mgl,$$

i.e.
$$\tfrac{25}{18}mv_Q^2 = mgl.$$

$$\therefore \ v_Q = \sqrt{\left(\frac{18gl}{25}\right)}.$$

(iii) A particle of mass m is released from rest at the top of a fixed rough inclined plane of inclination α. The particle acquires a speed of v ft/sec in sliding a distance s ft down the plane. Find an expression for the coefficient of friction between the particle and the plane.

The work–energy equation for the particle is

$$mgs\sin\alpha - \tfrac{1}{2}mv^2 = \mu\, mgs\cos\alpha,$$

where μ is the coefficient of friction.

$$\therefore \ \mu = \frac{2gs\sin\alpha - v^2}{2gs\cos\alpha}.$$

(iv) A particle of mass m slides down the smooth inclined face of a wedge of mass $4m$, and inclination α, which is itself free to move in a horizontal plane, (Fig. 118). Use equations of momentum and

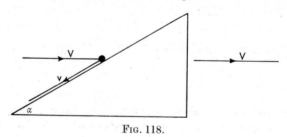

Fig. 118.

energy to obtain an expression for the velocity of the particle *relative to the wedge* when the particle has moved a relative distance l from rest down the inclined face of the wedge.

If, when the particle is in its displaced position, the velocity of the wedge is V and the velocity of the particle relative to the wedge is v, then the magnitude of the resultant velocity of the particle is $\sqrt{(V^2 + v^2 - 2Vv\cos\alpha)}$. The energy equation for the particle and the wedge is:

$$2mV^2 + \tfrac{1}{2}m(V^2 + v^2 - 2Vv\cos\alpha) = mgl\sin\alpha. \qquad (1)$$

By conservation of *horizontal* momentum, since there is no *horizontal* force acting on the system,

$$mv\cos\alpha - mV - 4mV = 0.$$

$$\therefore \ V = \tfrac{1}{5}v\cos\alpha.$$

Then substitution in equation (1) gives

$$2m\frac{v^2\cos^2\alpha}{25} + \frac{1}{2}m\left(\frac{v^2\cos^2\alpha}{25} + v^2 - \frac{2v^2\cos^2\alpha}{5}\right) = mgl\sin\alpha.$$

$$\therefore \ v^2\left(\frac{5 - \cos^2\alpha}{10}\right) = gl\sin\alpha.$$

$$\therefore \ v = \sqrt{\left(\frac{10gl\sin\alpha}{4 + \sin^2\alpha}\right)}.$$

(v) A particle of mass m is attached to one end B of an elastic string AB of natural length l. The end A of the string is fixed and the particle falls vertically from rest at A. In the subsequent motion, the greatest depth of the particle below A is $3l$. Calculate the modulus of elasticity λ of the string.

The velocity of the particle at its lowest point is zero, and the energy equation for the particle in this position is

$$\frac{\lambda(2l)^2}{2l} - mg(3l) = 0.$$

[Elastic P.E. + gravitational P.E. = Energy at A.]

$$\therefore \ \lambda = \frac{3mg}{2}.$$

(vi) A light rod AB of length l connects a smooth ring of mass M, attached at A, to a particle of mass m attached at B. The ring is threaded on to a thin smooth horizontal wire. The rod AB is held in a horizontal position and released from rest. Find the velocity of the particle at B at the instant when the rod AB becomes vertical.

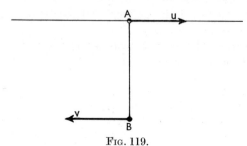

FIG. 119.

Figure 119 shows the position of the rod when it becomes vertical and the velocities of A and B then. *At this instant*, B is moving horizontally. Then,

(a) because no horizontal force acts on AB during the motion, the *horizontal* momentum of the system remains constant,

$$\therefore \ Mu - mv = 0;$$

(b) by the principle of conservation of energy,

$$\tfrac{1}{2}Mu^2 + \tfrac{1}{2}mv^2 = mgl.$$

It follows that

$$M\left(\frac{mv}{M}\right)^2 + mv^2 = 2mgl.$$

i.e.

$$v = \sqrt{\left(\frac{2Mlg}{M+m}\right)}.$$

*10.3. The Relation between the Energy Equation and the Equation of Motion

For a particle of constant mass m moving under the action of a conservative system of forces, the energy equation is

$$\tfrac{1}{2}m\dot{x}^2 + \varphi(x) = \text{constant}, \tag{8.1}$$

where $\dot{x}\,(=v)$ is the velocity of the particle at displacement x from the origin and $\varphi(x)$ is a function of x which represents the potential energy at this displacement.

Differentiation with respect to x gives,

$$m\dot{x}\frac{\mathrm{d}\dot{x}}{\mathrm{d}x} + \varphi'(x) = 0,$$

i.e. $$mf + \varphi'(x) = 0,$$

where f is the acceleration at this displacement. This is an equation of motion for the particle.

Alternatively

Differentiating equation (8.1) with respect to t gives

$$m\dot{x}\ddot{x} + \varphi'(x)\dot{x} = 0,$$

$$\therefore\ m\ddot{x} + \varphi'(x) = 0 \quad \text{as before.}$$

Example. An elastic string AB, of natural length l and modulus mg, is fixed at one end A and to the other end is attached a particle of mass m. The particle hangs in equilibrium vertically below A. The particle is now pulled vertically downwards a distance $\frac{1}{2}l$ and released. Show that, in the subsequent motion, the acceleration is proportional to the displacement of the particle from a point M distant $2l$ vertically below A and find the acceleration of the particle when it is distant $7l/4$ below A.

The energy equation for the particle and the string is,

$$\frac{1}{2}m\dot{x}^2 - mg(2l+x) + \frac{mg(l+x)^2}{2l} = \text{constant},$$

[K.E. + gravitational P.E. + Elastic P.E. = constant]

where $2l + x$ is the length of the string when the velocity of the particle is $\dot{x}$.

Differentiation with respect to t gives:

$$m\dot{x}\ddot{x} - mg\dot{x} + \frac{2mg(l+x)\dot{x}}{2l} = 0.$$

$$\therefore\ \ddot{x} = -\frac{g}{l}x,$$

i.e. the acceleration of the particle is proportional to its displacement from M.

When $x = -\frac{1}{4}l$, $\ddot{x} = \frac{1}{4}g$, i.e. the acceleration of the particle is 8 ft/sec² *downward*, when the particle is $\dfrac{7l}{4}$ below A.

Clearly this example could have been worked by using the equation of motion $P = mf$ directly. The alternative methods are available because of the close relationship between the equation of motion and the equation of energy which we have discussed in this section.

MISCELLANEOUS EXERCISES. X

In exercises 1–10, *use the equation of energy*, combined where necessary with the conservation of momentum equation, to obtain the result asked for.

1. Particles of mass $3m$ and m hang at the ends of a light inextensible string which passes over a smooth pulley. Find an expression for the speed of either particle when the mass $3m$ has moved downwards from rest through a distance x.

2. An inextensible string lies across a smooth table, one end of the string hanging down over each of the opposite edges of the table. The string is in a vertical plane at right angles to these edges. To one end of the string is attached a particle of mass 2 lb, to the other end a particle of mass 1 lb, and to the part of the string on the table a particle of mass 4 lb. Calculate the speed of each of the particles when the particle on the table has moved a distance of 2 ft from rest while remaining on the table.

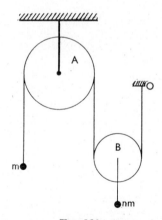

FIG. 120.

3. Figure 120 shows a system of two light smooth pulleys and an inextensible string. Pulley A is fixed, pulley B is movable and carries a mass nm; a mass m is attached to the free end of the string. The other end of the string is attached to a fixed point O. Show that, when the mass m has descended from rest through a distance x, the speed of B is $\sqrt{\left\{ gx\left(\dfrac{2-n}{4+n}\right)\right\}}$ and find the acceleration of B when $n = 3/2$.

4. Figure 121 shows two particles each of mass m connected by a light string which passes over a smooth pulley at the top of a fixed double inclined plane, the highest point of which is at a height h above its horizontal base. Particle A starts from rest close to the pulley and moves down the plane. Find an expression for the speed with which it reaches the foot of the incline.

5. Figure 122 shows a light smooth ring of mass m threaded on to a smooth vertical wire and connected by an inextensible string which passes over a small smooth pulley, which is at a distance a from the wire, to a mass $4m$

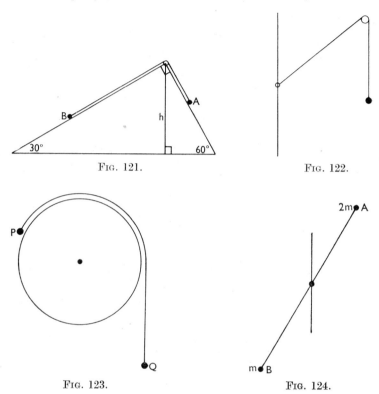

FIG. 121.   FIG. 122.

FIG. 123.   FIG. 124.

hanging freely. The system starts to move from rest when the string attached to the ring is horizontal. Calculate the velocity of the ring when this string makes an angle of $45°$ with the vertical.

6. Figure 123 shows two particles P and Q each of mass m connected by a light inextensible string which hangs in a vertical plane over a fixed smooth cylinder. Initially the system is at rest with the diameter through P horizontal. Prove that, when P reaches the highest point of the cylinder, the velocity of Q is $\sqrt{\{gr(\frac{1}{2}\pi - 1)\}}$. The particle P remains in contact with the cylinder throughout the motion.

7. Figure 124 shows two particles of masses $2m$ and m respectively attached to the ends A and B of a light rod AB of length $2a$ which turns about a horizontal axis through its mid-point. Initially, the rod is vertical with the particle of mass $2m$ at rest above the axis. Find an expression for the speed of the particles when the rod makes an angle of $60°$ with the vertical:

(i) with A above B,

(ii) with B above A.

8. A particle P of mass m is connected by a light *elastic* string of natural length l and modulus $\frac{1}{2}mg$ to a fixed point O on a smooth horizontal table. The particle lies on the table with $OP = l$ and it is given an impulse $m\sqrt{(lg)}$ in the direction OP. Find an expression for the maximum extension of the string.

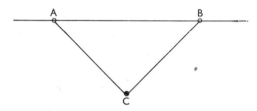

FIG. 125.

9. Figure 125 shows two small smooth rings A and B each of mass m and free to slide on a smooth horizontal wire. The rings are attached by equal inextensible strings to a particle of mass $2m$ at C where $AC = BC = 2$ ft and A, B and C are in a vertical plane. The system starts from rest with $\angle ABC = 30°$. Calculate the velocity of A at the instant that BC becomes vertical.

10. Two masses of $(M + m)$ and $(M - m)$ respectively are connected by a light inextensible string which passes over a small smooth pulley. When the larger mass has moved a distance l from rest, a mass $2m$ is removed from it; immediately afterwards an equal mass $2m$ is added to the smaller mass. Find how much further each of the masses moves before next coming to instantaneous rest.

*11. A light vertical spiral spring is suspended by one end and a particle A of mass 10 lb is attached to the other. Another particle B of mass 20 lb is hung from A by an inextensible string. When B is initially supported, and under the influence of A alone, the spring elongates 0·01 ft. B is then let go and acquires a velocity of 16 ft/sec just before the string becomes taut. Calculate the maximum elongation produced in the spring. (L.)

*12. A uniform heavy chain, of length $3a$, placed over a smooth peg, with lengths $2a$ and a hanging vertically, is released from rest. Prove that if $x(< 3a)$ is the length of the longer section after motion has begun, the velocity v of the chain is given by

$$a v^2 = \tfrac{2}{3}g(x^2 - 3ax + 2a^2).$$ (O.C.)

*13. A mass of 10 lb is attached to one end B of an elastic string AB of natural length 2·25 ft. The modulus of the string is 48 lb wt. If the end A is fixed and the mass falls from rest at A, find the extension of the string when B reaches its lowest point. (N.)

*14. Prove that the potential energy of an elastic string of modulus λ, natural length l and extension x is $\frac{1}{2}\lambda x^2/l$.

A heavy circular elastic ring, of modulus λ and weight w, has a natural length $2\pi a$. It is placed with its plane horizontal over a smooth cone, of semi-vertical angle $45°$, fixed with its axis vertical and vertex upwards. When at rest in contact with the cone at a depth a below the vertex, the ring is allowed to fall. Prove that it descends a vertical distance $wa/\lambda\pi$ before first coming to instantaneous rest. (L.)

*15. A light inelastic string passes round small smooth pulleys A, B in the same horizontal line at a distance $2a$ apart, and carries masses m_1 at each end and a mass m_2 ($< 2m_1$) at its middle point. The system is released from rest with m_2 at the middle point of AB. By applying the principle of the conservation of energy, show that the system comes to instantaneous rest when m_2 has fallen a distance $4am_1m_2/(4m_1^2 - m_2^2)$. (O.C.)

*16. A mass of 4 oz is suspended vertically from a fixed point O by an elastic cord of modulus 2 lb wt. and natural length 2 ft, the mass being in equilibrium. A ring of mass $\frac{1}{2}$ oz, initially at rest at O, is allowed to fall freely until it strikes the suspended mass, with which it then remains in contact during the subsequent motion. Use the principles of momentum and energy to find (i) the speed with which the combined masses begin to move, and (ii) the greatest length and the least length of the string in the subsequent motion. (Give your answers to (ii) to the nearest 0·01 in.) (N.)

*17. A particle of mass m is attached by a light inextensible string, of length l, to a small ring of mass $2m$ which can slide along a smooth horizontal rod. The system is released from rest with the string taut and the particle touching the rod. Find the speed of the particle and of the ring when the string passes through the vertical position.

If at this instant the particle collides with and sticks to another particle of mass m which was at rest, show that the whole system comes to instantaneous rest when the string is next inclined to the vertical at an angle $\cos^{-1}(2/3)$. (L.)

*18. A light inextensible string ABC, having the end A fixed, passes over a smooth peg P in the same horizontal line as A, where $AP = 2a$, and carries a particle of mass m at C. Another particle of mass $2m$ is attached to the string at B, where $AB = a$. If initially the portion of the string from A to P is horizontal and the system is then released, show that it comes to rest instantaneously when AB has turned through an angle θ given by

$$\sin\theta + \cos\theta = \cos^2\theta.$$

Show also that the speed of B when ABP is a right angle is $\sqrt{(\frac{2}{3}ga)}$. (N.)

19. A smooth circular wire of radius a is fixed with its plane vertical. A small bead of mass m can slide on the wire and it is attached to the highest point A of the wire by a light elastic string of natural length a. The bead is held at the point A with the string slack and then displaced slightly. If the modulus of the string is $4mg$, show that the bead will come to rest at the lowest point of the wire. Find the velocity of the bead (i) when the string is inclined at $60°$ to the vertical, (ii) when the string is inclined at $30°$ to the vertical. (N.)

CHAPTER XI

THE IMPACT OF ELASTIC BODIES

11.1. Direct Collision of Elastic Spheres

When two spheres moving along the line joining their centres collide, the collision is described as a *direct collision*. As discussed in Chapter X, § 10.2, the effect of the collision is a temporary distortion of shape of the spheres and a resulting loss of kinetic energy. The magnitude of the loss of energy is related to the velocities of the particles by the *Law of Restitution*, an experimental law discovered by Newton, and stated here in the form:

The relative velocity after impact has a magnitude which is a fixed ratio for the spheres concerned of the relative velocity before impact and it is in the opposite direction to the relative velocity before impact.

This fixed ratio, which is less than or equal to 1, is called *the coefficient of restitution for the two bodies concerned*, and is denoted by e.

In the ideal case, unattainable in practice, in which $e = 1$, the two bodies are said to be *perfectly elastic*. In the case in which $e = 0$, when the bodies do not separate after collision, the collision is said to be an *inelastic* one.

The motion of the spheres is subject also to the principle of conservation of momentum. In algebraic terms, if the masses of the spheres are m_1 and m_2, their velocities before impact u_1 and u_2 along the positive direction of the line of centres, and their velocities after impact v_1 and v_2 each in this direction, then

$$m_1 u_1 + m_2 u_2 = m_1 v_1 + m_2 v_2, \quad \text{(Momentum equation)},$$
$$-e(u_1 - u_2) = v_1 - v_2, \quad \text{(Restitution equation)}. \tag{11.1}$$

Examples. (i) Two spheres of masses 5 lb and 2 lb move towards one another in opposite directions along their line of centres with speeds 2 ft/sec and 5 ft/sec respectively. Given that the coefficient of restitution between the spheres is $\frac{1}{2}$, calculate their velocities after collision.

Figure 126 shows the velocities of the spheres before and after the collision.

In such an exercise as this it is of advantage always to mark the velocities in the chosen positive direction of motion and to attach to those velocities the appropriate sign.

For this collision,

the momentum equation is $0 = 5U + 2V$

and the restitution equation is $-\frac{1}{2}(2 + 5) = U - V.$

$$\therefore \ U = -1, \quad V = 2\frac{1}{2}.$$

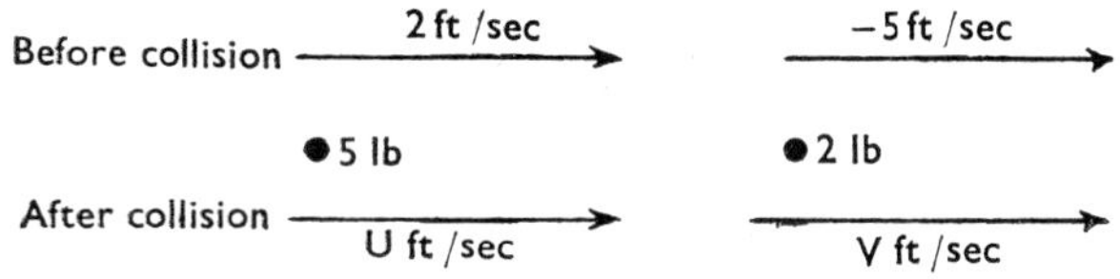

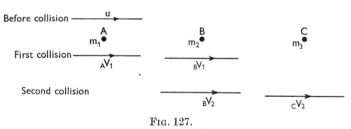

Fig. 126.

After the collision each sphere is moving in a direction opposite to its original direction of motion, the 5 lb sphere with a speed of 1 ft/sec and the 2 lb sphere with a speed of $2\frac{1}{2}$ ft/sec.

(ii) Three particles A, B, C of masses m_1, m_2, m_3 respectively lie at rest in a straight line on a smooth horizontal table. The particle A is projected towards B so that A collides with B and subsequently B collides with C, the coefficient of restitution at each impact being equal to m_2/m_3. Prove that after the second collision B will be at rest and that, if $m_2^2 > m_1 m_3$, A and C will be moving away from B.   (N.)

Before collision ────── u

  $\quad$ A $\quad\quad\quad\quad\quad\quad$ B $\quad\quad\quad\quad\quad\quad$ C

  $\quad$ m_1 ● $\quad\quad\quad\quad\quad$ m_2 ● $\quad\quad\quad\quad\quad$ m_3 ●

First collision ────── $\rightarrow$

  $\quad\quad$ ${}_A V_1$ $\quad\quad\quad\quad\quad\quad$ ${}_B V_1$

Second collision $\quad\quad\quad\quad\quad$ $\rightarrow$

  $\quad\quad\quad\quad\quad\quad$ ${}_B V_2$ $\quad\quad\quad\quad\quad$ ${}_C V_2$

Fig. 127.

Figure 127 shows the velocities of the particles initially and after collision. Here, and subsequently when we are concerned with problems involving more than one collision we use the notation ${}_A V_r$ to indicate *the velocity of A after the rth collision of the series.*

19*

For the first collision,

(1) the momentum equation is $m_1 u = m_1 {}_A V_1 + m_2 {}_B V_1$,

(2) the restitution equation is $\dfrac{-m_2 u}{m_3} = {}_A V_1 - {}_B V_1$.

$$\therefore {}_A V_1 = \frac{\left(m_1 - \dfrac{m_2^2}{m_3}\right) u}{m_1 + m_2} = \frac{(m_1 m_3 - m_2^2) u}{m_3 (m_1 + m_2)},$$

$$_B V_1 = \frac{\left(m_1 + \dfrac{m_1 m_2}{m_3}\right) u}{m_1 + m_2} = \frac{m_1 (m_3 + m_2) u}{m_3 (m_1 + m_2)}.$$

For the second collision,

(1) the momentum equation is $m_2 {}_B V_1 = m_2 {}_B V_2 + m_3 {}_C V_2$,

(2) the restitution equation is $-\dfrac{m_2}{m_3} {}_B V_1 = {}_B V_2 - {}_C V_2$.

$$\therefore {}_B V_2 = \frac{m_2 - \dfrac{m_2}{m_3} m_3}{m_2 + m_3} {}_B V_1 = 0.$$

Therefore, after the second collision the particle B is at rest. Also

$$_C V_2 = \frac{m_2}{m_3} {}_B V_1.$$

But $_B V_1$ is positive and therefore $_C V_2$ is positive. It follows that after the second collision C is moving in the original direction of motion of A.

But $_A V_1$ is negative if $m_2^2 > m_1 m_3$, Therefore, if $m_2^2 > m_1 m_3$, A and C move away from B after the second collision.

(iii) Three exactly equal smooth spheres stand at rest on a smooth horizontal table, their centres A, B and C being collinear and the distances AB, BC being equal to one another and greater than the diameter of a sphere. The first sphere is projected with velocity u directly towards the second. If e (< 1) is the coefficient of restitution between any two spheres, show that the first sphere is involved in two collisions. Show also that the third is involved in only one collision if e is greater than $3 - 2\sqrt{2}$. (L.)

With the notation used in example (ii) and if the mass of each sphere is m, we have:

First Collision

Momentum $\qquad m u = m_A V_1 + m_B V_1,$

Restitution $\qquad - e u = {}_A V_1 - {}_B V_1.$

$$\therefore \; {}_A V_1 = \frac{(1 - e) u}{2}, \quad {}_B V_1 = \frac{(1 + e) u}{2}.$$

Second Collision

The mechanical conditions are unchanged from the first collision so that we use the results of that collision again and obtain

$$ {}_B V_2 = \frac{(1 + e) u}{2} \times \frac{1 - e}{2} = \frac{(1 - e^2) u}{4}, $$

$$ {}_C V_2 = \frac{(1 + e) u}{2} \times \frac{1 + e}{2} = \frac{(1 + e)^2 u}{4}. $$

Each of ${}_A V_1$, ${}_B V_2$ and ${}_C V_2$ is positive and therefore the particles are moving, after two collisions, in the same direction.

Because $\qquad \dfrac{1 + e}{2} < 1,$

$$ \therefore \; \frac{(1 - e) u}{2} > \frac{(1 - e^2) u}{4}. $$

Also $\qquad \dfrac{(1 - e^2) u}{4} < \dfrac{(1 + e)^2 u}{4}.$

It follows that, after two collisions, A is overtaking B but B is not overtaking C, i.e. there is a third collision which is a collision between A and B.

Third Collision

Momentum $\qquad \dfrac{m u (1 - e)}{2} + \dfrac{m u (1 - e^2)}{4} = m_A V_3 + m_B V_3,$

Restitution $\qquad - e \left\{ \dfrac{u (1 - e)}{2} - \dfrac{u (1 - e^2)}{4} \right\} = {}_A V_3 - {}_B V_3.$

$$ \therefore \; {}_A V_3 = \tfrac{1}{8} u (3 + e^2)(1 - e) > 0, \quad {}_B V_3 = \tfrac{1}{8} u (1 - e^2)(3 - e) > 0. $$

Also $\qquad {}_B V_3 - {}_A V_3 = \tfrac{1}{4} u e (1 - e)^2 > 0.$

Therefore, after the third collision, all three spheres are moving in the same direction (that of the original motion of A). There are no more collisions, i.e. C is involved in one collision only, if

$$_CV_2 > {}_BV_3,$$

i.e. if $\qquad \frac{1}{4}u(1+e)^2 > \frac{1}{8}u(1-e^2)(3-e),$

i.e. if $\qquad (e+1)(e^2-6e+1) < 0,$

i.e. if $\qquad e^2-6e+1 < 0.$

Therefore, if the value of e lies between the roots of $e^2-6e+1=0$, C is involved in only one collision. Therefore, since e is positive and e is less than 1, C is involved in only one collision if $e > 3 - 2\sqrt{2}$.

EXERCISES 11.1.

1. A sphere of mass 4 lb moving at 6 ft/sec overtakes a sphere of mass 2 lb moving in the same line and in the same direction at 4 ft/sec. Calculate the velocities of the spheres after impact, given that $e = \frac{1}{3}$.

2. A sphere of mass 4 lb moving at 4 ft/sec impinges on a sphere of mass 2 lb moving in the same line and in the opposite direction at 6 ft/sec. Given that $e = \frac{1}{2}$, calculate the velocities of the spheres after impact.

3. A sphere of mass 2 lb collides directly with a sphere of mass 5 lb. The coefficient of restitution between the spheres is $\frac{1}{2}$. If the ratio of the velocities of the spheres before impact was $-\frac{1}{2}$, calculate the ratio of their velocities after impact.

4. A sphere of mass 6 lb moving with velocity 4 ft/sec collides directly with a sphere of mass 4 lb moving in the same line in the same direction at 2 ft/sec. After the impact the velocity of the second sphere is $3\frac{1}{2}$ ft/sec. Calculate e for the two spheres.

5. A sphere of mass m moving at speed kv overtakes a sphere of mass km moving at speed v. After the collision, the overtaking sphere is at rest. Show that $k \geq 3$ and state the velocity of the second sphere after the collision in terms of v only.

6. A smooth sphere of mass 25 gm is projected on a smooth horizontal table so as to impinge directly on a sphere, of the same radius and of mass 50 gm, at rest on the table. Show that, if the coefficient of restitution e is greater than $\frac{1}{2}$, the projected sphere will have its direction of motion reversed by the impact.

If $e = \frac{1}{5}$, find what fraction of the kinetic energy is lost by the collision. (N.)

7. A smooth sphere of mass 4 gm moving with speed 5 cm/sec, collides directly with another smooth sphere of mass 6 gm moving in the same direction with speed 3 cm/sec. The coefficient of restitution is $\frac{3}{4}$. Prove that the momentum of each sphere is changed by an amount equal to 42/5 absolute units.

Calculate the loss of kinetic energy due to the collision. (N.)

8. Two spheres of mass 3 lb and 2 lb moving in opposite directions with velocities of 4 ft/sec and 1 ft/sec respectively impinge directly. If the coefficient of restitution is 1/3, find their velocities immediately after impact. Calculate in ft lb wt. the loss of kinetic energy due to the impact.   (L.)

9. Three small smooth spheres A, B, C of masses 1 oz, 2 oz, 4 oz respectively rest on a smooth table with their centres collinear so that B lies between A and C. The sphere A is projected directly towards B with velocity 8 ft/sec, and C moves with velocity 2 ft/sec after it has been struck by B. If the coefficient of restitution between A and B is equal to that between B and C, show that its value is $\frac{1}{2}$, and prove that A and B are brought to rest.   (N.)

10. A particle A of mass $2m$ is at rest on a smooth horizontal table. A second particle B of mass m moving along the table with velocity u collides directly with A. If the direction of motion of B is reversed by the impact, show that the coefficient of restitution must exceed $\frac{1}{2}$.

If the coefficient of restitution is e, find the loss of kinetic energy due to the impact and show that if the direction of motion of B is reversed, this loss cannot exceed $\frac{1}{4}mu^2$.   (N.)

11. A particle A, of mass 5 lb, moving with velocity u, impinges directly on a particle B, of mass 3 lb, moving in the same direction as A with velocity v. After the impact the velocity of A is in the same direction as before impact, but its magnitude is reduced by one-half. If e is the coefficient of restitution between the particles, prove that $3v(1 + e) = u(3e - 1)$.

Taking $u = 18$ ft/sec and $v = 2$ ft/sec, calculate the ratio of the kinetic energy of the particles after impact to that before impact.   (O.C.)

12. Two spheres of masses m, $2m$, moving in the same straight line with velocities $2u$, u in opposite directions, impinge. Prove that their velocities are reversed in direction by the impact and become $2eu$, eu respectively, where e is the coefficient of restitution between the spheres.

Find the velocities after collision if the sphere of mass m, moving with velocity $2u$, overtakes the sphere of mass $2m$, moving with velocity u in the same direction and along the same straight line.

Compare the losses of kinetic energy in the two collisions.   (O.C.)

13. A particle A of mass m moving with velocity u collides with a particle B of mass M moving with velocity U in the *same* direction as A ($u > U$). If A is brought to rest as the result of the impact, prove that the coefficient of restitution between the particles is

$$\frac{mu + MU}{M(u - U)}.$$

If the particles had been moving in *opposite* directions with the same speeds, u and U, as before, the velocity of A would have been reversed in direction by the impact, with its magnitude unchanged. Prove that $u = 3U$ and that $M \geqq 3m$.   (O.C.)

14. Three spheres A, B, C, of equal radii but of masses m, $2m$, m respectively, lie in that order in a straight horizontal groove. Sphere A is projected towards sphere B with speed u. After the impact of A and B the sphere A is at rest. Calculate the coefficient of restitution and, assuming this to be the same at each impact, express the sum of the final kinetic energies of B and C as a fraction of the original kinetic energy of A. (L.)

15. Three smooth spheres A, B, C, of equal size and of masses $2m$, $7m$, $14m$ respectively, are at rest on a smooth horizontal table with their centres in that order on a straight line. The coefficient of restitution between each pair of spheres is $\frac{1}{2}$. The sphere A is now projected so that it impinges directly on B. Prove that, after two impacts have taken place, B is at rest and A and C are moving with equal speeds in opposite directions. Find what fraction of the original kinetic energy remains after both impacts have taken place. (N.)

16. Two equal spheres B and C, each of mass $4m$, lie at rest on a smooth horizontal table. A third sphere A, of the same radius as B and C but of mass m, moves with velocity V along the line of centres of B and C. The sphere A collides with B, which then collides with C. If A is brought to rest by the first collision, show that the coefficient of restitution between A and B is $\frac{1}{4}$.

If the coefficient of restitution between B and C is $\frac{1}{2}$, find the velocities of B and C after the second collision. Show that the total loss of kinetic energy due to the two collisions is $27mV^2/64$. (N.)

17. Two small balls of masses m and m' are hung from a fixed point by two light inextensible strings each of length l. The ball of mass m is raised so that its string is fully extended horizontally, and then released from rest. If e is the coefficient of restitution, find the velocities of the balls immediately after impact. (L.)

18. OA and OB are two light inextensible strings, each of length l, with their ends attached to a fixed point O; small spheres, of equal radii and of masses M and $\frac{3}{2}M$ are attached to the ends A and B respectively. With the strings taut, the spheres are released from rest when OA and OB are horizontal, and in the same vertical plane, with O between A and B. If the coefficient of restitution between the spheres is $\frac{1}{2}$, find the height above its lowest position to which A rises after impact has occurred. (O.C.)

19. Two equal spheres, A and B, each of mass $5m$, lie nearly touching on a smooth horizontal plane. A third sphere C, of the same radius as A and B, but of mass $3m$, approaching with velocity V along the line of centres strikes A. If the coefficient of restitution between A and each of the other spheres is e find the velocity of B immediately after the second collision. Show that if $e > \frac{1}{3}$ there are no further collisions between the spheres. (L.)

20. Two simple pendulums A and B, each of length 2 ft, are suspended from the same point and their bobs are small smooth spheres of masses 4 oz and 2 oz respectively. The pendulum A hangs freely at rest and the pendulum B is released from rest in the position in which its string is taut and inclined at $60°$ to the downward vertical. If the coefficient of restitution between the bobs is $\frac{1}{2}$, prove that, after impact, the pendulum B will remain at rest, and find the cosine of the angle through which the pendulum A swings. (L.)

21. A smooth wire in the form of a circle of radius a is fixed with its plane horizontal and two small beads of equal masses are threaded on the wire. One bead is initially at rest and the other is projected along the wire with speed u. If e is the coefficient of restitution between the beads, find the speed of each bead after the second collision and also the time which elapses between the first and second collisions. (L.)

22. A and B are points in a vertical line, B being at a height h above A. A particle is projected vertically upwards from A with velocity $2\sqrt{(gh)}$ and at the same instant a second particle is projected vertically upwards from B with velocity $\sqrt{(gh)}$. Show that the particles collide at a height $3h/2$ above A.

If the particles are of equal mass and the coefficient of restitution between them is $\frac{1}{2}$, find the speed of the first particle when it returns to A. (L.)

*11.2. Impulsive Reaction and Loss of Kinetic Energy

When two particles of masses m_1 and m_2 and velocities u_1 and u_2 collide directly,

$$m_1 u_1 + m_2 u_2 = m_1 v_1 + m_2 v_2,$$
$$-e(u_1 - u_2) = v_1 - v_2,$$

(11.1)

where v_1 and v_2 are the respective velocities of the particles after collision and e is the coefficient of restitution between them. From these fundamental equations,

$$v_1 = \frac{u_1(m_1 - em_2) + m_2 u_2(1 + e)}{m_1 + m_2},$$
$$v_2 = \frac{m_1 u_1(1 + e) + u_2(m_2 - em_1)}{m_1 + m_2}.$$

The impulse I_{12} of the second particle on the first is equal to the change in momentum of the first particle.

$$\therefore I_{12} = m_1 u_1 - m_1 v_1$$
$$= m_1 \left\{ \frac{m_1 u_1 + m_2 u_1 - u_1(m_1 - em_2) - m_2 u_2(1 + e)}{m_1 + m_2} \right\}$$
$$= \frac{m_1 m_2 (1 + e)(u_1 - u_2)}{m_1 + m_2}.$$

The impulse I_{21} of the first particle on the second is therefore given by

$$I_{21} = \frac{m_1 m_2}{m_1 + m_2} (1 + e)(u_2 - u_1).$$

The loss of kinetic energy in this impact is

$$\tfrac{1}{2} m_1 u_1^2 + \tfrac{1}{2} m_2 u_2^2 - \tfrac{1}{2} m_1 v_1^2 - \tfrac{1}{2} m_2 v_2^2.$$

This quantity is evaluated algebraically in terms of m_1, m_2, u_1, u_2 e from equations (11.1). Squaring each equation gives,

$$m_1^2 v_1^2 + m_2^2 v_2^2 + 2 m_1 m_2 v_1 v_2 = m_1^2 u_1^2 + m_2^2 u_2^2 + 2 m_1 m_2 u_1 u_2,$$
$$v_1^2 + v_2^2 - 2 v_1 v_2 = e^2 u_1^2 + e^2 u_2^2 - 2 e^2 u_1 u_2.$$

Multiplying the second of these equations by $m_1 m_2$ and adding gives,

$$v_1^2 m_1(m_1 + m_2) + v_2^2 m_2(m_1 + m_2) = u_1^2 m_1(m_1 + e^2 m_2) +$$
$$+ u_2^2 m_2(m_2 + e^2 m_1) + 2m_1 m_2 u_1 u_2(1 - e^2).$$

$$\therefore\ (m_1 + m_2)(m_1 v_1^2 + m_2 v_2^2) = (m_1 + m_2)(m_1 u_1^2 + m_2 u_2^2)$$
$$- m_1 m_2 u_1^2(1 - e^2) - m_1 m_2 u_2^2(1 - e^2) + 2m_1 m_2 u_1 u_2(1 - e^2).$$

$$\therefore\ \frac{1}{2}(m_1 u_1^2 + m_2 u_2^2) - \frac{1}{2}(m_1 v_1^2 + m_2 v_2^2) = \frac{m_1 m_2(1 - e^2)(u_1 - u_2)^2}{2(m_1 + m_2)}$$

and this is the loss of kinetic energy in the impact.

*11.3. The Collision between a Smooth Sphere and a Fixed Smooth Plane

For impacts of *smooth* bodies other than spheres, the impulsive action and reaction between the bodies are each *along the common normal* at the point of contact. In this case we generalize Newton's rule and state that:

"When two smooth bodies collide the component relative velocity along the common normal at the point of contact is changed in the ratio $1 : -e$ and the component velocities of the bodies at right angles to the common normal are unchanged by the impact."

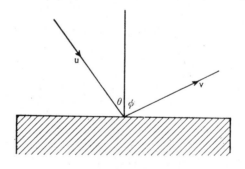

FIG. 128.

When a smooth sphere strikes a smooth plane, the algebraic interpretation of this law is

$$eu \cos\theta = v \cos\varphi,$$
$$u \sin\theta = v \sin\varphi,$$

$$(11.2)$$

where u at an angle θ to the normal is the striking velocity of the sphere and v at an angle φ with the normal is the rebounding velocity (Fig. 128).

(Note that it is convenient here to choose θ and φ so that the normal components of velocity of the striking and rebounding sphere are each defined as positive but are in opposite directions.)

The equations (11.2) determine any two of the quantities e, v, θ, φ if u and the other two are known.

Examples. (i) A smooth sphere falls freely from a height of 8 ft to strike a smooth horizontal plane. The coefficient of restitution between the sphere and the plane is $\frac{1}{2}$. Calculate the time which elapses before the sphere comes finally to rest.

The velocity acquired by the sphere in falling 8 ft is

$$\sqrt{(16g)} \text{ ft/sec} = 16\sqrt{2} \text{ ft/sec}.$$

The time taken by the sphere to fall 8 ft is $\frac{1}{2}\sqrt{2}$ sec.

The sphere rebounds vertically from the plane with speed $8\sqrt{2}$ ft/sec and returns to collide with the plane again in time $\frac{1}{2}\sqrt{2}$ sec with a speed of $8\sqrt{2}$ ft/sec. When the rebounding velocity is V the time for the next complete bounce is $2V/g$; when the striking velocity is V the rebounding speed is $\frac{1}{2}V$ and the time for the next complete bounce is V/g. The time taken for each bounce is therefore half the time taken for the preceding bounce.

Therefore, the total time during which the sphere is in motion is

$$\left\{ \frac{\sqrt{2}}{2} + \left(\frac{\sqrt{2}}{2} + \frac{\sqrt{2}}{4} + \frac{\sqrt{2}}{8} + \cdots \right) \right\} \text{ sec}$$

$$= \left\{ \frac{\sqrt{2}}{2} + \frac{\sqrt{2}}{2} \middle/ \left(1 - \frac{1}{2} \right) \right\} \text{ sec} = \frac{3\sqrt{2}}{2} \text{ sec}.$$

(ii) A smooth billiard ball is projected from the corner A of a rectangular table $ABCD$ so as to strike first the side BC, then the side CD, and then return to the point A. Show that this is impossible unless $e_1 < e_2$, where e_1 and e_2 are the coefficients of restitution of the ball with BC and CD respectively.

Prove also that the final velocity of the ball is

$$\sqrt{(e_1^2 \cos^2\alpha + e_2^2 \sin^2\alpha)}$$

times its initial velocity, where α is the angle which its initial direction of motion makes with AB.   (L.)

Suppose the ball strikes BC with velocity u, rebounds from BC with velocity V at an angle β to the normal, and rebounds from CD with velocity V' at an angle γ with the normal, Fig. 129. Then

$$u \sin\alpha = V \sin\beta,$$

$$e_1 u \cos\alpha = V \cos\beta,$$

$$V \cos\beta = V' \sin\gamma,$$

$$e_2 V \sin\beta = V' \cos\gamma.$$

$$\therefore e_1 \cot\alpha = \cot\beta,$$

$$e_2 \tan\beta = \cot\gamma.$$

$$\therefore e_1 \cot\alpha \cot\gamma = e_2,$$

i.e.
$$e_2 \tan\alpha = e_1 \cot\gamma.$$

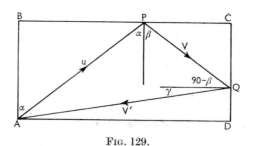

FIG. 129.

From Fig. 129 it is clear that the particle cannot return to A unless $\angle APQ + \angle AQP < 180°$, i.e. unless $\alpha + \gamma < 90°$,

i.e. unless
$$\tan\alpha < \tan(90 - \gamma),$$

i.e.
$$\tan\alpha < \cot\gamma.$$

But
$$e_2 \tan\alpha = e_1 \cot\gamma.$$

Therefore, for the particle to return to A,

$$e_2 > e_1.$$

The momentum parallel to CD is reduced by the impact at P in the ratio $e_1 : 1$ and it is unaltered by the impact at Q. Therefore the component of velocity parallel to CD on return to A is $e_1 u \cos\alpha$. Similarly the component of velocity parallel to BC is unaltered by the impact at P but is reduced in the ratio $e_2 : 1$ at Q. Therefore on return to A

the velocity component parallel to CB is $e_2 u \sin \alpha$. The resultant velocity on return to A is therefore

$$u \sqrt{(e_1^2 \cos^2 \alpha + e_2^2 \sin^2 \alpha)}.$$

(iii) A ball is projected with speed V at an inclination β to the horizontal from a point K distant a from a smooth vertical wall. After striking the wall the ball returns to K. If e is the coefficient of restitution between the ball and the wall, show that

$$e V^2 \sin 2\beta = ga(1 + e).$$

Show also that the height above K of the point of impact with the wall is $(a \tan \beta)/(1 + e)$. (N.)

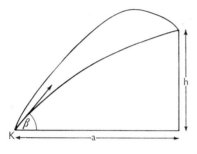

Fig. 130.

When the ball strikes the wall, the horizontal component of its velocity becomes $eV \cos \beta$ in magnitude and the vertical component of its velocity is unchanged (Fig. 130). Therefore the time of flight from K to the wall and back, deduced from the horizontal component of the motion, is $\dfrac{a}{V \cos \beta} \left(1 + \dfrac{1}{e} \right)$, and this time deduced from the vertical component of the motion is $\dfrac{2V \sin \beta}{g}$.

$$\therefore \frac{2V \sin \beta}{g} = \frac{a(1 + e)}{eV \cos \beta}.$$

$$\therefore e V^2 \sin 2\beta = ga(1 + e).$$

If h is the height above K of the point of impact with the wall,

$$h = Vt \sin \beta - \tfrac{1}{2}gt^2,$$

where t is the time of flight from K to the wall.

$$\therefore \ h = \frac{V a \sin \beta}{V \cos \beta} - \frac{g a^2}{2 V^2 \cos^2 \beta}$$

$$= a \tan \beta \left(1 - \frac{g a}{V^2 \sin 2 \beta} \right)$$

$$= a \tan \beta \left(1 - \frac{e}{1 + e} \right) = \frac{a \tan \beta}{1 + e}.$$

(iv) A small smooth sphere falls freely from rest through a distance h and then strikes a fixed smooth plane which is inclined at an angle α to the horizontal. If the coefficient of restitution between the sphere and the plane is $\frac{1}{2}$, prove that the distance between the first and fourth points of impact is $\frac{105}{16} h \sin \alpha$.   (L.)

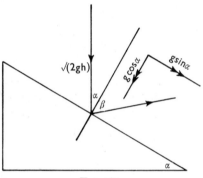

Fig. 131.

The sphere strikes the plane with a velocity $\sqrt{(2gh)}$ vertically (Fig. 131), i.e. at an angle α with the normal to the plane. The sphere rebounds with a component of velocity parallel to the plane unchanged at $\sqrt{(2gh)} \sin \alpha$ and a component of velocity perpendicular to the plane of $\frac{1}{2}\sqrt{(2gh)} \cos \alpha$.

Then, *for the first bounce*, the time of flight t_1 is given by

$$0 = \frac{1}{2}\sqrt{(2gh)} t_1 \cos \alpha - \frac{1}{2} g t_1^2 \cos \alpha,$$

$$\therefore \ t_1 = \sqrt{\left(\frac{2h}{g} \right)}.$$

For the second bounce, the initial component of velocity perpendicular to the plane is $\frac{1}{4}\sqrt{(2gh)} \cos \alpha$ and the time of flight is $t_2 = \frac{1}{2}\sqrt{\left(\frac{2h}{g} \right)}$.

For the third bounce, the initial component of velocity perpendicular to the plane is $\dfrac{1}{8}\sqrt{(2gh)}\cos\alpha$ and the time of flight is $t_3 = \dfrac{1}{4}\sqrt{\left(\dfrac{2h}{g}\right)}$.

Therefore the total time for three bounces is $\dfrac{7}{4}\sqrt{\left(\dfrac{2h}{g}\right)}$.

The equation of motion in the direction parallel to the plane, which gives the total distance R between the first and fourth points of impact is

$$R = \sqrt{(2gh)}\sin\alpha \cdot \frac{7}{4}\sqrt{\left(\frac{2h}{g}\right)} + \frac{1}{2}g\sin\alpha \cdot \frac{49}{16}\frac{2h}{g}.$$

$$\therefore\ R = \frac{105}{16}h\sin\alpha.$$

*EXERCISES 11.3.

*1. A smooth sphere falls freely from a height h above a smooth horizontal plane. The coefficient of restitution between the sphere and the plane is e. Find an expression for the total time during which the sphere is in motion.

In questions 2–6 a smooth sphere strikes a smooth plane with velocity u at an angle α with the normal to the plane and rebounds with velocity v at an angle β with the normal. The coefficient of restitution between the sphere and the plane is e.

*2. $u = 10$ ft/sec, $\alpha = 30°$, $e = \frac{1}{3}$; calculate v, β.

*3. $v = 20$ ft/sec, $\alpha = 60°$, $e = \frac{1}{2}$; calculate u, β.

*4. $\alpha = 45°$, $\beta = 60°$; calculate e.

*5. $\tan\alpha - k\tan\beta = 0$; calculate e.

*6. $u : v = \sqrt{3} : 1$, $\alpha = 30°$; calculate e.

*7. An elastic particle falls from rest through a height of 25 ft onto a smooth plane making an angle $30°$ with the horizontal. If the coefficient of restitution is e, show that the range of its first bounce is $50e(1 + e)$ ft.   (N.)

*8. Two spheres A and B, of equal radii but of mass 4 lb and 5 lb respectively, lie on a smooth horizontal table. A is given a horizontal velocity u and impinges directly on B, which in turn hits a smooth vertical wall normally. After rebounding from the wall, B hits A a second time. If the coefficient of restitution between A and B, and also that between B and the wall, is $\frac{1}{2}$, show that B will be reduced to rest after its second impact with A.   (L.)

*9. A small smooth sphere is moving with speed V on a fixed horizontal plane directly towards a fixed vertical wall. Before the sphere reaches the wall it impinges directly on an equal sphere at rest. If the coefficient of restitution is 0·5 at *all* impacts, show that the spheres will collide twice only. If the first collision is distant a from the wall, find the time that elapses between these two collisions.   (L.)

*10. A small smooth elastic sphere A of mass m, moving with velocity V on a smooth horizontal table, impinges directly upon an equal sphere B at rest on the table. If the coefficient of restitution between the spheres is $\frac{1}{2}$, find the velocities of A and B immediately after the collision. Find also the loss in kinetic energy due to the collision.

The spheres are so small that at the instant of impact they can both be assumed to be at the same distance $3a$ from a smooth vertical wall which is perpendicular to the direction of motion. The sphere B subsequently rebounds from this wall and meets the sphere A at a point distant a from the wall. Find the coefficient of restitution between B and the wall.   (N.)

11. A sphere A of mass $2M$ moving on a smooth floor and at right angles to a vertical wall, impinges directly on a stationary sphere B of mass $3M$. After B rebounds from the wall the spheres again collide directly. If the coefficient of restitution between the spheres is $\frac{1}{2}$ and between B and the wall is $\frac{1}{4}$, prove that B is brought to rest by the second impact of the spheres.   (O.C.)

12. A bucket of mass M is supported by a light string which passes over a smooth fixed pulley and carries at its other end a counterpoise of equal mass. A ball of mass m is dropped vertically so as to strike the bucket with velocity v. Prove that the bucket begins to move with velocity $m(1 + e)\, v/(m + 2M)$, where e is the coefficient of restitution.

Find also the time which elapses between the first and second impacts of the ball and bucket.   (O.C.)

13. A small metal ball falls vertically and strikes a fixed smooth inclined plane. Explain why the component of the velocity of the ball parallel to the plane is not affected by the impact.

If the inclination of the plane to the horizontal is θ (less than $45°$) and the ball rebounds horizontally, find the coefficient of restitution e in terms of θ, and show that a fraction $(1 - e)$ of the kinetic energy is lost during the impact. Also show that the impulse on the plane is

$$mu \sec\theta,$$

where m is the mass of the ball and u its speed just before impact.   (N.)

14. A small sphere falls from rest through a distance h on to a smooth fixed plane inclined at an angle α to the horizontal and then rebounds. The sphere and the plane are perfectly elastic. Prove that the greatest distance from the plane reached by the sphere during the rebound is $h \cos\alpha$, and that the next point of impact is at a distance $8h \sin\alpha$ further down the plane.   (N.)

15. A fixed smooth plane is inclined at $45°$ to the horizontal. From a point O on the plane a particle is projected so that it moves under gravity, the components of its velocity of projection being U perpendicular to the plane and $2U$ up the line of greatest slope through O. Show that the particle strikes the plane at right angles.

If the coefficient of restitution at impact is e, find the distance from O of the point at which the particle next strikes the plane.   (N.)

16. A particle, of mass m, moving with velocity V on a smooth horizontal table, impinges on a smooth plane inclined at an angle α to the horizontal, the line of intersection of the plane with the table being perpendicular to the direction of motion of the particle. The coefficient of restitution between the plane and the particle is e. Prove that after the impact the particle travels freely in space for a time, and that it lands on the table or the plane according as $e >$ or $< \cot^2\alpha$.

Prove also that the impulse at the impact is

$$mV(1 + e)\sin\alpha. \qquad \text{(O.C.)}$$

*17. A particle can move freely in a smooth straight tube, of length l, whose ends are closed. The tube is placed on a smooth horizontal table and the particle, whose mass is equal to that of the tube, is projected along it. If the coefficient of restitution between the ends of the tube and the particle is 1/2, prove that just before the third impact, the tube has travelled a distance $3l$. (L.)

*18. An elastic ball strikes a fixed smooth plane obliquely. Show that if α, β are the inclinations to the plane of the directions of motion just before and just after impact, then $\tan\beta = e\tan\alpha$ where e is the coefficient of restitution.

A horizontal circular tray has a vertical rim round its edge. Show that, if a small smooth sphere is projected along the tray from a point in the edge in a direction making an angle α with the radius to the point and after two impacts on the rim, returns to its starting point, then $\tan^2\alpha = e^3/(1 + e + e^2)$. (O.C.)

*11.4. Oblique Impact of Smooth Elastic Spheres

Two smooth spheres A and B, of masses m_1 and m_2 respectively, collide. Immediately before impact the velocity of A is u at an angle α with the line of centres of the spheres and the velocity of B is v at an angle β with the line of centres (Fig. 132). There is no impulse between the spheres in the direction of their common tangent at the point of contact and the momentum of each sphere in this direction is, therefore, unchanged by the impact. Hence the component velocities after collision in this direction are $u\sin\alpha$ for A and $v\sin\beta$ for B. If the component velocities in the direction of the line of centres after impact are x and y respectively, then

by conservation of momentum,

$$m_1 x + m_2 y = m_1 u \cos\alpha + m_2 v \cos\beta,$$

by the law of restitution, $\quad x - y = -e(u\cos\alpha - v\cos\beta).$ (11.3)

These two equations are sufficient to determine x and y, and hence the velocities of A and B after the collision.

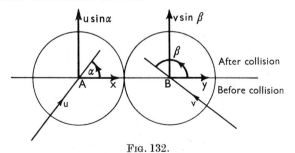

FIG. 132.

Examples. (i) A smooth sphere, of centre A and mass $2m$, moving with speed $2v$ collides with a smooth sphere, of centre B and mass m, moving with speed v. The velocities of the spheres immediately before impact are inclined at angles of 60° and 90° respectively to the direction of AB at the moment of impact (Fig. 133). The coefficient of restitution between the spheres is $\frac{1}{2}$. Calculate the velocities of the spheres after impact and the loss of kinetic energy sustained by the system during the impact.

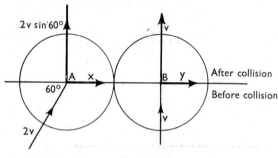

FIG. 133.

Figure 133 shows the velocities of the spheres immediately before and immediately after the impact. Equations (11.3), applied to this case, are:

Momentum $4mv\cos 60° = 2mx + my,$

Restitution $-v\cos 60° = x - y.$

$$\therefore x = \tfrac{1}{2}v, \quad y = v.$$

Therefore, immediately after the impact the velocity of the sphere A

is $\sqrt{\{(v\sqrt{3})^2 + (v/2)^2\}}$ at $\tan^{-1}(2\sqrt{3})$ with AB,

i.e. $\dfrac{v\sqrt{13}}{2}$ at $\tan^{-1}(2\sqrt{3})$ with AB;

the velocity of the sphere B is $v\sqrt{2}$ at 45° with AB.
The loss of kinetic energy is

$$\left\{\frac{1}{2}(2m)\,4v^2 + \frac{1}{2}mv^2\right\} - \left\{\frac{1}{2}(2m)\frac{13v^2}{4} + \frac{1}{2}m\cdot 2v^2\right\} = \frac{1}{4}mv^2.$$

(ii) An elastic sphere impinges on an equal sphere at rest. Show that, whatever the coefficient of restitution, the deviation in the

direction of motion of the first sphere cannot exceed a right angle;
and that, if the coefficient of restitution is less than unity by a small
quantity ε, the maximum deviation is less than a right angle by
approximately $\sqrt{(2\varepsilon)}$ radians.   (O.C.)

Figure 134 shows the velocities of the spheres (with centres A, B)
immediately before and immediately after impact. Equations (11.3)
for this case are,

Momentum $mx + my = mu\cos\theta$, where m is the mass of each sphere,
Restitution $x - y = -eu\cos\theta$.

$$\therefore\ x = \tfrac{1}{2}u(1-e)\cos\theta,\quad y = \tfrac{1}{2}u(1+e)\cos\theta.$$

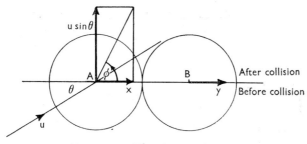

FIG. 134.

The sphere with centre A therefore moves after impact with a velocity which makes an angle φ with AB, where

$$\tan\varphi = \frac{u\sin\theta}{\tfrac{1}{2}u(1-e)\cos\theta} = \frac{2\tan\theta}{1-e}.$$

The deviation in the direction of motion of this sphere is $(\varphi - \theta)$, and

$$\tan(\varphi - \theta) = \frac{\dfrac{2\tan\theta}{1-e} - \tan\theta}{1 + \dfrac{2\tan^2\theta}{1-e}} = \frac{(1+e)\tan\theta}{2\tan^2\theta + 1 - e}.$$

Since the greatest value of θ which makes the collision geometrically
possible is $90°$, $\tan\theta$ is positive; since also $e \leq 1$, $\tan(\varphi - \theta)$ is
positive for all possible values of θ and e. The deviation $\varphi - \theta$ cannot
therefore exceed $90°$.

20*

Differentiating $\tan(\varphi - \theta)$ with respect to $\tan\theta$, we have

$$\frac{\mathrm{d}\{\tan(\varphi - \theta)\}}{\mathrm{d}(\tan\theta)} = (1 + e)\left\{\frac{(2\tan^2\theta + 1 - e) - 4\tan^2\theta}{(2\tan^2\theta + 1 - e)^2}\right\}$$

$$= \frac{(1 + e)(1 - e - 2\tan^2\theta)}{(2\tan^2\theta + 1 - e)^2}.$$

Therefore $\tan(\varphi - \theta)$ is stationary when $\tan\theta = +\sqrt{\left(\frac{1 - e}{2}\right)}$, and this stationary value is a maximum because $1 - e - 2\tan^2\theta$ is positive if $\tan\theta < \sqrt{\left(\frac{1 - e}{2}\right)}$ and negative if $\tan\theta > \sqrt{\left(\frac{1 - e}{2}\right)}$. The deviation $\varphi - \theta$ is therefore a maximum when $\tan\theta = \sqrt{\left(\frac{1 - e}{2}\right)}$.

If $e = 1 - \varepsilon$, where ε is small, and the deviation is δ,

$$\tan\delta = \frac{(2 - \varepsilon)\sqrt{\dfrac{\varepsilon}{2}}}{2\varepsilon}.$$

$$\therefore \tan\left(\frac{1}{2}\pi - \delta\right) = \frac{2\varepsilon}{(2 - \varepsilon)\sqrt{\dfrac{\varepsilon}{2}}}$$

$$= (1 - \tfrac{1}{2}\varepsilon)^{-1}\sqrt{(2\varepsilon)}$$

$$\doteqdot \sqrt{(2\varepsilon)},$$

if powers of ε higher than the first are neglected.

$$\therefore \tfrac{1}{2}\pi - \delta \doteqdot \sqrt{(2\varepsilon)} \text{ as required.}$$

*EXERCISES 11.4.

In exercises 1–6 a smooth sphere of centre A and mass m_1 collides with a smooth sphere of centre B and mass m_2. The coefficient of restitution between the spheres is e. Immediately before impact A is moving with velocity u at an anticlockwise angle α with the positive direction AB and B is moving with velocity v at an anticlockwise angle β with the positive direction AB. Immediately after the collision A is moving with velocity u_1 at an angle α_1 with AB and B is moving with velocity v_1 at an angle β_1 with AB.

*1. $m_1 = 2$ lb, $m_2 = 4$ lb, $u = 4$ ft/sec, $v = 2$ ft/sec, $\alpha = 45°$, $\beta = 135°$, $e = \frac{1}{2}$; calculate u_1, α_1, v_1, β_1.

*2. $m_1 = m_2 = m$, $\alpha = 45°$, $v = 0$, $e = \frac{1}{2}$; calculate u_1, v_1, α_1, β_1.

*3. $m_1 = m_2 = m$, $\alpha = 90°$, $\beta = 180°$, $u = v = V$, $e = \frac{1}{2}$; calculate u_1, v_1, α_1, β_1.

*4. $m_1 = m$, $m_2 = 2m$, $\alpha = 30°$, $\beta = 150°$, $u = v = V$, $e = \frac{2}{3}$; calculate u_1, v_1, α_1, β_1.

*5. $m_1 = m$, $m_2 = nm$, $\alpha = 60°$, $u = V$, $v = 0$, $\alpha_1 = 90°$; calculate e, u_1, v_1, β_1.

*6. $m_1 = m_2 = m$, $v = 0$, $\alpha = 45°$, $e = \frac{3}{4}$; calculate α_1.

*7. A smooth sphere collides with an equal smooth sphere which is at rest and the line of centres makes an acute angle α with the direction of motion just before impact. If the coefficient of restitution is e, find the angle through which the first sphere is deflected by the impact and show that this angle is greatest if $2\tan^2\alpha = 1 - e$. (L.)

*8. A ball B is at rest. It is struck by another ball A, of equal mass and volume, which is moving so that its centre is travelling along a tangent to the ball B. It is noticed that the direction of A is turned through an angle of $30°$ by the impact. Find the coefficient of restitution. (L.)

*9. A smooth sphere of mass m impinges obliquely on a heavier sphere of the same radius, but of mass km, at rest on a horizontal table. If, after impact, the directions of motion of the two spheres are perpendicular, prove that the coefficient of restitution must be $1/k$.

If, when $k = 2$, the kinetic energy lost due to the impact is one quarter of the original kinetic energy, determine the inclination of the initial direction of motion to the line of centres. (L.)

*10. Two smooth spheres with equal momenta approach each other from opposite directions, their coefficient of restitution being e. After impact, each moves perpendicular to its original direction. If, at the moment of impact, their common normal is inclined at an angle θ to the original direction of motion, find θ. (L.)

MISCELLANEOUS EXERCISES. XI

1. A smooth sphere A of mass 6 oz, moving at the rate of 4 ft/sec, strikes directly another smooth sphere B of mass 8 oz which is at rest. If the velocity of the sphere B immediately after impact is 2 ft/sec, what is the coefficient of restitution between them?

What fraction of the initial kinetic energy is lost in the impact? (L.)

2. Two equal marbles, A and B, lie on a smooth horizontal circular groove at opposite ends of a diameter. A is projected along the groove and at the end of time t impinges on B. Show that the second impact will occur after a further time $2t/e$, where e is the coefficient of restitution. (L.)

3. A body of mass 50 lb is released from rest and after falling freely through a distance of 25 ft strikes a pile of mass 200 lb embedded in the ground. After the impact the body adheres to the pile which is driven a distance 3 in. into the ground. Find the resistance to penetration, assumed constant.

If the body had rebounded to a height of 4 ft instead of adhering, find how far the pile would have penetrated after the first impact. (N.)

*4. Two small smooth spheres, of equal size and masses m, $2m$, are moving initially with equal speeds on a smooth horizontal floor. The spheres collide when their centres are on a line AB which is parallel to and distant a from a smooth vertical wall towards which the spheres are moving. Before collision the directions of motion are at right angles to each other, and each is inclined at

$45°$ to AB. The coefficient of restitution at all the impacts is e. Find the distance apart of the points at which the spheres strike the wall.

Show that after rebounding from the wall the centres of the spheres cross the line AB simultaneously, and that their distance apart is then $2a(1 + e)$.   (N.)

*5. Two equal smooth billiard balls, whose coefficient of restitution is e, moving with equal speeds v in opposite directions, impinge obliquely, the line of centres on impact being inclined at $45°$ to the direction of motion. Prove that the loss of energy is half what it would be if the impact were direct.   (L.)

6. A ball of mass m moves at a speed V towards a stationary ball of mass $2m$; after the impact the second ball moves at a speed V_1 and meets a third ball, of mass m, which is coming towards it at a speed kV. The third ball is brought to rest by the impact. The coefficient of restitution at each impact is $e(< \frac{1}{2})$. Find the value of V_1 in terms of e and V, and the value of k in terms of e.   (O.C.)

7. A smooth circular wire hoop, of radius a, is fixed in a vertical plane. A bead, free to slide along the wire, starts from rest at the end of a horizontal radius. At the lowest point of the wire the bead strikes a second bead, of equal mass, which is also free to slide along the wire. The coefficient of restitution between the two beads is e. Find the heights above the point of impact to which the beads rise after the first collision.   (O.C.)

8. A wire is bent into the form of a circle and fixed in a vertical plane. Beads of masses m and m', which can slide smoothly along the wire, are at the highest and lowest points of the wire, respectively. The upper bead is slightly displaced and comes into collision with the lower bead. Prove that the latter will just reach the highest point of the wire if the coefficient of restitution for the impact is equal to m'/m.   (O.C.)

9. Two equal small smooth spheres, A and B, lie in a horizontal circular groove at opposite ends of a diameter. A is initially at rest and B is projected along the groove. If the first impact takes place after 3 sec and the second after a further 12 sec, find the coefficient of restitution between the spheres.   (L.)

*10. A uniform smooth sphere A, of mass m, moving along a horizontal plane with speed u, impinges directly on another smooth uniform sphere B, of the same radius, at rest. If the mass of B is double that of A, and A is reduced to rest by the impact, show that the coefficient of restitution between the spheres is $\frac{1}{2}$.

B then moves along the plane and impinges directly on a fixed vertical wall, the coefficient of restitution between B and the wall being $\frac{3}{4}$. Find the impulsive reaction between B and the wall and if, after rebounding, B again strikes A, show that after this last impact the velocity of A is twice that of B.   (L.)

11. A sphere of mass m moving with velocity v impinges directly on an identical sphere moving in the same direction with velocity u. If the coefficient of restitution is e, find the velocity of the second sphere after impact.

Show that the magnitude of the impulse on either of the two spheres is

$$\tfrac{1}{2}m(1 + e)(v - u),$$

and find, from first principles, the kinetic energy lost in the impact.   (N.)

12. A smooth sphere of mass m moving with speed u impinges directly on another smooth sphere of mass km moving with speed λu in the same sense. If the sphere of mass m is brought to rest by the impact, show that the coefficient of restitution is

$$\frac{1 + k\lambda}{k(1 - \lambda)}$$

and deduce that, for this to be possible, k must be greater than 1.   (L.)

*13. A number of equal balls rest on a smooth horizontal table with their centres in a straight line, no two balls being in contact. The first ball is projected with a velocity u along the line of centres towards the second ball. Find the velocity with which the nth ball begins to move if e is the coefficient of restitution.   (N.)

14. Three smooth spheres A, B, C have equal radii and masses $9m$, m, $9m$ respectively. They are at rest on a smooth horizontal table with their centres in a straight line and B lies between A and C. The sphere B is now projected directly towards C with speed V. The coefficient of restitution at all impacts is $\frac{2}{3}$. Find the velocity of each sphere after three impacts have taken place, and show that there can be no further collisions.   (N.)

15. Two spheres of masses M, m impinge directly when moving in opposite directions with speeds u, v respectively, and the sphere of mass m is brought to rest by the collision; prove that

$$\frac{m}{M} = e + (1 + e)\,\frac{u}{v}.$$

After this collision the sphere of mass M is acted on by a constant retarding force which brings it to rest after travelling a distance a. Prove that the magnitude of this force is

$$\frac{M\,e^2\,(u + v)^2}{2\,a}.$$ (N.)

16. Three balls of masses m, m, $2m$ respectively lie at rest on a smooth floor with their centres collinear; e_1 is the coefficient of restitution between the first and the second; e_2 is the coefficient of restitution between the second and the third. The first ball is projected towards the second. Prove that, if

$$e_2 > \frac{2e_1 - 1}{e_1 + 1},$$

then, after the second ball has hit the third, the first ball will again collide with the second.   (O.C.)

17. Two masses m, m', whose coefficient of restitution is e, moving in opposite directions with velocities u, u' impinge directly. Write down equations which give their velocities after impact.

If , before impact, the masses have equal and opposite momenta, prove that the ratio of the kinetic energy of the first to the kinetic energy of the second is unaltered by the impact.   (O.C.)

18. A particle A, of mass $2m$, moving with a velocity u ft/sec impinges directly on a stationary particle B, of mass m, placed at a distance d ft from a wall which is at right angles to the direction of motion of A. After B rebounds from the wall, a second impact occurs between A and B, T sec after the first impact. Prove that, if the coefficient of restitution between A and B is $\frac{1}{2}$ and between B and the wall is e, then

$$T = \frac{2\,d\,(1+e)}{u\,(1+2\,e)}.$$
(O.C.)

19. Two uniform smooth spheres of the same radius but of different masses $5m$ and $4m$ stand at rest on a smooth horizontal table, their closest points being joined by a slack light inextensible string. The sphere of mass $4m$ is suddenly projected, without rotation with velocity V along the line of centres and away from the other sphere. Find the velocity with which the sphere of mass $5m$ begins to move.

When both spheres are in motion the sphere of mass $4m$ impinges on a vertical wall which is perpendicular to the direction of motion. If the coefficient of restitution between the two spheres and between the spheres and the wall is $\frac{1}{2}$, prove that, when the spheres first collide, one of them is reduced to rest. (N.)

20. An elastic particle of mass m is projected horizontally with velocity u from the centre of a circular ring, of mass nm and radius a, lying at rest on a smooth horizontal table. If e is the coefficient of restitution between the particle and the ring, find the velocities of the ring and the particle after each of the first two impacts.

Show that at the moment of the second impact the ring has moved through a distance $2a(1+e)/(n+1)\,e$. (N.)

*21. A smooth elastic sphere of mass m fits into a long straight tube of mass M with closed ends, so that it is free to move, without friction, along the length of the tube. The coefficient of restitution between the sphere and the ends of the tube is e. The tube is placed on a smooth horizontal table and is given an initial velocity V in the direction of its length. Find the velocity of the sphere after its second impact in the tube.

Show that ultimately, the velocities of the sphere and tube are equal. (L.)

*22. A small sphere A rests on a smooth horizontal floor at a distance d from a straight wall. An equal sphere B is projected along the floor with speed V towards the wall in a direction perpendicular to it and strikes A so that the line of centres on impact is inclined at an angle α to the wall. The coefficient of restitution between the spheres is e, and the diameter of each sphere is negligible compared with d. Show that the components of the velocity of B after impact, along and perpendicular to the line of centres are $\frac{1}{2}V(1-e)\sin\alpha$ and $V\cos\alpha$ respectively. Deduce the components of this velocity parallel and perpendicular to the wall, and show that the spheres strike the wall at points distant

$$\frac{2\,d\,\cot\alpha}{2-(1+e)\sin^2\alpha}\,.$$

apart. (N.)

*23. A sphere collides obliquely with another sphere of equal mass which is at rest, both spheres being smooth and perfectly elastic. Show that their paths after the collision are at right angles.

Three smooth perfectly elastic spheres of equal masses and radii r have their centres at the vertices of an isosceles triangle PQR with $PQ = QR = l$ and $\angle PQR = \varphi(> 90°)$. The sphere at P is to be projected so as to strike the sphere at Q and then to impinge directly on the sphere at R. Show that the initial direction of the sphere at P makes with PQ an angle α satisfying the equation

$$l^2 \sin \alpha + 2r\sqrt{(l^2 - 4r^2)} \cos(\alpha + \varphi) = 4r^2 \sin(\alpha + \varphi).$$ (O.C.)

*24. A sphere of mass m strikes a sphere of mass m'. The latter sphere is at rest and the former is moving in a direction inclined at an angle θ to the line of centres at impact. Prove that, if the direction of motion of the first sphere is turned through a right angle by the impact, then $\tan^2\theta = (em' - m)/(m + m')$, where e is the coefficient of restitution. (O.C.)

*25. A sphere moving with speed v on a smooth horizontal plane strikes in succession two vertical walls which are perpendicular. Prove that if the coefficient of restitution at both walls has the same value e, the sphere is finally moving with speed ev opposite to its original direction.

If the coefficient of restitution at the second wall is $e'(> e)$ and the sphere is initially moving parallel to the bisector of the angle between the walls, prove that the final direction of motion makes an angle $\tan^{-1}[(e' - e)/(e' + e)]$ with the bisector. (L.)

*26. Two equal smooth spheres, of diameter d, are moving with equal speeds whit their centres on two parallel lines, distant $a(a < d)$ apart, and towards each other. Prove that after impact, they move away from each other with equal speeds with their centres on two parallel lines distant b apart, where

$$b^2\{e^2d^2 + (1 - e^2)a^2\} = a^2d^2,$$

and e is the coefficient of restitution between the spheres. (L.)

*27. The centres of two equal smooth spheres, each of mass m and radius a, are moving with equal speeds u in opposite directions along two parallel lines at a distance $2a \sin \alpha$ apart. Prove that the loss of kinetic energy due to the impact of the spheres is $mu^2(1 - e^2)\cos^2\alpha$, where e is the coefficient of restitution between them.

Find also the angle through which the direction of motion of either sphere is deflected. (O.C.)

*28. Show that if two smooth spheres whose masses are equal are perfectly elastic and one impinges obliquely on the other which is at rest, then their subsequent directions of motion are at right angles.

Three smooth perfectly elastic spheres of diameter a and equal mass have their centres at the corners A, B, C of a square $ABCD$ of side c. The sphere at A is to be projected so as to strike in turn the spheres at B and C and finally move parallel to AB. Show that the direction of projection makes with AB an angle θ given by

$$a \cos(\theta - \varphi) = c \sin\theta,$$

where

$$\cos\varphi = a/(c - a).$$ (O.C.)

*29. A smooth sphere of mass m is lying at rest on an inelastic horizontal floor when it is struck by a second equal sphere moving with velocity V towards it in a direction inclined downwards from the horizontal at an angle α. The impact is direct, that is, the line of centres at the instant of impact is the line of original motion of the centre of the second sphere, and the coefficient of restitution between the spheres is e. Find the velocities of the spheres after impact and prove that the loss of kinetic energy is

$$\frac{1}{2} m V^2 \frac{1 - e^2}{1 + \cos^2\alpha}.$$ (L.)

*30. A particle projected from a point O on a smooth inclined plane strikes the plane normally at the second impact. At the sixth impact it is again at O. If e is the coefficient of restitution, show that

$$e^4 + e^2 - 1 = 0.$$ (N.)

*31. A straight narrow tube, of mass $2m$ and length l, has the shape of a right circular cylinder and is closed by plane ends A and B. A ball of mass m just fits inside the tube and can run smoothly along it. When the ball reaches an end it rebounds, the coefficient of restitution being e. Initially the tube is at rest on its side on a smooth horizontal floor, with the ball at rest at B. The tube is then suddenly set in motion in the direction AB with velocity V. Find the velocity of the tube when the ball is next leaving the end B, and find how far relative to the floor the ball has then travelled. (N.)

*32. A smooth sphere A moving in a straight line strikes an equal smooth sphere B at rest. If α, β are the angles which the directions of motion of A, B respectively make, after impact, with the initial direction of A's motion, show that

$$\tan(\alpha + \beta) = \frac{2}{1 - e} \tan\beta,$$

where e is the coefficient of restitution. (L.)

*33. Two equal smooth spheres are joined by an inextensible string and lie on a smooth horizontal table with the string taut. A third equal sphere moving on the table at an angle α with the string hits one of the spheres directly, so that the string remains taut. Prove that the third sphere rebounds if the coefficient of restitution is greater than $\frac{1}{2}(1 + \sin^2\alpha)$. (L.)

CHAPTER XII

POWER

12.1. Definition and Units

Power is defined as a *rate of working*. If work is being done by a force or a system of forces, and if W, the work done at time t, can be expressed as a function of t,

the power at time t is $\dfrac{\mathrm{d}\,W}{\mathrm{d}\,t}$.

If W_1 is the total work done by the system of forces from time t_1 to time t_2,

the average power from time t_1 to time t_2 is $\dfrac{W_1}{t_2 - t_1}$.

The absolute unit of power in the FPS system is 1 ft pdl/sec. This unit is too small for most purposes and the unit which is called 1 horse power (historically associated with James Watt) is the unit of power, in this system of units, which is in common use.

$$1 \text{ horse power (1 h.p.)} = 550g \text{ ft pdl/sec}$$
$$= 550 \text{ ft lb wt./sec}.$$

In the metric system of units, the absolute unit of power is 1 erg/sec which, again, is too small for most practical purposes.

$$1 \text{ watt} = 1 \text{ joule/sec}, \quad \text{i.e.} \quad 10^7 \text{ erg/sec},$$
$$1 \text{ kilowatt} = 1000 \text{ joules/sec}$$

are more commonly used units of power.

Units of Electrical Energy

Electrical energy is used through the medium of appliances which determine the *rate* at which electric energy is converted into other forms of energy such as mechanical energy and heat energy. Thus a 100 W light bulb in use is converting energy *at the rate of* 100 W, i.e. *at the rate of* 100 J/sec. Because energy is converted by the appliance at an approximately uniform rate, the quantity of energy converted is obtained by multiplying the constant rate of conversion by the time. The 100 watt bulb thus converts $100 \times 60 = 6000$ J of energy in one minute. An equivalent quantity of energy to that converted at the rate of 1 kW for a period of 1 hr is sold for conversion as 1 *unit* or 1 *kilowatt-hour*. Thus

$$1 \text{ unit} = 1000 \text{ J/sec} \times 3600 \text{ sec}$$
$$= 3 \cdot 6 \times 10^6 \text{ J}.$$

This, for example, is the quantity of energy converted in 1 hr by a bar of an electric fire which is described as being a 1 kW bar.

Comparison between FPS and CGS Units of Power

If we take 1 ft as 0·3048 m, 1 kgm as 2·205 lb, and g as 980·7 cm/sec,

$$1 \text{ h.p.} = 550 \text{ ft lb wt./sec}$$
$$= \frac{550 \times 30 \cdot 48}{0 \cdot 002205} \text{ cm gm wt./sec}$$
$$= \frac{550 \times 30 \cdot 48 \times g}{0 \cdot 002205 \times 10^7} \text{ J/sec}$$
$$= \frac{550 \times 30 \cdot 48 \times 980 \cdot 7}{0 \cdot 002205 \times 10^7} \text{ W}$$
$$\doteqdot 746 \text{ W} = 0 \cdot 746 \text{ kW}.$$

EXERCISES 12.1.

1. Express a rate of working of 220 ft ton wt./hr in horse power.

2. Calculate, in joules, the work done by a machine working at the rate of 220 kW for 5 min.

3. Calculate, in horse power, the average effective power of a machine which lifts a load of 11 cwt once every 25 sec through a vertical distance of 40 ft.

4. Calculate the amount of an electricity bill calculated at 6d. per unit for the first 80 units, 1·25d. per unit for the next 400 units and 0·9 d. per unit for the remaining units, when the consumer has used:

five 100-W light bulbs each for a total of 240 hr,

one 2-kW electric fire for a total of 500 hr, and

one 3-kW immersion heater for a total of 36 hr.

5. The work W ft pdl done by a force at time t sec from the time it commenced to act is given by the equation

$$W = 5\pi \sin\left(\frac{\pi t}{5}\right).$$

Calculate the power of the force at time $t = 2 \cdot 5$.

6. Calculate the power at time $t = 2$ of a force which acts on a particle of mass 100 gm and moves the particle in a straight line so that the distance s cm of the particle from a fixed point in the line at time t sec from the beginning of the motion is given by

$$s = 5t + 2t^2.$$

12.2. Power with a Constant Force

A constant force P acts on a body of constant mass m which moves in a straight line in the direction of P so that its velocity is v at time t. The work done by P in moving the body from displacement x to displacement $x + \delta x$ from a fixed point in the line of motion is $P\delta x$. Therefore, the average rate of working of P for this displacement is $\dfrac{P\delta x}{\delta t}$. Hence, the power of P at time t is

$$\lim_{\delta t \to 0} P\frac{\delta x}{\delta t} = P\frac{\mathrm{d}x}{\mathrm{d}t} = Pv. \tag{12.1}$$

When P is not constant but is a function of the time, the work done by P in the small interval of time δt lies between $P\delta x$ and $(P + \delta P)\,\delta x$ and it follows, as above, that the power of P at time t is Pv, calculated at time t.

If we make the assumption that, if $y = \displaystyle\int_{x_1}^{x} f(x)\,\mathrm{d}x$ then $\dfrac{\mathrm{d}y}{\mathrm{d}x} = f(x)$, we can demonstrate the truth of this last statement thus:

If W is the work done between displacement x_1 and displacement x from the origin,

$$W = \int_{x_1}^{x} P\,\mathrm{d}x = \int_{t_1}^{t} P\frac{\mathrm{d}x}{\mathrm{d}t}\,\mathrm{d}t.$$

$$\therefore \frac{\mathrm{d}W}{\mathrm{d}t} = P\frac{\mathrm{d}x}{\mathrm{d}t} = Pv,$$

i.e. the power at time t is Pv, calculated at time t.

Examples. (i) A motor truck, of mass 5 tons, with an engine capable of developing 32 h.p., has a maximum speed of 50 m.p.h. on a level road. Calculate the total resistances in lb wt. at this speed.

Assuming the resistances to be proportional to the square of the speed, calculate in horse-power the rate of working of the engine when the truck is climbing a gradient of 1 in 224 at 37·5 m.p.h. and has, at that instant, an acceleration of 0·08 ft/sec². (L.)

When the truck is moving at its maximum speed it is not accelerating and the force exerted by the engine on the truck is equal to the total resistance to motion of the truck.

Therefore, if this resisting force is Rg pdl, the *power equation* for the motion of the truck is,

$$\text{force} \times \text{velocity} = \text{power},$$

i.e. $$Rg \times 50 \times \tfrac{22}{15} = 32 \times 550g.$$

$$\therefore R = 240.$$

The total resistance in lb wt. at this speed is 240 lb wt. *on the incline.*

The forces acting on the truck in the direction of motion are, as shown in Fig. 135,

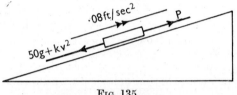

FIG. 135.

(a) the force P pdl exerted by the engine on the truck,

(b) the resistance to the motion of the truck (this force is equal to kv^2 lb wt. where k is constant and v ft/sec is the speed of the truck at the instant concerned), and

(c) the component of the weight of the truck in the direction down the plane.

When the speed is 50 m.p.h., the resistance is 240 lb wt.

$$\therefore 240 = k(50)^2, \quad k = \frac{240}{(50)^2}.$$

(This value of k is obtained from the variation equation by substituting a value of v in *miles per hour* and a value of the corresponding resistance in *pounds weight*. When the value of k thus obtained is used in the *variation equation*, values of v and of the resistance will be in m.p.h. and lb wt. respectively.)

Therefore, when the speed is 37·5 m.p.h., the resistance is S lb wt. where

$$S = \frac{240}{(50)^2} \times (37\cdot5)^2 = 135.$$

Therefore, at the instant when the acceleration of the truck is 0·08 ft/sec², the equation of motion for the truck is

$$P - 135g - \frac{5 \times 2240g}{224} = 5 \times 2240 \times 0\cdot08 .$$

$$\therefore P = 213g .$$

Therefore, the power of the engine at this instant is

$$\frac{213g \times 37\cdot5 \times \frac{22}{15}}{550g} \text{ h.p.}$$

$$= 21\cdot3 \text{ h.p.}$$

(ii) A car of mass 1 ton moves along a horizontal road against a resistance of 80 lb wt. Find the greatest speed attainable (in m.p.h.), if the engine cannot exert more than 20 h.p.

Find the pull in the tow rope if the car (still subject to the resistance of 80 lb wt.) pulls a trailer of mass 12 cwt which is resisted by a force of 60 lb wt., when the speed is 15 m.p.h. and the engine is working at 20 h.p.   (L.)

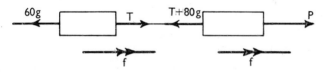

FIG. 136.

The power equation for the motion of the car at maximum speed is

$$80gv = 20 \times 550g,$$

where v ft/sec is the maximum speed.

$$\therefore v = \frac{550}{4} .$$

Therefore, the greatest speed obtainable is $\frac{550}{4} \times \frac{15}{22}$ m.p.h. = $= 93\frac{3}{4}$ m.p.h.

When the car is pulling the trailer, the forces acting on the car and those acting on the trailer are as represented in Fig. 136, where T pdl is the pull in the tow rope and f ft/sec² the acceleration of car and trailer. The power equation is

$$20 \times 550g = P \times 22 .$$

$$\therefore P = 500g .$$

Therefore, from the equations of motion for the engine and the trailer separately,
$$f = \frac{420g - T}{2240} = \frac{T - 60g}{\frac{3}{5} \times 2240},$$
whence
$$T = 195g.$$

The pull in the tow rope is 195 lb wt.

(ii) A car of mass m tons, with its engine working at H h.p., can attain a speed of V m.p.h. when running down a slope of 1 (vertically) in n (along the slope). Assuming that the resistance to motion varies as the square of the speed and that the maximum speed attainable up the same slope with the same horse-power is $\frac{1}{2} V$ m.p.h., prove that

$$\frac{Hn}{Vm} = \frac{64}{15}. \tag{L.}$$

When the car is running down the incline at its maximum speed of V m.p.h., the power equation is

$$550 H g = \frac{22 P V}{15},$$

where P pdl is the force exerted by the engine.
The equation of motion is

$$P + \frac{2240 m g}{n} = k V^2,$$

where k is a constant such that $k V^2$ pdl is the resistance to the motion of the car at V m.ph.
Eliminating P between these two equations we have,

$$550 H g = \frac{22 V}{15} \left(k V^2 - \frac{2240 m g}{n} \right).$$

For the motion up the incline at the maximum speed of $\frac{1}{2} V$ m.p.h. the power equation is
$$550 H g = \frac{22 P_1 V}{30},$$

where P_1 pdl is the force exerted by the engine.
The equation of motion is

$$P_1 - \frac{2240 m g}{n} = \frac{k V^2}{4}.$$

Eliminating P_1 between the last two equations we have

$$550 H g = \frac{22 V}{30} \left(\frac{k V^2}{4} + \frac{2240 m g}{n} \right).$$

Hence, eliminating k,

$$7 \times 550 Hg = \frac{5 \times 2240\,mg}{n} \times \frac{22\,V}{15}.$$

$$\therefore \; \frac{Hn}{Vm} = \frac{64}{15}.$$

12.3. Energy and Power

The relation between the work done by a force and the mechanical energy produced makes it possible to calculate the power of a force by calculating the rate at which it is producing or destroying mechanical energy. If the energy E produced by a force is expressible as a function of the time t measured from an arbitrary origin, then the power of the force at time t is $\dfrac{\mathrm{d}E}{\mathrm{d}t}$.

In problems in which the rate at which energy is produced is evaluated in order to calculate power, it is frequently the average rate of working, i.e. the average power, which can be deduced.

Example. Water flows to the water-wheel of a mill through a rectangular channel 10 ft wide. If the water is 2 ft deep and flows at 11 ft/sec, calculate the mass of water reaching the water-wheel per sec. Assuming an efficiency of 75 per cent calculate the available horse power of the wheel.   (L.)

[1 ft^3 of water is of mass $62\frac{1}{2}$ lb.]

The term *efficiency* as used here is defined as the ratio of the energy *output* of the machine to the energy *input*.

The mass of water reaching the wheel per sec is

$$(2 \times 10 \times 11 \times 62\tfrac{1}{2})\,\text{lb} = 13{,}750\,\text{lb}.$$

Therefore the rate of energy input is

$$\tfrac{1}{2} \times 13{,}750 \times 11^2\,\text{ft pdl/sec}.$$

Therefore the rate of energy output = available power

$$= \frac{\tfrac{3}{4} \times \tfrac{1}{2} \times 13{,}750 \times 121}{550 \times 32}\,\text{h.p.} = 35 \cdot 4\,\text{h.p.}$$

12.4. The Acceleration and the Maximum Speed of a Car

The constructional details of the engine and mechanical traction system of a car determine the maximum *power* at which the car can work and the maximum *tractive force* which the engine can exert. The maximum power determines the maximum speed of which the car is capable against a given resistance and the maximum tractive force determines the maximum acceleration of which the car is capable against a given resistance and at a given speed.

Example. Car A of mass m lb can work at a maximum horse-power H and has a maximum tractive force of P lb wt. Car B of mass $2m$ lb can work at a maximum horse-power $2H$ and has a maximum tractive force $5P/4$ lb wt. Show that when both cars are travelling in the same direction at speed v ft/sec, A against a resistance of $P/6$ lb wt. and B against a resistance of $P/4$ lb wt., and when both cars are employing maximum possible acceleration, A will gain ground on B if $v < \dfrac{825H}{P}$. Calculate the maximum speed of each car.

When the limitation of power allows B to use maximum tractive force, the equation of motion for B is

$$\frac{5Pg}{4} - \frac{Pg}{4} = 2mf,$$

i.e.
$$f = \frac{Pg}{2m}$$

and from the power equation this acceleration is possible for B if

$$1100Hg \geqq \frac{5Pg}{4}v,$$

i.e. if
$$v \leqq \frac{880H}{P}.$$

When A employs maximum tractive force its acceleration is $\dfrac{5Pg}{6m}$ and A can attain a greater acceleration than $\dfrac{Pg}{2m}$ so long as its maximum power is greater than the power required to overcome the resistance and provide this acceleration,

i.e.   so long as $550Hg > \left(\dfrac{Pg}{6} + \dfrac{Pg}{2} \right) v,$

.e.   so long as $v < \dfrac{825H}{P}.$

Therefore A gains ground on B so long as $v < \dfrac{825H}{P}.$

A's maximum speed is given by the power equation as V_1 ft/sec, where

$$500\,Hg = \frac{Pg}{6}\,V_1,$$

i.e.
$$V_1 = \frac{3300\,H}{P}.$$

B's maximum speed is V_2 ft/sec, where

$$1100\,Hg = \frac{Pg}{4}\,V_2,$$

i.e.
$$V_2 = \frac{4400\,H}{P}.$$

MISCELLANEOUS EXERCISES. XII

1. A cyclist working at $\frac{1}{10}$ h.p. rides at 30 m.p.h. *down* a slope of inclination θ, where $\sin\theta = \frac{1}{100}$. If the total mass of the rider and his machine is 125 lb, show that the frictional force opposing his motion is $2\frac{1}{2}$ lb wt.

The lowest speed at which the cyclist can ride without falling off is 3 m.p.h. Calculate the inclination of the steepest slope *up* which he can ride, assuming that he works at the same rate as before and that the frictional resistance remains unchanged.   (N.)

2. A motor cyclist travels along a level road at a constant speed of 50 m.p.h. The engine works at the rate of 5 h.p. Show that the frictional resistance opposing the motion is $37\frac{1}{2}$ lb wt.

The total mass of the rider and his machine is 270 lb. Assuming that the engine works at the same rate as before and that the frictional resistance remains unchanged, calculate the steady speed, in miles per hour, at which the motor cyclist can ride up a slope of inclination θ, where $\sin\theta = \frac{1}{12}$. Show that, when his speed is 45 m.p.h. up the incline, his retardation is $2\frac{14}{81}$ ft/sec^2.   (N.)

3. A motor truck of mass 10 tons travels along a level road at a constant speed of 50 m.p.h. The engine works at the rate of 40 h.p. Show that the frictional resistance opposing the motion is 300 lb wt.

The truck comes to a slope of inclination θ, where $\sin\theta = \frac{1}{112}$. Assuming that the engine works at the same rate as before and that the frictional resistance remains unchanged, calculate the retardation of the truck when its speed has been reduced to 40 m.p.h.   (N.)

4. The maximum rate of working of the engines of a ship is 2500 h.p. The greatest steady speed of the ship is 15 m.p.h. If the ship is of mass 10,000 tons, show that the resistance opposing the motion is equivalent to $6\frac{1}{4}$ lb wt./ton.

Find the acceleration of the ship when its speed is $7\frac{1}{2}$ m.p.h. and the engines are working at the rate of 2000 h.p. It may be assumed that the resistance remains unchanged.   (N.)

5. (*a*) A car of mass 1 ton travels up a slope of inclination θ, where $\sin\theta = \frac{1}{10}$. The engine works at the rate of 22 h.p. and the frictional resistance opposing the motion is constant and of magnitude 51 lb wt. Calculate the steady speed at which the car travels.

21*

(b) A pump raises 180 gal of water per min from a depth of 57 ft; the water is delivered at a speed of 24 ft/sec. Assuming that 1 gal of water is of mass 10 lb, find (i) the potential energy, (ii) the kinetic energy, gained by the water delivered each second. Give your answers in ft lb wt.

Show that, neglecting frictional losses, the pump is working at the rate of $3\frac{3}{5}$ h.p.   (N.)

6. A plane is inclined at 30° to the horizontal and a mass of 1 ton is being pulled up the plane by a force of 1 ton wt. If the coefficient of friction is 0·3 what will the acceleration up the plane be? When the velocity has reached 5 m.p.h. at what h.p. will the force be working?   (N.)

7. A car of mass 1 ton can ascend a gradient of $\sin^{-1}\frac{1}{6}$ at a steady speed of 18 m.p.h. Working at the same horse-power it can ascend a gradient of $\sin^{-1}\frac{1}{12}$ at a steady speed of 30 m.p.h. In each case the resistances can be considered as constant and the same. Find the horse-power and the total resistance in lb wt.   (C.)

8. A fire engine can just send a jet of water from a pipe of cross-section of area $\frac{1}{20}$ ft^2 to a height of 100 ft. Calculate:
   (i) the speed of the water as it leaves the pipe,
   (ii) the mass of water in lb which leaves the pipe each second (1 ft^3 of water is of mass 62·5 lb),
   (iii) the least horse power required to project the water.   (L.)

9. A boy whose mass is 7 stone cycles up a slope of 1 in 8 (i.e. $\sin\theta = \frac{1}{8}$) at a steady speed of 3 m.p.h., the total resistances due to wind and surface being 4 lb wt. Find the force he is exerting and the horse power at which he is working. If he cycles down using the same force show that his acceleration will be 8·0 ft/sec^2.   (N.)

10. An engine, working at the rate of 210 h.p., drives a train of total mass 100 tons up a slope of 1 vertically in 40 along the slope at a constant speed of 10 m.p.h.
   (i) Find the resistance, in lb wt., due to friction.
   (ii) What would be the maximum speed on the level against the same friction if the engine continued to work at the same rate?   (L.)

11. A car of mass 1 ton climbs a hill of uniform gradient at a uniform speed of 15 m.p.h. The total length of the hill is 1100 ft and the vertical rise in this distance is 121 ft. Frictional and other resistances amount to a constant retarding force of 60 lb wt. Calculate in ft lb wt. the total work in climbing the hill.

Find the horse-power at which the engine is working.   (L.)

12. The resistance to motion of a train, whose mass including that of the engine is 200 tons, is 15 lb wt./ton. If the greatest horse-power of the engine is 360, find the greatest possible speed of the train on the level.

Find also the greatest possible acceleration of the train when its speed is 30 m.p.h., assuming that the resistance to motion is still 15 lb wt./ton.   (N.)

13. A locomotive of 2000 available horsepower can haul a train of mass 500 tons (including the locomotive itself) on a level track at a maximum speed of 75 m.p.h. Calculate the resistance to motion in lb wt./ton.

Assuming that this resistance remains constant, find the maximum speed attainable at full horsepower up a slope of 1 (vertically) in 50 (along the slope).   (L.)

14. If a gun fires a 7 lb shell every 5 sec with a muzzle velocity of 1200 ft/sec, at what h.p. is the gun working? (N.)

15. A locomotive working at the constant rate of 500 h.p. is pulling a train up an incline of 1 in 200 (measured along the track). The total mass of the train and locomotive is 250 tons. When the speed is 15 m.p.h. the acceleration is $\frac{1}{2}$ ft/sec². Find the acceleration when the speed is 30 m.p.h., assuming that the resistance remains unchanged. Find also the greatest speed that the train can reach up this incline. (L.)

16. The total mass of a train and engine is 250 tons. Its maximum speed on a level track is 60 m.p.h. and its maximum speed up a slope of inclination $\sin^{-1}(1/224)$ is 30 m.p.h. Assuming that both the horse-power and the resistance are constant, find the maximum speed up a slope of inclination $\sin^{-1}(1/112)$. (L.)

17. A car of mass 2000 lb is driven along a horizontal road against a resistance of 80 lb wt. Find the greatest speed, in miles per hour, and the pull of the engine if the engine cannot exert more than 15 h.p.

The car now pulls a trailer of mass 1200 lb against an additional resistance of 60 lb wt., the engine working at 15 h.p. Find, in lb wt., the tension in the towrope at the instant when the speed is 20 m.p.h. (L.)

18. A cyclist with his machine is of mass 200 lb. He freewheels at uniform speed down a straight road which is inclined to the horizontal at an angle θ where $\sin\theta = 1/80$. Find the horse-power at which he must work if he cycles up the incline at a constant speed of 9 m.p.h.

If he cycles along a horizontal road, working at the same rate, the resistance to his motion being unchanged, find (i) his maximum speed (in miles per hour) and (ii) his acceleration (in ft/sec²) when his speed is 9 m.p.h. (O.C.)

19. The resistance to a train, of mass 150 tons, travelling at V m.p.h., is $(a + bV)$ lb wt./ton. When the engine is working at 278 h.p. the maximum speed up an incline of 1 in 140 is 30 m.p.h., and when the engine is working at 312 h.p. the maximum speed up an incline of 1 in 70 is 20 m.p.h. Prove that the value of a is $6\frac{2}{3}$, and find the value of b.

Also find the maximum speed on the level when the engine is working at 150 h.p. (O.C.)

20. A lorry has a maximum speed of 54 m.p.h. on the level when the engine is working at 36 h.p. Calculate the total resistance to motion (in lb wt.) at this speed.

Assuming that the resistance varies as the square of the speed and that the mass of the lorry is 4 tons, find the acceleration of the lorry at the instant when its speed down an incline of 1 in 112 (i.e. $\sin^{-1}\frac{1}{112}$) is 36 m.p.h., if the engine is now working at 18 h.p. (C.)

21. The resistance to the motion of a cyclist is proportional to the square of his speed. The total mass of the man and his bicycle is 180 lb. If he can freewheel down a slope of inclination $\sin^{-1}(\frac{1}{45})$ at a steady speed of 9 m.p.h., prove that when he is ascending a slope of inclination $\sin^{-1}(\frac{1}{72})$ at the same steady speed he is working at a rate of 0·156 h.p.

If he continues to work at the same rate, find his steady speed on the level. (N.)

22. A locomotive, of mass 100 tons, is allowed to run, with steam shut off, down a slope of 1 vertically to 30 along the slope, and is observed to reach a maximum speed of 80 m.p.h. Find the resistances to motion in tons wt.

If the resistances are proportional to the square of the speed and the engine develops 1120 h.p., calculate the acceleration of the locomotive on a level track when its speed is 60 m.p.h.   (L.)

23. (i) An engine, pumping water from a well 33 ft deep, discharges 20 gal/sec with a speed of 22 ft/sec. Find the horse-power of the engine, given that 1 gal of water is of mass 10 lb.

(ii) A lorry of mass M tons, with its engine working at H h.p., has a maximum speed on the level of u m.p.h. If the maximum speed up a road inclined at an angle α to the horizontal is v m.p.h. when the rate of work and the resistance are unchanged, prove that

$$75H(u - v) = 448Muv \sin\alpha.$$ (O.C.)

24. A pump raises 300 gal of water per min from a depth of 40 ft and delivers it at a speed of 16 ft/sec. If a gallon of water is of mass 10 lb, calculate

  (i) the total work done on the water in ft lb/sec, and

  (ii) the least horse-power of the pump.   (L.)

25. A car of mass 25 cwt, travelling along a level road with the engine shut off, has its speed reduced from 30 m.p.h. to 15 m.p.h. in 200 yd. Calculate the resistances in lb wt.

If the resistances remain constant, calculate the horse-power required to drive the car up an incline of 1 in 14 at a uniform speed of 15 m.p.h.   (L.)

26. An engine, working at constant horse-power, can draw a train, of total mass W tons, at a maximum speed of 50 m.p.h. on the level, of 30 m.p.h. up an incline of 1 in 150, and of V m.p.h. down a slope of 1 in 350, the resistance in all three cases being the same. Find the value of V and, if the mass of the train is 120 tons, find the constant horse-power at which the engine was working.   (O.C.)

27. A sledge, of mass m lb, is pulled up a slope inclined at an angle α to the horizontal. Work at the rate of H h.p. is required to maintain a constant velocity V ft/sec up the slope when the coefficient of friction between the sledge and the ground is μ. Express V in terms of H, m, μ, and α.

If $\mu = 1$ and $\alpha < 45°$, and if work at the same rate of H h.p. will maintain either a constant velocity v ft/sec down the slope or a constant velocity u ft/sec along level ground, prove that u^2 is the harmonic mean between V^2 and v^2.   (O.C.)

28. A train of mass M starts from rest at A and travels with uniform acceleration for a time t_1. Steam is then shut off, and the train comes to rest at B (without the brakes being touched). The distance from A to B is a, and the total time taken is t. The resistance due to friction is k times the weight of the train. Prove that $t - t_1 = 2a/kgt$, and that the greatest rate of working of the engine during the journey is $\dfrac{2aMk^2g^2t}{kgt^2 - 2a}$.   (O.C.)

29. The total mass of a train and engine is 200 tons. Its maximum speed up a slope of $\sin^{-1}(1/80)$ is 15 m.p.h. and its maximum speed up a slope of $\sin^{-1}(1/280)$ is 30 m.p.h. Assuming that the horse-power and the resistance are constant, find the maximum speed on a level track.   (L.)

30. A tractor and plough are of mass 3 tons and the engine of the tractor can develop a maximum of 50 h.p. When ploughing a furrow up an incline of 7° to the horizontal the maximum ploughing speed is 3 m.p.h. Show that the frictional resistance, assumed constant, to ploughing is 5430 lb wt. approximately.

Find the maximum ploughing speed when the furrow is (a) on the level, (b) down the incline, the frictional resistance having the same value as before. (L.)

31. A car, of mass m tons, with its engine working at H h.p., can attain a maximum speed of v m.p.h. when running down a slope inclined at $\sin^{-1}(1/n)$ to the horizontal. If the resistance to motion can be assumed to vary directly as the speed and the maximum speed attainable when running up the same slope (at the same horse-power) is $v/3$ m.p.h., prove that $75\,Hn = 224\,mv$. (L.)

32. An engine working at 480 h.p. can pull a train of total mass 200 tons at a steady speed of 60 m.p.h. on the level, or at a steady speed of 25 m.p.h. up an incline of $\sin^{-1}(1/100)$. If the resistance to motion at speed v m.p.h. is $(a + bv^2)$ lb wt., where a and b are constants, find the values of a and b. (L.)

33. A locomotive exerting constant tractive force pulls a train of total mass 300 tons along a level line against a constant resistance of 3850 lb wt. The train starts from rest and in 2 min reaches a speed of 30 m.p.h. At the moment when this speed is reached the tractive force is reduced to half its former value for a further 4 min after which the speed is kept constant. Find the horse-power developed by the locomotive while the train is running at constant speed. (N.)

34. A fire engine is pumping water through a pipe from a reservoir, and delivering it through a circular nozzle of 3 in. diameter with a velocity of 70 ft/sec. Show that the volume pumped is between 3·43 and 3·44 ft³/sec.

If the nozzle is at the level of the surface of the water in the reservoir, show that (neglecting frictional losses) the horse power developed by the engine is just under 30. Find the additional horsepower required if the nozzle is 40 ft above the water surface. (Take the mass of 1 ft³ of water as 62·5 lb.) (N.)

35. A train whose total mass is 560 tons starts from rest on a level track. During the first 30 sec of its motion the engine exerts a force of $(25 - \tfrac{2}{3}t)$ tons weight, where t sec is the time from the commencement of the motion. The total resistance to motion is constant and equal to 5 tons wt. Show that the acceleration at time t sec is

$$\frac{4\,(30 - t)}{105} \text{ ft/sec}^2,$$

and find the speed in terms of t.

Also find (to the nearest unit) the horse-power developed by the engine when $t = 30$. (N.)

36. An engine of mass 80 tons works at 500 h.p. while pulling forty trucks, each of mass 13 tons, at a steady speed of 20 m.p.h. along a level line. If the resistance experienced by each part of the train is proportional to the weight of that part, find, in lb wt., the tension in the coupling between the engine and the first truck.

Find the acceleration of the train when the speed is 10 m.p.h. if the engine continues to work at the same rate as before, but the resistance to motion is only one-quarter of what it was when the speed was 20 m.p.h. (N.)

37. (a) A variable force F acts in a given straight line. Write down, in the form of an integral, an expression for the work done by the force when its point of application moves a distance a in the direction in which the force is acting.

(b) A particle of mass 10 gm moves in a fixed straight line under the action of a variable force. At time t sec after the commencement of the motion the magnitude of the force is $2(50 - t)$ dyn. Assuming that $t \leq 50$ and that the particle starts from rest, find its speed as a function of the time.

Find also the value of t when the rate of working of the force is greatest. (N.)

38. The total mass of a motor-cyclist and his machine is W lb. His steady speed up a hill inclined at an angle α to the horizontal is v m.p.h.; down the hill it is V m.p.h. Assuming that the resistance to motion is proportional to the speed and that full power is always being used, show that the horse-power of the machine is

$$\frac{W V v \sin \alpha}{375(V - v)}.$$

Find, in terms of V and v, the maximum steady speed in miles per hour along a horizontal road.   (N.)

39. Prove that the horse-power exerted by a force of P lb wt. moving a body at v m.p.h. is $Pv/375$.

A train of total mass 300 tons is travelling along a level line at a speed of 30 m.p.h. with an acceleration $\frac{1}{5}$ ft/sec^2. If the horse-power exerted by the engine is 596, find, in lb wt., the tractive force of the engine and the total frictional resistance to motion.

If the mass of the engine alone is 50 tons and the tension in the coupling between the engine and the rest of the train is 6000 lb wt., find the rate at which energy is being wasted by friction in the rest of the train.   (N.)

40. In tests with a car it was found that when driven on a level track at uniform speeds of (i) 20 m.p.h., (ii) 40 m.p.h., (iii) 60 m.p.h., the horse-power developed by the engine was 4, 10 and 20 respectively. Show that these observations are consistent with the assumption that the forces retarding the car are a constant force together with a force which is proportional to the square of the speed.

Assuming this relation to hold for all speeds, find the greatest horse-power at which the engine can work if the greatest speed attainable on the level is 75 m.p.h.   (N.)

41. A lorry of mass 3 tons runs down a slope, which falls 1 ft vertically for 140 ft along the road, at constant speed with the engine off. Find the horse-power necessary to pull it up the same slope at a uniform speed of 25 m.p.h.

If, after slowing down, the lorry regains speed up the same slope with the engine working at the same horse-power, find the rate (in ft lb wt./sec) at which the kinetic energy of the lorry is changing at the instant when its speed is 15 m.p.h. The frictional resistance has the same value throughout. (N.)

CHAPTER XIII

MOTION IN A CIRCLE

13.1. The Motion of a Particle which is not moving in a Straight Line

Newton's first law states that a body remains in a state of rest or of *uniform speed in a straight line* unless it is acted upon by a force. If follows from this hypothetical law that a force is necessary to maintain the motion of a body which is moving in a curve and, in particular, a force is necessary to maintain the motion of a body which is moving in a circle. We assume here,

(a) that, at a particular instant, *the direction of motion of a particle* which is moving in a curve is along the tangent to the curve at the position occupied by the particle at that instant,

(b) that the speed of the particle in the curve is defined as $\dfrac{\mathrm{d}s}{\mathrm{d}t}$,

where s is the length of the arc of the curve traversed by the particle at time t measured from an arbitrary origin. If a particle, P, is moving with *uniform speed* in a circle, any component of force in the direction of the tangent to the circle at P would change the speed of the particle in that direction, contrary to the hypothesis of uniform speed. The force which maintains a particle in a state of *uniform speed* in a circle must therefore be directed along the radius of the circle to the particle.

13.2. Angular Velocity and Angular Acceleration

If P is a particle describing a circle about a point O, fixed in the frame of reference. OX is a straight line fixed in that frame, and $\angle XOP = \theta$, [Fig. 137], then the rate of change of θ with respect to time, i.e. $\dfrac{\mathrm{d}\theta}{\mathrm{d}t}$ or $\dot{\theta}$, is defined as the angular velocity of OP. The angular acceleration of OP is $\dfrac{\mathrm{d}^2\theta}{\mathrm{d}t^2}$ or $\ddot{\theta}$. By convention, θ is measured in radians so that the units of angular velocity are rad/sec (dimensions time^{-1}) and the units of angular acceleration are rad/sec^2 (dimensions time^{-2}). In the work which follows we shall also refer to $\dot{\theta}$ and $\ddot{\theta}$

319

as the angular velocity, and angular acceleration respectively *of the particle P*. In Fig. 137, Q is the point at which the circle of motion of P cuts OX. Then, if θ is measured in radians,

$$\text{arc } PQ = a\theta,$$

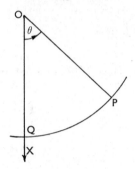

FIG. 137.

where $OP = a = $ the radius of the circle of motion.

$$\therefore \frac{\mathrm{d}(\text{arc } PQ)}{\mathrm{d}t} = a\frac{\mathrm{d}\theta}{\mathrm{d}t}.$$

$$\therefore v = a\omega, \tag{13.1}$$

where v is the speed of the particle in the direction of the tangent to the circle at P and ω is the angular velocity of P.

It can be shown that equation (13.1) is true also of a particle moving *instantaneously* in a circle of radius a about a fixed point O but not necessarily maintaining its motion in that circle.

13.3. Uniform Speed in a Circle

A particle P is moving with uniform speed in a circle of radius a about a fixed point O (Fig. 138). Ox and Oy are fixed rectangular axes through O. At time t (measured from an arbitrary origin) $\angle POx = \theta$ and the coordinates of P are $x = a\cos\theta$, $y = a\sin\theta$. Then

$$\dot{x} = -a\dot{\theta}\sin\theta, \quad \dot{y} = a\dot{\theta}\cos\theta,$$

where $\dot{x}$ and $\dot{y}$ are the components of velocity of P in the directions Ox and Oy respectively. Also, since $\dot{\theta}$ is constant,

$$\ddot{x} = -a\dot{\theta}^2\cos\theta, \quad \ddot{y} = -a\dot{\theta}^2\sin\theta,$$

where $\ddot{x}$ and $\ddot{y}$ are the components of acceleration of P in the directions Ox and Oy respectively. Therefore, the acceleration of P towards O is

$$-\ddot{x}\cos\theta - \ddot{y}\sin\theta$$

$$= a\dot{\theta}^2(\cos^2\theta + \sin^2\theta)$$

$$= a\dot{\theta}^2.$$

(In agreement with the hypothesis of uniform speed in the circle, the acceleration of P in the direction at right angles to OP is $\ddot{y}\cos\theta - \ddot{x}\sin\theta = 0$.)

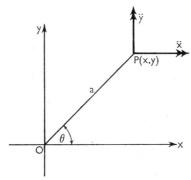

FIG. 138.

The acceleration of a particle moving with uniform angular velocity ω in a circle of radius a is $a\omega^2$ directed towards the centre of the circle. (13.2)

The acceleration of a particle moving with uniform speed v in a circle of radius a is v^2/a directed towards the centre of the circle. (13.3)

If a particle of mass m is moving with uniform angular velocity ω (and uniform speed v) in a circle of radius a, it must be acted upon by a force, directed towards the centre of the circle, of magnitude

$$m a \omega^2 = \frac{m v^2}{a}. \tag{13.4}$$

Examples. (i) A particle P of mass 10 gm is connected by a taut inextensible string of length 1 m to a fixed point O of a smooth horizontal table on which the particle rests. The breaking tension of the string is 800 gm wt. Calculate the greatest possible speed, in m/sec, at which P can describe a circle of radius 1 m about O.

The force towards the centre of the circle which maintains P in its circular motion is the tension in the string. In the usual notation, this force is therefore equal to mv^2/a and, since it must be less than the breaking tension of the string,

$$\frac{10\,V^2}{100} < 800g,$$

where V cm/sec in the greatest possible speed of the particle.

$$\therefore\ V^2 < 800 \times 980 \times 10,$$

taking g as 980 cm/sec²,

$$\therefore\ V < 2800.$$

The greatest possible speed of the particle is approximately 28 m/sec.

(ii) A particle of mass m gm is connected by a light elastic string of modulus mg dyn and natural length l cm to a fixed point O on a smooth table and is describing a horizontal circle about O at a rate of n/π rev/sec, where $n^2 < g/(4l)$. Find an expression for the radius of the circle.

$$n/\pi \text{ rev/sec} = 2n \text{ rad/sec}.$$

The force towards the centre of revolution is the tension in the string.

$$\therefore\ mx(2n)^2 = \frac{\lambda(x-l)}{l},$$

where λ is the modulus of elasticity of the string and x cm is the radius of the circle.

$$\therefore\ 4mn^2x = \frac{mg(x-l)}{l}.$$

$$\therefore\ x = \frac{gl}{g - 4n^2l}.$$

EXERCISES 13.3.

1. Calculate, in kgm wt. correct to the nearest unit, the force necessary to maintain a body of mass 2 kgm in uniform angular speed of 2 rev/sec in a circle of radius 20 cm.

2. Calculate, in lb wt., the force necessary to maintain a body of mass 3 cwt in uniform speed of 32 ft/sec in a circle of radius 14 ft.

3. A car of mass 15 cwt moves in a horizontal circle of radius $\frac{1}{4}$ mile at 30 m.p.h. What is the component of force acting on the car in a direction towards the centre of the circle.

4. A mass of 3 lb is revolving at the end of a string 2 ft long on a smooth horizontal table, and making 1 rev/sec. Find the tension in the string.

If the string would break under a tension of 40 lb wt. find the greatest possible speed of the mass. (N.)

5. A particle of mass 2 lb is fastened by a string of length 3 ft to a point 2 ft above a smooth horizontal table, and is describing a circle on the table with uniform speed of 1 rev in 2 sec. Find the force exerted on the table and the tension in the string, stating the units in which the magnitudes are given. (N.)

6. One end of a light inextensible string of length l ft is fastened to a smooth table at O, and to the other end of the string a particle of mass m lb is attached and revolves about O on the table. If the string breaks when its tension exceeds Mg pdl, find the greatest number of rev/min that the particle can make. (N.)

7. One end of a light inextensible string of length $2l$ ft is fastened to a fixed point O of a smooth horizontal table; the string carries two masses of m lb, one at A, the midpoint of the string, and one at the other end B. If the masses, moving in contact with the table, describe circles with angular velocity ω about O as centre, while OAB remains a straight line, find in lb wt. the tensions in OA and AB. (N.)

8. Two particles commence simultaneously to move from the end A of a diameter AB of a circle of radius 2 ft. One moves along the diameter and the other around the circumference, each with constant speed both reaching the point B after π sec. Find the velocity and acceleration of the particle on the circumference relative to that on the diameter when the latter has moved 1 ft. (L.)

13.4. Some Examples of Uniform Circular Motion in a Horizontal Circle

For a particle which is describing a circle with uniform speed in a horizontal plane, the two principles which determine the motion are:

1. The sum of the components towards the centre of revolution of the forces acting on the particle is equal to $ma\omega^2$, where m is the mass of the particle, a is the radius of the circle of revolution and ω is the angular velocity of the particle.

2. The sum of the vertical components of the forces acting on the particle is zero.

Examples. (i) A rough horizontal turntable can rotate about a vertical axis and a heavy particle is placed on the table at a distance of 8 in. from the axis. The table is made to rotate with gradually increasing angular velocity. If the coefficient of friction between the particle and the table is $\frac{1}{3}$, show that the particle will not move relative to the table if the number of rev/min does not exceed 38. (L.)

The forces acting on the particle are its weight, mg pdl, the normal component, R pdl, of the reaction between the table and the particle and the frictional force, F pdl, between the table and particle, which acts in the direction necessary to prevent relative motion (Fig. 139).

The equations of motion for the particle, when it is not moving relative to the table, are

$$R = mg,$$

$$F = m \cdot \tfrac{2}{3}\omega^2,$$

where ω rad/sec is the angular velocity of the table.

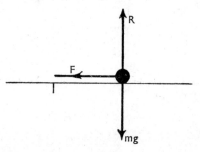

FIG. 139.

Since
$$\frac{F}{R} \leqq \frac{1}{3},$$

$$\therefore \ \frac{2}{3}\frac{\omega^2}{g} \leqq \frac{1}{3},$$

$$\therefore \ \omega^2 \leqq 16.$$

$$\therefore \ \omega \leqq 4.$$

$$4 \text{ rad/sec} = \frac{4}{2\pi} \times 60 \text{ rev/min} \doteqdot 38 \cdot 2 \text{ rev/min}.$$

Therefore the particle will not move relative to the table if the number of rev/min does not exceed 38.

(ii) A particle hangs by a light inextensible string of length l from a fixed point O, and a second particle of the same mass hangs from the first by an equal string. The whole system moves with constant angular speed ω about the vertical through O, the upper and lower strings making constant angles α and β respectively with the vertical. Show that

$$\tan \alpha = p(\sin \alpha + \tfrac{1}{2}\sin\beta),$$

and that
$$\tan\beta = p(\sin\alpha + \sin\beta),$$
where $p = l\omega^2/g$. (N.)

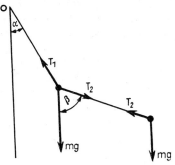

FIG. 140.

Let the mass of each particle be m. The forces acting on each particle are as shown in Fig. 140.

The equations of motion for the first particle are:

$$mg + T_2\cos\beta = T_1\cos\alpha, (1)$$

$$T_1\sin\alpha - T_2\sin\beta = ml\omega^2\sin\alpha. (2)$$

The equations of motion for the second particle are:

$$T_2\cos\beta = mg, (3)$$

$$T_2\sin\beta = m(l\sin\alpha + l\sin\beta)\omega^2. (4)$$

Therefore, from (1) and (3),

$$T_1\cos\alpha = 2mg.$$

Therefore, from (2) and (3),

$$2mg\tan\alpha - mg\tan\beta = ml\omega^2\sin\alpha,$$

i.e. $$2\tan\alpha - \tan\beta = p\sin\alpha. (5)$$

From (3) and (4),

$$mg\tan\beta = ml\omega^2(\sin\alpha + \sin\beta).$$

$$\therefore \tan\beta = p(\sin\alpha + \sin\beta). (6)$$

Therefore, from (5) and (6),

$$\tan\alpha = \tfrac{1}{2}p\sin\alpha + \tfrac{1}{2}\tan\beta$$
$$= \tfrac{1}{2}p\sin\alpha + \tfrac{1}{2}p(\sin\alpha + \sin\beta)$$
$$= p(\sin\alpha + \tfrac{1}{2}\sin\beta).$$

The Conical Pendulum

A particle of mass m is attached to a fixed point O by an inelastic string of length l and describes a horizontal circle of constant radius with uniform speed in a horizontal plane below O. Such a system as this is called a conical pendulum.

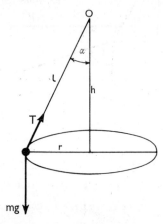

FIG. 141

Figure 141 shows the two forces acting on the particle, viz. its weight mg and the tension T in the string. The equations of motion for the particle are

$$T \cos \alpha = mg,$$

$$T \sin \alpha = ml\omega^2 \sin \alpha,$$

where α is the semi-vertical angle of the cone of the string's motion and ω is the angular velocity of the particle. Hence

$$\omega = \sqrt{\left(\frac{g}{l \cos \alpha}\right)}$$

and the time taken for one revolution of the conical pendulum is P, where

$$P = \frac{2\pi}{\omega} = 2\pi \sqrt{\left(\frac{l \cos \alpha}{g}\right)}.$$

The time of revolution P may be variously expressed as

$$P = 2\pi \sqrt{\left(\frac{h}{g}\right)} \quad \text{or} \quad P = 2\pi \sqrt{\left(\frac{r \cot \alpha}{g}\right)} \quad \text{or} \quad P = 2\pi \sqrt{\left\{\frac{(l^2 - r^2)^{\frac{1}{2}}}{g}\right\}},$$

where h is the vertical height of the point of suspension above the plane of revolution of the particle and r is the radius of the circle of revolution.

The Motion of a Railway Carriage on a Banked Track

A vehicle describing a circle on a level track must be acted upon by a force towards the centre of the circle; this force could be provided, for example, by the friction between a car and the road or by the force between the outer rail and the flange of the wheel in the case of a railway carriage. Such forces create considerable practical disadvantages (such as, for example, the tendency to overturn the vehicle) which can be lessened by banking the track so that the outer

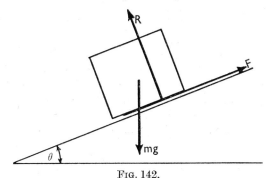

FIG. 142.

wheels are higher than the inner wheels. Figure 142 represents a railway carriage of mass m on a track which is banked at an angle θ with the horizontal. The track is part of a circle of radius a and the carriage moves with uniform speed v.

The equations of motion for the carriage are,

(i) $$R\cos\theta + F\sin\theta = mg,$$

(ii) $$R\sin\theta - F\cos\theta = \frac{mv^2}{a}.$$

From these equations, multiplying (i) by $\sin\theta$ and (ii) by $\cos\theta$, and then subtracting the second equation from the first, we have

$$F(\sin^2\theta + \cos^2\theta) = mg\sin\theta - \frac{mv^2}{a}\cos\theta.$$

$$\cdot\ F = mg\sin\theta - \frac{mv^2}{a}\cos\theta.$$

Similarly $$R = mg\cos\theta + \frac{mv^2}{a}\sin\theta.$$

The following considerations arise in special cases:

(a) There is no sideways pressure on the rails, i.e. $F = 0$, when $\tan\theta = v^2/ag$.

(b) When $\theta > \tan^{-1}(v^2/ag)$, F is positive and there is an inward thrust on the inner rail.

When $\theta < \tan^{-1}(v^2/ag)$, F is negative and there is an outward thrust on the outer rail. The angle θ is normally chosen so that $F = 0$ for the usual speed at which trains take the curve. In the case of a banked track for cars, the angle of banking increases towards the outside of the track so that a higher value of θ can be chosen as v increases.

(c) When there is no sideways pressure on the rails, since the carriage does not overturn in the plane of the diagram, the resultant normal reaction R must act through the centre of mass. The normal reactions at the outer and inner rails must therefore be equal. (It is assumed that the centre of mass of the carriage lies on the perpendicular bisector of a line joining the centres of the outer and inner wheels.)

(d) If the track is a horizontal plane, $\theta = 0$, $F = -\dfrac{mv^2}{a}$ and $R = mg$. In this case, since the sum of the moments of the forces acting on the carriage about the centre of mass is zero,

$$mgx = \frac{mv^2}{a}h,$$

where x is the distance of the line of action of R from the centre of mass and h is the height of the centre of mass above the rails.

It follows that x is positive for all values of v and therefore that the normal pressure on the outer wheel is always greater than the normal pressure on the inner wheel. Also, since we must have $x < b$ where $2b$ is the width of the carriage,

$$v^2 < \frac{agb}{h}.$$

The carriage will upset if $v > \sqrt{\left(\dfrac{agb}{h}\right)}$.

(e) Figure 143 represents the forces acting on a cyclist riding round a horizontal circular track of radius a. The cyclist with his machine leans towards the centre of the track at an angle θ with the vertical, R is the normal action of the track on the cycle and F is the frictional force of the track on the cycle. The combined mass of cyclist and cycle is m and their centre of mass is at G. When the cyclist rides at a speed v round the track,

(i) $$R = mg,$$

(ii) $$F = \frac{mv^2}{a},$$

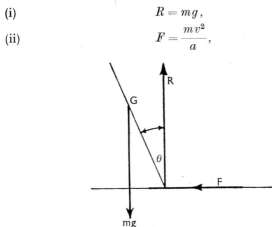

FIG. 143.

and if the cyclist is not to overturn, the moment-sum of the forces about G must be zero, i.e. the resultant of R and F must pass through G. Therefore

(iii) $$\tan\theta = \frac{F}{R}.$$

$$\tan\theta = \frac{v^2}{ag}.$$

Motion of a Satellite in a Circular Orbit

A small satellite revolving about a planet in a circular orbit is maintained in that orbit by the gravitational attraction of the planet. Because the mass of an artificial satellite is small compared with that of the earth, calculations concerning the motions of such satellites can be concluded with a sufficient degree of accuracy if the earth is treated as a fixed body in space. In the same way, for the purpose of a first approximation, we can treat the sun as fixed and neglect

22*

the interaction between the planets in determining the separate motions of the planets.

Example. A small satellite of mass m revolves uniformly in a circular orbit of radius a about a fixed spherical planet of mass M and radius c. Given that the gravitational attraction between two spherical bodies of mass m_1, m_2 whose centres are r apart is $Gm_1 m_2/r^2$ (where G is a universal constant), show that the period T of revolution of the satellite is $2\pi \sqrt{(a^3/gc^2)}$, where g is the force per unit mass at the planet's surface due to its own gravity.

Three satellites A, B, C, each of mass m, are each describing uniformly the same circular orbit of radius a such that ABC is always an equilateral triangle. Show that their period of revolution is

$$T\left(1 + \frac{m}{M\sqrt{3}}\right)^{-\frac{1}{2}}. \qquad \text{(N.)}$$

Because the force of gravitation acting on a body of mass m at the earth's surface is mg, and because the force of gravitation between two spherical bodies of fixed mass is inversely proportional to the square of the distance between their centres, the force of gravitation acting on the satellite in its orbit is mgc^2/a^2 directed towards the centre of the planet. Therefore, if ω is the uniform angular velocity of the satellite about the planet,

$$\frac{mgc^2}{a^2} = ma\omega^2.$$

$$\therefore \omega = \sqrt{\left(\frac{gc^2}{a^3}\right)}.$$

$$\therefore T = 2\pi \sqrt{\left(\frac{a^3}{gc^2}\right)}.$$

Figure 144 shows the forces acting on satellite A when the three satellites move in the same orbit. These are

(1) the force of gravitational attraction due to the satellite C acting along the line AC and equal to $Gm^2/3a^2$ (since $AC = a\sqrt{3}$),

(2) a force $Gm^2/3a^2$ acting along AB due to the gravitational attraction of the satellite B,

(3) the force GMm/a^2 along AO, where O is the centre of the planet, due to the gravitational attraction of the planet.

The resultant of these three forces is

$$Gm\left(\frac{2m}{3a^2}\cos 30^\circ + \frac{M}{a^2}\right) \text{ along } AO.$$

But
$$\frac{GMm}{c^2} = mg, \quad \therefore \ GM = c^2 g.$$

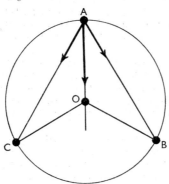

Fig. 144.

Therefore the resultant force towards O acting on satellite A is

$$\frac{c^2 g\, m}{M}\left(\frac{m}{a^2\sqrt{3}} + \frac{M}{a^2}\right).$$

$$\therefore \ \frac{c^2 g\, m}{M}\left(\frac{m}{a^2\sqrt{3}} + \frac{M}{a^2}\right) = m\, a\, \Omega^2,$$

where Ω is the uniform angular velocity of satellite A.

$$\therefore \ \Omega = \sqrt{\left\{c^2 g\left(\frac{m}{M\, a^3\sqrt{3}} + \frac{1}{a^3}\right)\right\}} = \frac{2\pi}{T}\sqrt{\left(1 + \frac{m}{M\sqrt{3}}\right)}.$$

Therefore the period of revolution of each of the satellites is

$$T\left(1 + \frac{m}{M\sqrt{3}}\right)^{-\frac{1}{2}}.$$

EXERCISES 13.4.

1. Two light rods AB, AC, each of length 100 cm, are joined by smooth hinges to a particle of mass 300 gm at A; the rods are smoothly hinged at B and C to two points of a vertical spindle such that B is above C and $BC = 100$ cm. The spindle is made to rotate so that the particle describes a horizontal circle at a uniform speed of 1 rv/sec. Find in gm wt. the tension or thrust in AB. (N.)

22**

2. A particle is attached by two equal light inextensible strings to two points A and B distant a apart in the same vertical line and rotates in a horizontal circle with uniform angular velocity ω. Show that for both strings to remain stretched ω must exceed $\sqrt{(2g/a)}$, and that, if the tensions in the strings are in the ratio of 2 to 1, then $\omega = \sqrt{(6g/a)}$. (N.)

3. Two small masses, of 2 oz and 1 oz respectively, are connected by a light inextensible string, a foot long, which passes through a small smooth fixed ring. The 2 oz mass hangs at a distance 9 in. below the ring, while the 1 oz mass describes a horizontal circle. Show that the plane of this circle is $1\frac{1}{2}$ in. below the ring, and show also that the 1 oz mass makes very approximately 153 rev/min. (O.C.)

4. The ends of a light string, of length $18a$, are attached to two fixed points L, M in the same vertical line, M being at a depth $12a$ below L. A small smooth ring R of mass m is threaded on the string. The ring revolves in a horizontal circle with M as centre and the string taut. Show that $MR = 5a$ and that the tension in the string is $13\,mg/12$. Find the period of revolution. (N.)

5. A particle P is attached by two equal strings to two points A and B in the same vertical line. The system revolves with constant angular velocity ω about AB, so that P describes a horizontal circle. If $AB = 9$ ft, and $\omega = 8/3$ rad/sec, prove that the tension in one string is zero, and that if $\omega = 16/3$ rad/sec, the tensions in the strings are in the ratio 5 : 3. (L.)

6. AC, of length a, and BC are two light rods hinged at C, the mass of the hinge being M lb. The ends A and B are hinged to two points, A being vertically above B; $\angle ACB = 90°$ and $\angle BAC = \theta$. If the system revolves with uniform angular velocity, ω, about AB, prove that both rods are in tension if

$$\cos\theta > \frac{g}{a\omega^2}.$$

If either rod can withstand a maximum tension of $5\,Mg$ pdl, find the maximum value of ω if $a = 1\frac{1}{3}$ ft and $\theta = 60°$. (O.C.)

7. A particle moving inside a smooth spherical bowl of radius a is describing a horizontal circle at a distance $\frac{1}{2}a$ below the centre of the bowl. Prove that its speed is $\frac{1}{2}\sqrt{(6ga)}$. (N.)

8. A circular cone of semi-vertical angle α is fixed with its axis vertical and its vertex upwards. An inextensible string of length l is attached at one end to the vertex and at the other to a particle of mass m resting on the smooth external surface of the cone. The particle then revolves with uniform angular velocity ω in a horizontal circle in contact with the cone. Show that $\omega^2 < (g\sec\alpha)/l$ and find the tension of the string. (N.)

9. A rough circular disc rotates with constant angular velocity about a vertical axis through its centre O and perpendicular to its plane making n rev/sec. A particle P is placed on the disc at a distance r from O, the coefficient of friction between P and the disc being μ. Prove that P remains on the disc provided that

$$\mu \geqq 4\pi^2 n^2 r/g.$$ (O.C.)

10. A car of mass 1 ton describes a horizontal circle of radius 242 ft, at 30 m.p.h. on a track which is banked at an angle α to the horizontal. If $\tan\alpha = \frac{1}{4}$, prove that there is no lateral frictional force between the tyres and the track.

If the speed of the car is increased to 60 m.p.h. and the car describes the same path, find the lateral frictional force between the tyres and the track, and prove that if there is no sideslip the coefficient of friction must be greater than 0·6.   (N.)

11. Two particles of masses m_1 amd m_2 are attached to the ends of a string which passes through a small smooth ring. The position of the ring is fixed, but it is capable of free rotation about the vertical axis passing through itself. Show that if the system revolves in such a way that each particle describes a horizontal circle, the two circles must be at the same level. If l_1 and l_2 are the lengths of the two portions of the string, find the ratio l_1/l_2 in terms of the masses.
                                                                              (N.)

12. A particle of mass 4 oz is attached to an inextensible string of negligible mass and of length 3 ft to form a conical pendulum, which moves with the string inclined at a constant angle 60° to the vertical. Calculate the tension in the string, and the time of one complete revolution about the vertical.   (N.)

13. A motor-cyclist travels round a curved track of radius 847 ft at a speed of 60 m.p.h. The track is banked at an angle of $\tan^{-1}(2/11)$ to the horizontal. If R is the component of the reaction on the wheels perpendicular to the plane of the track, and S the component along the line of greatest slope of the track, calculate the ratio $R:S$.
For what speed would S be zero?   (L.)

14. A particle of mass 4 lb is whirled round at the end of a string 20 in. long, so as to describe a horizontal circle at 60 rev/min; calculate the tension in the string (in lb wt.) and prove that the fixed end of the string is a little less than 10 in. above the centre of the circle.   (O.C.)

15. A particle of mass m is suspended from a fixed point by an inextensible string of length l. It is describing a horizontal circle steadily with angular velocity ω. Prove that, if θ is the inclination of the string to the vertical,

$$\omega^2 \cos\theta = g/l.$$

If the string is elastic, of natural length a, and if the tension of the string when stretched a length x is λx, prove that in steady motion the equation connecting ω and θ is

$$\omega^2 \cos\theta = \frac{g}{a}\left(1 - \frac{m}{\lambda}\,\omega^2\right). \qquad \text{(O.C.)}$$

16. A car of mass 5 cwt travels at 30 m.p.h. round a circular track of radius 100 yd which is banked at an inclination of 10° to the horizontal. What is the frictional force exerted across the track, and in what sense does it act?
Show that 0·025 would be a sufficient coefficient of friction to prevent sideslip.   (O.C.)

17. The governor of a gramophone consists essentially of a particle on a light wire 2 in. long which rotates as a conical pendulum. The governor is geared to the turntable so that the angular velocity of the governor is twice that of the turntable. Find the semi-vertical angle of the conical pendulum when the turntable is rotating at 78 rev/min.   (C.)

18. A railway curve is an arc of a circle of radius R. The track is banked at an angle α to the horizontal such that there is no sideways force on the rails when a vehicle travels along the track with speed V. Express R in terms of V and α.

If a vehicle of weight W traverses the same curve at a speed $2V$ show that the sideways force on the rails is $3W \sin \alpha$. (L.)

19. A rough horizontal plate rotates with constant angular velocity ω about a fixed vertical axis. A particle of mass m lies on the plate at a distance $5a/4$ from this axis. If the coefficient of friction between the plate and the particle is $1/3$ and the particle remains at rest relative to the plate, show that

$$\omega \leq \sqrt{\{4g/(15a)\}}.$$

The particle is now connected to the axis by a horizontal light elastic string, of natural length a and modulus $3mg$. If the particle remains at rest relative to the plate and at a distance $5a/4$ from the axis, show that the greatest possible angular velocity of the plate is $\sqrt{\{13g/(15a)\}}$ and find the least possible angular velocity. (N.)

20. At any point P outside the Earth and at a distance x from its centre the acceleration f due to gravity is inversely proportional to x^2. If R is the radius of the Earth and g is the value of f at its surface, express f in terms of R, g and x.

Find the speed in miles per hour with which an artificial satellite would describe a circle of radius 4500 miles, concentric with the Earth and the time in minutes it would take to describe the circle once.

(Take R as 3960 miles and g as 79,000 m.p.h./hr.) (N.)

13.5. Motion in a Circle when the Speed is not Necessarily Uniform

The position of a particle P, moving in a circle of radius a about a fixed point O, is determined as in § 13.3 (and using Fig. 138) but in this case $\dot\theta$ is not necessarily constant.

We obtain the components of velocity and acceleration parallel to the x and y-axes thus:

$$x = a\cos\theta, \qquad\qquad y = a\sin\theta.$$
$$\dot{x} = -a\dot\theta \sin\theta, \qquad\qquad \dot{y} = a\dot\theta \cos\theta,$$
$$\ddot{x} = -a\dot\theta^2 \cos\theta - a\ddot\theta \sin\theta, \quad \ddot{y} = -a\dot\theta^2 \sin\theta + a\ddot\theta \cos\theta.$$

Therefore the acceleration of P towards O is

$$-\ddot{x}\cos\theta - \ddot{y}\sin\theta$$
$$= a\dot\theta^2(\cos^2\theta + \sin^2\theta) + a\ddot\theta(\sin\theta \cos\theta - \cos\theta \sin\theta)$$
$$= a\dot\theta^2.$$

The acceleration of P in the direction of the tangent to the circle is, by definition, $a\ddot\theta$ and this may be verified as being the value of $\ddot{y}\cos\theta - \ddot{x}\sin\theta$.

It follows that, for a particle of mass m moving in a circle of radius a, whose angular velocity at a particular instant is ω and whose linear speed at this instant is v:

the acceleration *at this instant* towards the centre of the circle is

$$a\omega^2 = v^2/a, \qquad (13.5)$$

the force *towards the centre of the circle*, acting on the particle at this instant is

$$m a\omega^2 = m v^2/a. \qquad (13.6)$$

The acceleration in the direction of the tangent to the circle and the force in that direction required to produce the acceleration are, respectively, $a\alpha$ and $m a\alpha$, where α is the value of the angular acceleration of the particle at this instant. (13.7)

Example. A smooth wire bent into the form of a circle of radius r is fixed in a horizontal plane. Two small rings, each of mass m, are threaded on the wire and are connected to each other by a light rod of length $2r\sin\alpha\,(\alpha < \tfrac{1}{2}\pi)$. The rod is initially at rest, and a force of constant magnitude F is applied to one of the rings in a direction always tangential to the wire and towards the other ring. Show that the thrust in the rod during the subsequent motion is $\tfrac{1}{2}F\sec\alpha$. Show also that at the instant when the rod has completed one revolution the force exerted by the wire on either particle is

$$F(\tfrac{1}{2}\tan\alpha + 2\pi). \qquad (N.)$$

Let θ be the angle made at time t by OA with the initial position of OA. Then the forces acting on the rings will be as shown in Fig. 145, where T is the tension in the light rod and R, S are the normal

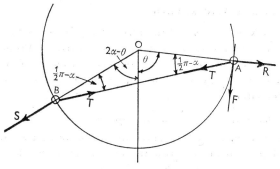

Fig. 145.

actions of the wire on the rings A and B respectively. The force F acts upon the ring A. The equations of motion for the rings are:

for A, $T \sin \alpha - R = m r \dot{\theta}^2,$ (1)

$F + T \cos \alpha = m r \ddot{\theta},$ (2)

for B, $T \sin \alpha - S = m r (-\dot{\theta})^2,$ (3)

$T \cos \alpha = m r (-\ddot{\theta}),$ (4)

obtained using the equations $\dfrac{\mathrm{d}}{\mathrm{d}t}(2\alpha - \theta) = -\dot{\theta}$ and $\dfrac{\mathrm{d}^2}{\mathrm{d}t^2}(2\alpha - \theta) = -\ddot{\theta}$ to express the components of the acceleration of B in terms of $\dot{\theta}, \ddot{\theta}$. Equations (2) and (4) give

$$F = 2 m r \ddot{\theta}.$$

$$\therefore \ T = - m r \ddot{\theta} \sec \alpha = - \tfrac{1}{2} F \sec \alpha.$$

Therefore, the rod is in compression and the thrust in the rod is $\tfrac{1}{2} F \sec \alpha$.

Also equations (1) and (3) give

$$R = S = T \sin \alpha - m r \dot{\theta}^2 = - \tfrac{1}{2} F \tan \alpha - m r \dot{\theta}^2.$$

When the rod has completed one revolution the work–energy relationship gives, for $\theta = 2\pi$,

$$2 \pi r F = 2 \times \tfrac{1}{2} m r^2 \dot{\theta}^2.$$

Therefore, at this instant,

$$R = S = - \tfrac{1}{2} F \tan \alpha - 2 \pi F,$$
$$= - F (\tfrac{1}{2} \tan \alpha + 2 \pi).$$

The force exerted by the wire on either particle is towards the centre of the ring.

13.6. Motion in a Vertical Circle

In Chapter X we discussed the relationship between the equation of energy and the equation of motion of a particle. Problems concerning motion in a vertical circle are best considered by combining the equation of energy with the equation of motion towards the centre of the circle.

Motion on the Outside of a Smooth Sphere

A particle of mass m is slightly disturbed from rest and slides from the highest point P down the outside of a smooth sphere of radius a in a vertical plane, Fig. 146.

When the particle is at Q on the sphere where $\angle POQ = \theta$, the forces acting on the particle are its weight mg and the normal reaction R of the sphere on the particle acting along OQ. If v is the speed of the particle at Q, then

(i) the equation of motion for the particle in the direction QO is

$$mg \cos\theta - R = mv^2/a,$$

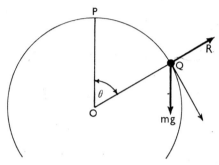

FIG. 146.

(ii) the energy equation for the particle is

$$mga(1 - \cos\theta) = \tfrac{1}{2}mv^2.$$

From (i) and (ii),

$$R = mg(3 \cos\theta - 2).$$

Therefore

since $\quad 3 \cos\theta - 2 > 0 \quad$ for $\quad \theta < \cos^{-1}\tfrac{2}{3}$

and $\quad 3 \cos\theta - 2 < 0 \quad$ for $\theta > \cos^{-1}\tfrac{2}{3}$,

the particle leaves the sphere when $\theta = \cos^{-1}\tfrac{2}{3}$. After leaving the sphere, the particle moves freely under gravity in a parabolic path, its initial velocity being $\sqrt{(2ga/3)}$ at an angle $\cos^{-1}\tfrac{2}{3}$ below the horizontal.

Motion of a Suspended Particle in a Vertical Circle

A particle of mass m is suspended vertically from a fixed point O by a light inextensible string of length a (Fig. 147). P is the initial position of the particle which is given an initial horizontal velocity u. When the particle reaches the point Q so that $\angle POQ = \theta$, the forces acting on it are its weight, vertically downwards, and the tension in the string acting in the direction QO. Then, if v is the speed of the particle in this position,

(i) the equation of motion for the particle in the direction QO is

$$T - mg\cos\theta = \frac{mv^2}{a},$$

(ii) the energy equation for the particle is

$$mga(1 - \cos\theta) + \tfrac{1}{2}mv^2 = \tfrac{1}{2}mu^2.$$

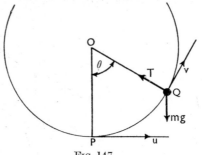

FIG. 147.

From (i) $T = mv^2/a + mg\cos\theta$, and T is therefore positive for all values of $\theta < \tfrac{1}{2}\pi$ so that the string does not go slack for positions of Q below the horizontal through O.

From (ii) $v = 0$ when $\theta = \tfrac{1}{2}\pi$ if $u = \sqrt{(2ga)}$, and if $u < \sqrt{(2ga)}$, $v = 0$ when $\theta = \alpha$ where $\alpha < \tfrac{1}{2}\pi$. It follows that if $u \leq \sqrt{(2ga)}$ the particle oscillates about P.

From (i) and (ii)

(iii) $$v^2 = u^2 - 2ga(1 - \cos\theta),$$

(iv) $$T = \frac{mu^2}{a} + mg(3\cos\theta - 2).$$

Hence both v^2 and T decrease as θ increases in the range $0 < \theta < \pi$. In order that the particle should describe complete vertical circles the string must never be slack (other than instantaneously), i.e. $T \geq 0$ for $0 \leq \theta \leq \pi$. This condition implies that the least value of T, i.e. $m(u^2/a - 5g)$, must not be negative. Therefore

(v) $$u^2 \geq 5ga$$

is a *necessary* condition that the particle should describe complete circles. In this case (iii) above implies $v^2 \geq ga$ and so v never vanishes. Therefore the particle continues to move in the same direction round the circle and, in fact, (v) is a *sufficient* condition that the particle describes vertical circles.

When $u^2 = 5ga$, T vanishes instantaneously when the particle is at the top of its path.

It follows that for $\sqrt{(2ag)} < u < \sqrt{(5ag)}$, the string slackens before the particle can reach the highest point of the circle. The particle then moves freely as a projectile under gravity.

Examples. (i) A particle, free to move on the inside of a smooth fixed hollow spherical bowl of internal radius a, is projected horizontally from its lowest position A with speed $2(ga)^{1/2}$. Show that the particle leaves the surface of the bowl when at a height $5a/3$ above A. Show also that the greatest height above A attained by the particle is $50a/27$.   (L.)

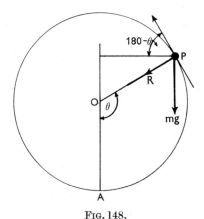

FIG. 148.

Figure 148 shows the forces acting on the particle when it reaches the point P of the surface of the bowl so that $\angle AOP = \theta$. R is the normal reaction of the bowl on the particle in the direction PO and mg is the weight of the particle. (The mass of the particle is m.) If the speed of the particle at the point P is v, the equation of motion of the particle in the direction PO is

$$- mg\cos\theta + R = \frac{m v^2}{a}$$

and the equation of energy is

$$mga(1 - \cos\theta) + \tfrac{1}{2} mv^2 = 2mga.$$
$$\therefore R = 2mg + 3mg\cos\theta.$$

The particle leaves the surface of the bowl at the point where $R = 0$, i.e. at the point where $\cos\theta = -\frac{2}{3}$ and at this point the particle is at a height $5a/3$ above A. The velocity of the particle is then $\sqrt{(-ag\cos\theta)} = \sqrt{(2ag/3)}$.

The particle now moves as a projectile freely under gravity, with initial vertical component of velocity

$$\sqrt{\left(\frac{2ag}{3}\right)}\sin\theta = \frac{\sqrt{5}}{3}\sqrt{\left(\frac{2ag}{3}\right)} = \sqrt{\left(\frac{10ag}{27}\right)}.$$

Therefore the particle rises to a height h above P where

$$\frac{10ag}{27} = 2gh, \quad \text{i.e.} \quad h = \frac{5a}{27}.$$

Therefore the greatest height above A attained by the particle is

$$\frac{5a}{27} + \frac{5a}{3} = \frac{50a}{27}.$$

(ii) A particle P, of mass m, is suspended by two equal light inextensible strings PA, PB, where A and B are fixed at the same level and each string is inclined at an angle α to the horizontal. Find the tension in either string.

If the string PB is suddenly cut so that P starts to move in a circular path, find the tension in the string PA when it is inclined at an angle θ to the horizontal.

If the tension in PA is suddenly halved when PB is cut, find the angle α. (N.)

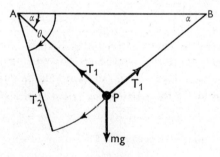

FIG. 149.

In the initial position of equilibrium $2T_1\sin\alpha = mg$, i.e. $T_1 = mg/(2\sin\alpha)$, where T_1 is the tension in either string (Fig. 149).

After the string PB is cut and when the string PA is inclined at an angle θ to the horizontal, by conservation of energy

$$mga\,(\sin\theta - \sin\alpha) = \tfrac{1}{2}mv^2,$$

where v is the speed of the particle and $PA = a$.

$$\therefore\; v^2 = 2ga(\sin\theta - \sin\alpha).$$

Therefore, if T_2 is the tension in the string PA in this new position, the equation of motion towards A for the particle P is

$$T_2 - mg\sin\theta = \frac{m\,v^2}{a} = \frac{2mga(\sin\theta - \sin\alpha)}{a}.$$

$$\therefore\; T_2 = mg\,(3\sin\theta - 2\sin\alpha).$$

If the tension in PA is suddenly halved when PB is cut, then $T_2 = mg/(4\sin\alpha)$ when $\theta = \alpha$.

$$\therefore\; \frac{mg}{4\sin\alpha} = mg\sin\alpha.$$

$$\therefore\; \sin^2\alpha = \tfrac{1}{4}, \quad \alpha = 30°.$$

(iii) A smooth narrow tube is in the form of a circle, of centre O and radius a, fixed with its plane vertical. Two particles A and B, of masses m and $2m$ respectively, are connected by a light inextensible string of length πa and are placed at opposite ends of the horizontal diameter of the tube, the string occupying the upper half of the tube. The system is released from rest. If OB makes an angle θ with the horizontal at time t after release and $0 < \theta < \tfrac{1}{2}\pi$, show by energy considerations that

$$a\left(\frac{d\theta}{dt}\right)^2 = \frac{2}{3}\,g\sin\theta.$$

Hence, or otherwise, find in terms of m, g and θ the tension in the string. Find also the force exerted by the tube on particle A.   (N.)

At time t after release, if the potential energy is measured from the initial position of the particles as origin (Fig. 150),

$$\text{potential energy of } A = mga\sin\theta,$$

$$\text{potential energy of } B = -2mga\sin\theta,$$

$$\text{kinetic energy of } A = \frac{1}{2}\,ma^2\left(\frac{d\theta}{dt}\right)^2,$$

$$\text{kinetic energy of } B = ma^2\left(\frac{d\theta}{dt}\right)^2.$$

23*

Therefore, by conservation of energy,

$$\frac{3}{2}\,m\,a^2\!\left(\frac{\mathrm{d}\theta}{\mathrm{d}t}\right)^2 - m g a \sin\theta = 0,$$

i.e.

$$a\!\left(\frac{\mathrm{d}\theta}{\mathrm{d}t}\right)^2 = \frac{2}{3}\,g\sin\theta.$$

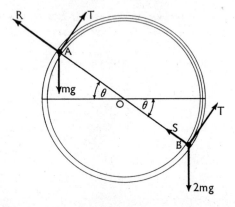

FIG. 150.

Differentiating this equation with respect to t, we have

$$2a\,\frac{\mathrm{d}\theta}{\mathrm{d}t}\,\frac{\mathrm{d}^2\theta}{\mathrm{d}t^2} = \frac{2}{3}\,g\cos\theta\,\frac{\mathrm{d}\theta}{\mathrm{d}t}.$$

$$\therefore\ \frac{\mathrm{d}^2\theta}{\mathrm{d}t^2} = \frac{g}{3a}\cos\theta$$

since $\mathrm{d}\theta/\mathrm{d}t \neq 0$ (except instantaneously at $t = 0$).

Then the equation of motion of the particle A in the direction of the string is

$$T - m g \cos\theta = m a\,\frac{\mathrm{d}^2\theta}{\mathrm{d}t^2} = \frac{1}{3}\,m g \cos\theta,$$

where T is the tension in the string.

$$\therefore\ T = \tfrac{4}{3}\,m g \cos\theta.$$

The equation of motion of the particle A in the radial direction is

$$m g \sin\theta - R = m a\!\left(\frac{\mathrm{d}\theta}{\mathrm{d}t}\right)^2,$$

where R is the force exerted by the tube on the particle.

$$\therefore R = mg\sin\theta - \tfrac{2}{3}mg\sin\theta = \tfrac{1}{3}mg\sin\theta.$$

Otherwise: the equations of motion for the particle A are,

(1) $$T - mg\cos\theta = ma\,\frac{\mathrm{d}^2\theta}{\mathrm{d}t^2},$$

(2) $$mg\sin\theta - R = ma\left(\frac{\mathrm{d}\theta}{\mathrm{d}t}\right)^2.$$

The equations of motion for the particle B are,

(3) $$2mg\cos\theta - T = 2ma\,\frac{\mathrm{d}^2\theta}{\mathrm{d}t^2},$$

(4) $$S - 2mg\sin\theta = 2ma\left(\frac{\mathrm{d}\theta}{\mathrm{d}t}\right)^2,$$

where S is the force exerted by the tube on this particle. Hence, solving for T and $\mathrm{d}^2\theta/\mathrm{d}t^2$ from equations (1) and (3) we have,

$$T = \frac{4}{3}mg\cos\theta, \qquad \frac{\mathrm{d}^2\theta}{\mathrm{d}t^2} = \frac{g}{3a}\cos\theta.$$

Therefore, by integration with respect to θ,

$$\int \frac{\mathrm{d}\left(\dfrac{\mathrm{d}\theta}{\mathrm{d}t}\right)}{\mathrm{d}t}\,\frac{\mathrm{d}\theta}{\mathrm{d}t}\,\mathrm{d}t = \frac{g}{3a}\sin\theta + C.$$

$$\therefore \int \frac{\mathrm{d}\theta}{\mathrm{d}t}\,\mathrm{d}\left(\frac{\mathrm{d}\theta}{\mathrm{d}t}\right) = \frac{g}{3a}\sin\theta + C.$$

$$\therefore \frac{1}{2}\left(\frac{\mathrm{d}\theta}{\mathrm{d}t}\right)^2 = \frac{g}{3a}\sin\theta + C.$$

$\left[\text{The result } \int \dfrac{\mathrm{d}^2\theta}{\mathrm{d}t^2}\,\mathrm{d}\theta = \dfrac{1}{2}\left(\dfrac{\mathrm{d}\theta}{\mathrm{d}t}\right)^2 + C \text{ is of frequent occurrence and should be remembered and quoted where necessary.}\right]$

Since $\dfrac{\mathrm{d}\theta}{\mathrm{d}t} = 0$ when $t = 0$, $C = 0$.

$$\therefore \left(\frac{\mathrm{d}\theta}{\mathrm{d}t}\right)^2 = \frac{2g}{3a}\sin\theta.$$

R can now be found from the equation of motion (2) as before.

The first of these two methods illustrates the obtaining of the equation of motion from the energy equation by differentiation and the second illustrates the reverse process of obtaining the energy equation from the equation of motion by integration.

EXERCISES 13.6.

1. A particle of mass 2 oz is suspended from a fixed point by a light inextensible string 1 ft long, and hangs in equilibrium. The particle is then projected with a horizontal velocity of 16 ft/sec. Calculate, in ounces weight, the tension when the string has turned through (i) 60°; (ii) 180°. (N.)

2. An aeroplane is flying in a vertical circle of radius 400 ft (looping the loop). If the pilot is of mass 140 lb, find the tension in the strap holding the pilot to his seat at the top of the circle if the plane is then going at 60 m.p.h. (N.)

3. A particle of mass 1 oz is attached to one end of a light inextensible string and is moved in a vertical circle, the other end of the string remaining fixed and the string being taut. The speeds at the highest and lowest points are 10 ft/sec and 22 ft/sec respectively. Calculate
(i) the radius of the circle;
(ii) the tension of the string when the particle is in its highest position. (N.)

4. A bead of mass m is allowed to slide down a smooth circular wire, whose plane is vertical, starting from rest at the end of a horizontal diameter. Prove that, when the radius through the bead makes an angle θ with the horizontal, the reaction on the bead is $3mg\sin\theta$. (O.C.)

5. A string of length a has one end attached to a fixed point O and hangs vertically at rest with a particle attached to the other end. The particle is given a horizontal velocity V; when it has risen to a height $\frac{1}{2}a$ above the level of O, the string becomes slack. Prove that

$$V^2 = \tfrac{7}{2}ga.$$ (O.C.)

6. A heavy particle, of mass m, oscillates through 180° on the inside of a smooth circular hoop of radius a fixed in a vertical plane. Prove that the force exerted on the hoop at any point ˙s $3mv^2/2a$. (O.C.)

7. The road over a hump-backed bridge is in the form of a circular arc of radius 42 ft. Assuming that the mass of a car may be regarded as concentrated at its centre of gravity 2 ft above road level, and that the car is moving with constant speed, find, in miles per hour, the greatest speed at which the car can cross the bridge without leaving the ground.

If the mass of the car is $1\frac{1}{2}$ tons, find in lb wt. the magnitude of the vertical reaction of the bridge on the car at the instant when it is passing over the crown of the bridge at 15 m.p.h. (C.)

8. A particle rests at the highest point of a fixed smooth sphere of radius a. If the particle is slightly displaced, find the angle through which the radius to it has turned when it leaves the sphere. With what speed does it leave the sphere?

With what horizontal speed must the particle be projected from the highest point if it is to leave the sphere when it has descended a vertical distance $\frac{1}{4}a$? (L.)

9. A small body is tied by a fine string to a fixed point and projected so as to describe a circle in a vertical plane. Prove that the sum of the tensions of the string when the body is at the opposite ends of a diameter is the same for all diameters. (L.)

10. A particle is projected horizontally with velocity u from the highest point of a fixed smooth sphere of radius a. Prove that, if $u^2 \geqq ga$, the particle leaves the sphere immediately, but that if $u^2 < ga$, the particle slides on the surface until the radius to it is inclined to the vertical at an angle θ such that

$$\cos\theta = (u^2 + 2ga)/3ga. \qquad \text{(L.)}$$

11. A particle of mass m, fastened to one end of a light inextensible string of length r, is describing a circle in a vertical plane about the other end, which is fixed. If u is the speed at the lowest point, show that when the string has turned through an angle θ from the downward vertical the tension in the string is

$$\frac{m\,u^2}{r} - m\,g\,(2 - 3\cos\theta).$$

If, for such a particle, the ratio of the maximum to the minimum tension of the string is $3:1$, show that the ratio of the maximum to the minimum speed is $\sqrt{2}:1$. (N.)

12. A particle is free to slide down the outside of a fixed smooth circular cylinder, of radius a, whose axis is horizontal. If the particle is slightly displaced from rest at a point on the highest generator of the cylinder, find its velocity at the instant it leaves the cylinder.

Find also the horizontal and vertical components of its velocity when it reaches the level of the lowest generator of the cylinder. (N.)

13. A particle of mass m is attached to one end of a light inextensible string of length a whose other end is fixed. When at rest in its lowest position the particle is projected horizontally with speed $\sqrt{(nga)}$. Show that while the string remains taut the tension in it when it has turned through an angle θ is

$$mg(n - 2 + 3\cos\theta).$$

If $n = 7/2$, find the value of θ for which the string slackens, and show that the particle reaches a height of $27a/16$ above the point of projection before beginning to fall. (N.)

14. A smooth tube is bent into the form of a circle of radius 1 ft and fixed with the plane of the circle vertical. Prove that a particle in the tube projected from the lowest point with a velocity of 12 ft/sec will go completely round the tube.

Prove also that it will not go completely round if the material of the tube facing the centre of the circle is cut away. (O.C.)

15. A particle inside and at the lowest point of a fixed smooth sphere of radius a is projected horizontally with speed $\sqrt{(7ga/2)}$. Show that it will leave the sphere at a height $3a/2$ above the lowest point and that its subsequent path meets the sphere again at the point of projection. (N.)

16. A particle of mass m is attached to one end of a light inextensible string of length l whose other end is tied to a fixed point O. When the particle is in its lowest position it is projected horizontally with speed V. Derive expressions for the speed of the particle and the tension in the string when the string has turned through an angle θ. Deduce the value of V which will just enable the particle (i) to rise to the level of O, (ii) to complete a circular path.

The particle is allowed to move from a position of rest in which the string is taut and horizontal. When the string has turned through 90° it catches against a small fixed peg. Find the least depth of the peg below O if the particle subsequently describes a complete circle about the peg.   (N.)

17. A particle P of mass m is attached to a fixed point O by a light inextensible string and is moving in a vertical circle about O as centre. The tension in the string is T_1 when P is at its lowest point. Prove that when OP makes an angle θ with the downward vertical the tension T in the string is $T_1 - 3mg(1 - \cos\theta)$. If $T = T_2$ when OP is horizontal, prove that for complete revolutions without the string slackening $T_2/T_1 \geqq \frac{1}{2}$.

If however $T_2/T_1 = \frac{1}{4}$, determine the value of θ when the string becomes slack.   (N.)

18. A mass of 8 oz is attached to two fixed points A, B, which are 18 in. apart and in the same horizontal line, by means of two strings each 15 in. in length. The mass is held with the strings taut in the horizontal plane through AB, and is then released. Find the tension of a string, when the mass is in the vertical plane through AB.   (O.C.)

19. A light inextensible rod of length b hangs vertically with the upper end smoothly pivoted to a fixed point O and the lower end A attached to a particle of mass m. The particle is projected horizontally with speed $5u$ and describes complete circles in a vertical plane. If $3u$ is the speed of the particle at the highest point of its circular path, show that $u^2 = \frac{1}{4}gb$.

When OA makes an angle θ with the downward vertical, show that

$$b(\mathrm{d}\theta/\mathrm{d}t)^2 = \tfrac{1}{4}(17 + 8\cos\theta)\, g$$

and find the tension in the rod.   (N.)

20. Two particles, of masses m and $2m$, are connected by a light inextensible string of length πr and are placed on the outside of a smooth vertical circle of radius r, so that the string is just taut and the particles are at opposite ends of the horizontal diameter. The system is then released from rest. Show that, in the subsequent motion, the lighter particle leaves the circular path after the radius to it has turned through an angle θ given by

$$4\theta = 5\sin\theta.$$ (L.)

MISCELLANEOUS EXERCISES. XIII

1. Two particles are connected by a light string of length l which passes through a small smooth ring which is free to rotate about a vertical axis. The heavier particle of mass m hangs vertically below the ring, and the lighter particle of mass m' moves with constant speed v in a horizontal circle; the particle m lies in the plane of this circle. Show that

$$v^2 = \frac{m - m'}{m'}\, gl.$$ (O.C.)

2. A ring is threaded on a smooth circular wire, centre O and radius a, fixed in a vertical plane. When at the highest point of the wire the ring is given a horizontal velocity $\sqrt{(ga)}$ in the plane of the wire. Prove that the magnitude of the horizontal component of the reaction of the wire on the ring is a maximum when the ring is at a vertical distance $a/2$ below O. (O.C.)

3. A motor car is running on a level road round a curve with a speed of v ft/sec. Its track width is $2a$ ft; the centre of mass of the car is describing an arc of a circle of radius r ft and its height above the road is h ft. Find the thrusts of the road on the near and offside wheels, and show that the car will turn over if $v > \sqrt{(gar/h)}$. Also find the minimum coefficient of friction to prevent sideslip when the car is on the point of turning over. (L.)

4. A rough horizontal disc is revolved at a constant angular speed about a fixed vertical axis through its centre, and on it is placed a particle at a distance of one foot from the axis. If the coefficient of friction between the disc and the particle is $\frac{1}{2}$ and the particle remains at rest relative to the disc, find the greatest possible angular speed of the disc. (L.)

5. A particle is projected with speed u from the lowest point of a fixed smooth hollow sphere of radius a so as to slide on the inner surface. Prove that, if $5ga > u^2 > 2ga$, the particle leaves the sphere at a height $(u^2 + ga)/(3g)$ above the starting point. (L.)

6. A conical pendulum consists of a light elastic string of natural length l_0 and modulus λ attached to a bob of mass m. Show that, when the pendulum rotates with an angular velocity ω, the inclination θ to the vertical is given by

$$\cos\theta = \frac{g(\lambda - m\omega^2 l_0)}{\lambda l_0 \omega^2}. \qquad \text{(N.)}$$

7. A conical pendulum of length l ft rotates steadily with its string inclined at a constant angle α to the vertical. Prove that the number of revolutions per second is

$$\frac{1}{2\pi}\sqrt{\left(\frac{g}{l\cos\alpha}\right)}.$$

If the pendulum performs one revolution in 2 sec and the string is inclined at $60°$ to the vertical, prove that the acceleration of the bob is $32\sqrt{3}$ ft/sec^2. (N.)

8. A railway carriage of mass 3 tons is moving at the rate of 30 m.p.h. on a curve of 770 ft radius. If the outer rail is not raised above the inner, find the lateral pressure on the outer rail in lb wt. (L.)

9. A particle attached to the end of a string 12 in. long, the other end of which is fixed, moves in a horizontal circle of diameter 12 in. Find approximately the number of revolutions described per minute. (L.)

10. A particle suspended by a fine string from a fixed point describes a circle uniformly in a horizontal plane. If it makes 3 complete revolutions every 2 sec, show that its vertical depth below the fixed point is 4·3 in. approximately. (Take $\pi = 22/7$.) (O.C.)

11. A particle of mass $2m$ hangs at rest at the end of an inextensible string of length l, the upper end of which is fastened to a fixed point. A particle of mass m is projected so as to impinge horizontally and directly on the first particle which then recoils until the string makes an angle of $60°$ with the downward vertical when it comes instantaneously to rest. If the coefficient of restitution for the particles is $\frac{1}{3}$, prove that the velocity of the particle of mass m before impact is $\frac{9}{4}\sqrt{(gl)}$.

Show also that the tension in the string immediately after impact is $4mg$.

(N.)

12. A particle of mass m lb is whirled round at the end of a light string of length l ft so as to describe a horizontal circle with an angular velocity ω. Show that the inclination of the string to the vertical is

$$\cos^{-1}(g/l\omega^2),$$

and deduce that steady circular motion is impossible if $l\omega^2 < g$.

Show that the inclination of the string to the vertical is increased by an increase in ω. (O.C.)

13. A particle is fastened to one end of a string, the other end of which is fastened to a fixed point O. The particle rotates with uniform angular velocity ω about the vertical through O, so that the string is inclined at an angle α to the downward vertical. Show that the length of the string is $g/\omega^2 \cos\alpha$.

If the point O, instead of being fixed, is descending with uniform accelera-tion f, the particle still rotating with uniform angular velocity ω, find f in order that the string may make an angle α with the *upward* vertical. (O.C.)

14. A small ring C can move freely on a light inextensible string the two ends of which are attached to points A and B, the point A being vertically above and at a distance c from B. When the ring C is describing a horizontal circle with constant angular speed ω the distances of C from A and B are b and a respectively. Prove that

$$2gc(a + b) = \omega^2(a - b)[c^2 - (a + b)^2].$$

(N.)

15. A heavy particle is attached to one end of a fine string of length l ft, the other end being fastened to a fixed point O. Initially it is held at rest in a posi-tion in which the string is taut and makes an angle θ with the downward vertical through O. It is then let go and, as the particle passes through its lowest position A, the mid-point of the string is held fast, without causing any change of velocity of the particle. The particle now rises on the other side to a point B, such that the lower half of the string is inclined at an angle φ to the downward vertical. Prove that

$$\cos^2 \tfrac{1}{2}\varphi = \cos\theta.$$

If φ is small and $l = 6\frac{1}{4}$, show that the particle will return from B to A in just under $\frac{1}{2}$ sec. (C.)

16. A particle of mass m, hangs in equilibrium at one end of a light in-extensible string, of length a, whose other end is attached to a fixed point O. If the particle is projected horizontally with velocity $2\sqrt{(ga)}$, prove that when the string is inclined at an angle θ to the upward-drawn vertical, the tension in the string is $mg(2 - 3\cos\theta)$.

Show also that, in the motion after the string becomes slack, the particle will describe part of a parabola and will pass through a point on the vertical line through O at a height $9a/16$ above O. (N.)

17. A particle P of mass $2m$ is attached by a light inextensible string of length a to a fixed point O and is also attached by another light inextensible string of length a to a small ring Q of mass $3m$ which can slide on a fixed smooth vertical wire passing through O. The particle P describes a horizontal circle with OP inclined at an angle $\frac{1}{3}\pi$ with the downward vertical.

(i) Find the tensions in the strings OP and PQ.

(ii) Show that the speed of P is $(6ga)^{\frac{1}{2}}$.

(iii) Find the period of revolution of the system. (N.)

18. Two particles of equal mass are connected by a fine inextensible string which passes through a small smooth hole in a smooth horizontal table. The particle on the table describes a circle with constant speed v, while the other particle hangs at rest. Calculate the radius of the circle in terms of v.

If the particle on the table is suddenly brought to rest by an impulse applied to it, find the magnitude of the impulse and the speed with which the particle reaches the hole. (N.)

19. A light inextensible string ABC is such that $AB = 20$ in. and $BC = 15$ in. A particle of mass m is attached to the string at C and one of mass $7m$ is attached at B. The end A is tied to a fixed point and the whole system rotates steadily about the vertical through A in such a way that B and C describe horizontal circles of radii 12 in. and 24 in. respectively. Show that the tension in BC is $5mg/3$.

Also find the tension in AB and the speed of B. (N.)

20. A light endless inextensible string, of length $2\pi a$, lies inside and along the bore of a fine smooth tube, bent into the form of a circle, of radius a. The tube is fixed in a vertical plane. A particle of mass M is attached to a point A of the string and a particle of mass $m(< M)$ is attached to the diametrically opposite point B. If the particles are released from rest when AB is horizontal, prove that, when A is at a depth h below the centre, the speed of each particle is

$$\sqrt{\left(\frac{M-m}{M+m}\,2g\,h\right)}.$$

Show also that the reactions at A and B at this instant are in the ratio $M(3M - m) : m(M - 3m)$. (N.)

21. One end A of a light inelastic string, of length a, is fixed at a height $2a$ above a horizontal floor. To the other end is attached a particle which is released from rest at a point distant a from A and $2a$ from the floor. The string breaks when it reaches the vertical position. At what horizontal distance from A does the particle strike the floor and what are the direction and magnitude of its velocity? (L.)

22. A cylindrical tube of internal radius a is made to rotate about its axis, which is horizontal, with constant angular velocity ω. A particle of mass m is placed on the inner surface of the tube and remains in contact with it without slipping. Calculate the normal component R and the tangential component F of the force exerted by the tube on the particle if the radius to the particle makes an angle θ with the upward vertical. Prove that $a\,\omega^2$ must not be less than g.

Putting $a\omega^2/g$ equal to $\sec\alpha$, show that F/R is greatest when $\theta = \alpha$, and find its value in this position. (C.)

23. A light string, of length l, has one end fixed at A; the other carries a particle of mass m. Initially, the particle is held so that the string is taut and horizontal; it is then let go. Determine, in terms of m, g, l, and θ,

(i) the kinetic energy of the particle,

(ii) the tension of the string,

when the string makes an angle θ with the downward vertical.

When the particle is vertically below A it coalesces with a stationary particle of mass M. Prove that the combined mass ascends until the string makes an angle
$$\cos^{-1} \frac{M\,(M + 2\,m)}{(M + m)^2}$$
with the vertical, and that the loss of energy due to the coalescing of the two particles is
$$\frac{M\,m}{M + m}\, g\,l\,. \tag{O.C.}$$

*24. A uniform smooth tube of small cross-sectional area is bent into a circular arc of radius a and angle $2(\pi - \alpha)$, where α is acute. The tube is held firmly in a vertical plane with its axis of symmetry vertical and its open ends uppermost. A particle is projected inside the tube from its lowest point with velocity u. The particle leaves the tube, moves freely under gravity, and then again enters the tube. Find the value of u^2, and show that its least possible value is $2(1 + \sqrt2)\,ga$, and that this value occurs when $\alpha = \pi/4$. Show also that the highest point reached by the particle is at height $a(\sec\alpha + \cos\alpha - 2)/2$ above the top of the completed circle. (N.)

*25. A small artificial satellite is required to encircle the earth in the plane of the equator with uniform speed, the period of revolution being $2\pi/\omega$. The earth is assumed to be a sphere of radius R and the gravitational acceleration at a height y above the earth's surface is $g R^2/(R + y)^2$.

(i) Show that, if $\omega^2 = g/(n^3 R)$, the height of the satellite must be $(n - 1)\,R$. If, in a particular case, this height is to be 300 miles, find to the nearest minute the period of revolution of the satellite, assuming that R is 3960 miles and g is 32 ft/sec^2.

(ii) Find the velocity, in terms of g, n and R, with which the satellite should be projected vertically from the earth's surface in order just to reach a height $(n - 1)\,R$. (N.)

*26. Two particles P, Q, each of mass m, are joined by a light inextensible string. The particle P is held at rest at a point on the highest generator of a smooth circular cylinder, of radius a, having its axis horizontal. The particle Q hangs freely and lies in the vertical plane through P at right angles to the axis of the cylinder. If P is now released, show that it will leave the surface of the cylinder when the radius through P makes with the vertical the angle α, where
$$2\cos\alpha - 1 - \alpha = 0\,.$$

Find in terms of α the tension in the string at the instant when P leaves the surface. (L.)

*27. Two particles are connected by a light string which passes over a fixed smooth vertical disc of radius a. The system starts from rest with the lighter particle, of mass m, at one end of the horizontal diameter of the disc and the heavier particle, of mass M, hanging freely. Find the reaction between the lighter particle and the disc in terms of θ, the angle which the radius drawn to the particle makes with the horizontal.

In the subsequent motion it is found that the particle leaves the disc after having risen a height $a/2$. Find the value of the ratio m/M and the velocity of the particle when contact ceases. (L.)

*28. A rough rod can turn in a vertical plane about one end Q, which is fixed. Two small, equally rough, heavy rings are put on the rod at A and B, where $QA = 1$ ft, $QB = 1\frac{1}{2}$ ft. When the rod is horizontal it is set rotating in a downward direction with angular velocity 4 rad/sec, which is kept constant. Show that, if the coefficient of friction is $3/4$, the ring at B will slip at once, and the ring at A will slip when the rod is inclined to the horizontal at an angle θ given by

$$3 \cos\theta - 4 \sin\theta = 2. \tag{L.}$$

*29. A small bead P of mass m is threaded on a smooth circular wire, of radius a and centre O, fixed in a vertical plane. The bead is initially at the lowest point A of the circle and is projected along the wire with a velocity which is just sufficient to carry it to the highest point. Denoting the angle POA by θ find the reaction between the wire and the bead in terms of θ.

Deduce from the energy equation by means of integration that the time for the bead to reach the position $\theta = \frac{1}{2}\pi$ is $(a/g)^{\frac{1}{2}} \log_e(1 + \sqrt{2})$. (L.)

*30. A smooth circular ring of radius a is fixed in a horizontal plane. A light elastic string has one end attached to a point at a height h vertically above the centre of the circle; the other end is attached to a heavy particle. The natural length of the string is $\sqrt{(h^2 + a^2)} = c$, and when the particle hangs in equilibrium the length of the string is $c + b$. Show that the particle can describe a horizontal circle with uniform angular velocity ω, the string passing through the ring but not touching it, provided that $\omega^2 < g/(h + b)$, and also show that the string will then be inclined at an angle α to the vertical, where $\omega^2(b + c \cos\alpha) = g$.

If however $\omega^2 > g/(h + b)$, show that the string will touch the ring, its lower part being inclined at an angle β to the vertical, where $\omega^2(b + a \cot\beta) = g$. (N.)

*31. The force of gravity acting on a particle of mass m at a distance r from the earth's centre O is mga^2/r^2, where a is the earth's radius and $r > a$. Show, by calculating the work done in raising the particle from the earth's surface, that its potential energy is

$$mga^2\left(\frac{1}{a} - \frac{1}{r}\right).$$

Find the velocity of a particle describing uniformly a circular orbit of radius r about O. Deduce an expression for its total energy, and show that if the radius of the orbit be increased by a small amount δr, the total energy will be increased by $(mga^2/2r^2)\,\delta r$ approximately.

If the motion of a satellite subject to a small retarding force F is represented as a series of uniformly described circles, decreasing in radius from r to $r - \varrho$ (ϱ small) in n rev, show that an estimate of the value of F is

$$(mga^2/4\pi n r^3)\,\varrho. \tag{N.}$$

*32. A particle lies in a thin rough tube, which is in the form of a circle of radius a. When the tube is stationary in a vertical plane, the radius to the highest point (P) in the lower half of the tube at which the particle can rest without slipping makes an acute angle β with the downward vertical. When the tube rotates with constant angular velocity ω about the vertical through the centre, shew that the particle can remain at the point P of the tube for all values of ω if $\beta \geq \frac{1}{4}\pi$. For what range of values of ω^2 is this possible if $\beta < \frac{1}{4}\pi$? (C.)

ANSWERS TO THE EXERCISES

MISCELLANEOUS EXERCISES. I (p. 8)

1. 10^6 dyn.   **2.** $3\frac{4}{7}$ ft/sec².   **3.** 80 lb.   **4.** $(m - R)\, g/m$.
5. 3.40×10^{-14} kgm wt.   **6.** (a) $m(g_1 - g_2)$ dyn; (b) d_1^2/d_2^2.
7. 20.   **8.** 121 $W/100$ lb.   **9.** $33\frac{3}{5}$.   **10.** 214,000 miles.

EXERCISES 2.6. (p. 17)

1. $R = \sqrt{61}$ lb wt. $= 7.81$ lb wt.; $\alpha = \tan^{-1}(2\sqrt{3}/7) = 26°\ 20'$.
2. $R = \sqrt{21}$ lb wt. $= 4.58$ lb wt.; $\alpha = \tan^{-1}(2/\sqrt{3}) = 49°\ 7'$.
3. $\alpha = 90°$; $\theta = 90° + \tan^{-1}(\frac{3}{4}) = 126°\ 52'$.
4. $Q = 6.01$ lb wt.; $\theta = 86°\ 16'$.
5. $P = Q = 4\sqrt{3}$ lb wt. $= 6.93$ lb wt.
6. $P = 10$ lb wt.; $Q = 10\sqrt{3}$ lb wt. $= 17.3$ lb wt.
7. $P = 8\sqrt{3}$ lb. wt. $= 13.9$ lb wt.; $Q = 16\sqrt{3}$ lb wt. $= 27.7$ lb wt.
8. $R = P\sqrt{7}$; $\alpha = \tan^{-1}(\frac{1}{2}\sqrt{3}) = 40°\ 54'$.
11. Each $8\frac{1}{3}$ lb wt.
12. $\sqrt{3}$ lb wt. $= 1.73$ lb wt.; 1 lb wt.
13. At angle $\sin^{-1}(5 \sin 5°) = 25°\ 51'$ with the direction of motion of the boat and $5° + \sin^{-1}(5 \sin 5°) = 30°\ 51'$ with the rope.
14. 237.5 lb wt., 174 lb wt.
15. $P\sqrt{3}$.   **16.** 8 lb wt., 6 lb wt.
18. $10\sqrt{3}$ lb wt. $= 17.3$ lb wt.; $X = 10$.
19. Force $= 10.7$ lb wt., tension $= 27.0$ lb wt., greatest inclination $53°\ 25'$.
20. (i) 1.73 oz wt.; (ii) 1 oz wt.
21. $6\sqrt{3}$ lb wt. $= 10.4$ lb wt.; 6 lb wt.

EXERCISES 2.7. (p. 24)

(i) 15 lb wt.; 19°.   (ii) 0.39 lb wt.; 180°.
(iii) 7.4 lb wt.; 20°.   (iv) 2.3 lb wt.; 155°.
(v) $(2 + \sqrt{2})\, P = 3.4\, P$; 0°.   (vi) $0.78\, P$; 350°.
7. 7.9 lb wt.; N. $62°\ 24'$ W.   **8.** 3.2 lb wt.; E. $37°$ N.
9. 63.5 lb wt.; W. $14°$ S.   **10.** 57 lb wt.; S. $40°$ E.
11. 6 lb wt. at $22°$ with BC on side remote from A.
12. 8.9 lb wt.; E. $28°$ N.   **13.** 8.2 lb wt. at $72°$ with Ox.
14. Bisecting the angle between the 6 lb wt. and 7 lb wt. forces.
15. $P = 2.52$ lb wt.; $\theta = 8°$.
16. $P = 2.83$ lb wt.; $Q = 10.83$ lb wt.
17. $\theta = 75\frac{1}{2}°$; $P = 2.55$ lb wt.
18. $P = 6\sqrt{2}$ lb wt. $= 8.49$ lb wt.; $Q = 2\sqrt{2}$ lb wt. $= 2.83$ lb wt.
19. 1.42 lb wt. at $4°$ above the horizontal and towards the 6 lb mass.
20. $k(AB + AD)\sqrt{2}$.

EXERCISES 2.10. (p. 36)

1. 13·2 lb wt. **2.** 26·4 lb wt.; at $36\frac{1}{2}°$ with the wall.

3. 15 lb wt.; along the beam.

4. $\frac{2}{3}\sqrt{3}$ lb wt.; at 30° with the vertical.

5. 140 lb wt.; at 33° with the vertical.

6. 3·95 lb wt.; 7·9 ft.

7. 1·96 lb wt.; 2·64 lb wt.; 0·98 ft from A.

8. 155 lb wt. at 52° with the horizontal.

9. At A, 33 lb wt. at 13° to AB and above AB; at B, 48 lb wt. at right angles to AB.

10. By the wall, 10·4 lb wt. perpendicular to the wall; by the plane, 37·5 lb wt. at 74° with the plane (14° with the beam).

11. $\frac{1}{2}W$; $\frac{1}{2}W\sqrt{3}$ at 30° to the upward vertical (and 30° to BA).

12. $10\sqrt{3}$ lb wt. = 17·3 lb wt.; 10 lb wt.; 60°.

13. *Either* the rod makes the angle $\sin^{-1}(\frac{4}{5}) = 53°$ with the upward vertical and the reaction at the hinge is $0·72\,W$ at $19\frac{1}{2}°$ with the upward vertical, *or* the rod makes the angle $\sin^{-1}(\frac{4}{5})$ with the downward vertical and the reaction at the hinge is $0·72\,W$ at $19\frac{1}{2}°$ with the upward vertical.

17. $30\sqrt{5} = 67$ lb wt.; $\tan^{-1}(\frac{1}{2}) = 26\frac{1}{2}°$ with the upward vertical.

18. $(2W\sin\alpha)/\sqrt{3}$. **19.** $Q = \frac{1}{2}P$, $R = \frac{1}{2}\sqrt{5}P$.

20. $30W/13$ lb wt.; $1·44\,W$.

21. $3\theta - \sin\theta = 3$; 76°.

24. If $1 \leq \dfrac{w}{2T} \leq \dfrac{c}{c-a}$, $x = (w-T)(c-a)/a$;

if $\dfrac{w}{2T} > \dfrac{c}{c-a}$, $x = \dfrac{w(c-a) + 2aT}{2T}$.

MISCELLANEOUS EXERCISES. II (p. 41)

1. $6·5P$; N. 38° W. **2.** 4·2 lb; S. 18° W.

3. 577. **4.** $\sqrt{17}$ lb wt.; $DY = 1$ in.

5. $x = 2\frac{1}{2}$, $y = \frac{1}{2}\sqrt{3}$; 6 lb wt. along AC.

6. 84 lb wt. in AC, 35 lb wt. in BC.

7. (i) 7·47 lb wt.; (ii) 61° 54'; (iii) 1·69 in.

8. $\frac{1}{2}W\cot\alpha$. **9.** 7·53 lb wt.; $119\frac{1}{2}°$.

11. $13W/10$; (i) $65W/12$; (ii) 39 : 25.

13. $14\frac{18}{23}$ gm wt.; $6\frac{2}{23}$ gm wt. **14.** 20 oz wt.; 15 oz wt.

15. (i) $\sqrt{7}$ lb wt. **16.** 1·5 ft. **17.** $w\sqrt{5}$.

19. $W(a^2 + l^2)/(2l^2)$. **20.** 30°; $w\sqrt{3}$, w, w.

22. $(5W\sqrt{2})/3$, $(W\sqrt{26})/3$, $(W\sqrt{41}/3$.

23. $(2PQ\sin\alpha)/\sqrt{(P^2 + Q^2 + 2PQ\cos 2\alpha)}$.

24. $W\sqrt{(1 + 8\cos^2\alpha)}$, $2W\sqrt{(1 + 8\cos^2\alpha)}$.

25. $mg/\{2(\cot\theta - \cos\theta)\}$.

26. 52°. **27.** $2W\cos\frac{1}{2}\alpha$ vertically downwards. **30.** $W/\sqrt{5}$.

31. $\dfrac{T}{\sin\beta} = \dfrac{R}{\sin\alpha} = \dfrac{W}{\sin(\alpha+\beta)}$; $W\sin\alpha$.

32. Tension in string of length a is $(2W\sqrt{2})/\sqrt{11}$, in string of length $2a$ is $(3W\sqrt{2})/\sqrt{11}$; reaction is $(W\sqrt{2})/\sqrt{11}$.

EXERCISES 3.2. (p. 56)

1. (i) 106 ft/sec; (ii) 162 ft/sec.
2. 3 ft/sec^2. **3.** 1·2 ft/sec^2.
4. (a) (i) $1\frac{1}{2}$ min; (ii) 3·2 miles; (b) 0·29 ft/sec^2, 1·17 ft/sec^2.
5. 4·1 miles, (ii) 5·9 miles/min$^2 \doteqdot 8\cdot7$ ft/sec^2; $4\frac{1}{2}$ min.
6. (i) $2\frac{7}{12}$ miles; (ii) $\frac{11}{36}$ ft/sec^2; (iii) $7\frac{1}{2}$ sec.
7. $51\frac{1}{2}$ ft.   **8.** 13·5 sec. **9.** 1·7 sec. **10.** 8·6 ft/sec^2.

EXERCISES 3.3. (p. 65)

1. $\frac{1}{2}$.   **2.** 8.   **3.** 16.   **4.** -24.
5. 12.   **6.** -5.   **7.** 32.   **8.** 2.
9. 32.   **10.** 19.   **11.** 2 or $1\frac{1}{2}$.
12. $u = 3$, $a = 2$, or $u = 7/3$, $a = 22/9$.
13. $u = 6$, $v = 2$, $t = 2$.   **14.** $\frac{1}{2}(n - 1)$.
15. $u = 4$, $a = -\frac{1}{2}$. **16.** (i) 6 sec; (ii) $2\frac{4}{9}$ ft/sec^2.
17. They meet after $2\frac{2}{3}$ sec and after 8 sec.
18. 36 sec, 12 sec, 12 sec.   **19.** 53 sec.   **20.** 42 and 210 ft.
21. 2 ft/sec^2; 55 sec; 3025 ft; 11 sec.
22. 21 ft/sec; 104 ft from O; 13 ft/sec; 3 sec and 9 sec after A passes O; 102 ft.
23. 60 ft/sec; $142\frac{1}{2}$ sec after leaving A.
24. (i) 220 sec; (ii) 9600 ft. **25.** 300 ft.
26. $75s/32$.   **27.** 18 ft/sec; $6\frac{1}{8}$ ft.
29. 45 m.p.h.; $-\frac{11}{40}$ ft/sec^2, $\frac{11}{80}$ ft/sec^2.
30. 16,500 yd; $17\frac{1}{2}$ min.

EXERCISES 3.4. (p. 70)

1. (i) 100 ft; 5 sec.   **2.** (i) -60 ft/sec; (ii) $2\frac{1}{2}$ sec.
3. 195 m/sec. **4.** $4\frac{1}{2}$ sec. **5.** 36 ft/sec.
7. $(3u + g)/(u + g)$ sec. **8.** $3\frac{1}{2}$ sec.
9. $\frac{1}{2}u$ ft/sec. **10.** 80 ft/sec.

MISCELLANEOUS EXERCISES. III (p. 71)

1. 27 sec; 729 ft. **2.** 1 sec, 4 sec; 48 ft/sec upwards, 48 ft/sec downwards.
3. $\frac{1}{4}$ sec; 6 ft above the ground, $\frac{3}{4}$ sec after the first ball is thrown up.
4. 24 ft; $2\frac{1}{2}$ sec. **5.** 196 ft; 6 sec.
6. 40 ft/sec.   **7.** $32\frac{1}{4}$ m.p.h.
9. (i) 6 miles; (ii) 11/50 ft/sec^2; (iii) $6\frac{1}{2}$ min.
10. Acceleration $\frac{44}{225}$ ft/sec^2, retardation $\frac{44}{75}$ ft/sec^2; 60 m.p.h.
11. (i) $7\frac{1}{2}$ min; (ii) $\frac{22}{27}$ ft/sec^2.
12. (a) $5\frac{1}{3}$ ft/sec^2; (b) 480 miles/hr^2.
13. (i) $4\frac{1}{2}$ miles; (ii) $7\frac{1}{3}$ min.
14. $8\frac{1}{4}$ miles.
15. (i) $(u - u_1)^2/(2f)$; (ii) $(2u - u_1)\,f/u$.
17. 110 sec.   **18.** 60 ft/sec; $11\frac{1}{4}$ sec; 36,450 ft; 10,800 ft.
19. $d - ut - \frac{1}{2}ft^2$; $(2fd - u^2)/2f$.
21. $\frac{8}{45}$ miles/min$^2 = \frac{176}{675}$ ft/sec^2; $1\frac{1}{4}$ min.

22. 72 ft/sec; 4840 ft; 28 min.
23. 15 ft/sec; 45 ft.
24. (i) 120 sec; (ii) $\frac{22}{75}$ ft/sec^2.
25. (i) 8 ft/sec; (ii) $\frac{4}{15}$ ft/sec; (iii) 65 sec.
26. Uniform velocity of 10 ft/sec for 10 sec, uniform acceleration of $1\frac{1}{2}$ ft/sec^2 for next 10 sec; 275 ft.
27. 27 m.p.h.; $\frac{11}{75}$ ft/sec^2. **28.** 30 min.
29. 30 m.p.h.; $52\frac{1}{2}$ m.p.h.; $2\frac{15}{16}$ miles.
30. $1\frac{1}{2}$ ft/sec^2; $\frac{3}{4}$ ft/sec^2. **31.** 6 miles; 36 m.p.h./min.
32. 48 m.p.h. **33.** (i) 2310 ft; (ii) 30 sec; (iii) 290 sec.
34. 20 ft/sec; 60 ft.

EXERCISES 4.1. (p. 77)

1. $(2, t)$; 1 unit/sec^2 parallel to Oy.
2. (i) $4\sqrt{2}$ units; (ii) $16y = 3x^2 + 4x$.

EXERCISES 4.2. (p. 85)

1. 25 ft; $16\sqrt{31} \doteqdot 88$ ft/sec at inclination $\tan^{-1}(7/5\sqrt{3}) \doteqdot 39°$ below horizontal.
2. 15 ft horizontally, 4 ft above top of tower; 3 sec; 45 ft.
3. $v/16$ sec; $v^2/8$ ft; $56\frac{1}{4}$ ft.
4. $165\frac{1}{4}$ ft; 361 yd; $3\frac{3}{4}$ sec.
5. $14\frac{1}{16}$ ft; 97 ft; 1·3 ft.
6. 120 ft/sec at 45° to horizontal; $15\sqrt{2}/4$ sec.
7. 90 ft; 4 sec.
8. $1\frac{1}{2}$ sec; (i) $56\frac{1}{4}$ ft; (ii) 300 ft.
10. $\tan^{-1}(\frac{4}{3}) \doteqdot 53°$; 200 ft/sec; 10 sec.
11. 25 ft. **12.** 7·3 ft; 27·8 ft/sec.
13. $20\sqrt{3} \doteqdot 34\frac{1}{2}$ ft; $2\frac{3}{4}$ sec.
15. 600 ft; $\tan^{-1}(\frac{4}{3}) \doteqdot 53°$; 200 ft/sec.
17. 320 ft/sec; $\tan^{-1}(\frac{1}{4}) \doteqdot 14°$ above the horizontal.
18. 384 ft, 448 ft; 14 sec.
19. $75\sqrt{3} \doteqdot 130$ ft; $20\sqrt{7} \doteqdot 53$ ft/sec at $\tan^{-1}\left(\dfrac{\sqrt{3}}{2}\right) \doteqdot 41°$ to horizontal.

EXERCISES 4.4. (p. 96)

3. $\sqrt{(13ga/3)}$. **4.** $\sqrt{(7696/3)} \doteqdot 50\cdot7$ ft/sec.
5. 71° 34′, $-18°$ 26′ to horizontal. **8.** 80 yd.

EXERCISES 4.5. (p. 100)

1. 2130 ft. **2.** 28·6 ft/sec at 8° 47′ (above) to the horizontal.
3. 1·83 sec. **4.** (i) 133 ft; (ii) 400 ft.
5. $\dfrac{u^2 \sin^2(\alpha - \theta)}{2g \cos\theta}$. **8.** (i) $\dfrac{V^2}{g(1 + \sin\alpha)}$; (ii) $\dfrac{V^2}{g(1 - \sin\alpha)}$.
10. $\dfrac{u \sin(\alpha - \beta)}{g \cos\beta}$; $\dfrac{u^2 \sin^2(\alpha - \beta)}{2g \cos\beta}$.

MISCELLANEOUS EXERCISES. IV (p. 101)

1. (i) 80 ft/sec; (ii) 173·2 ft; (iii) $\frac{1}{2}$ sec.
2. (i) 16 ft/sec; (ii) $56\frac{1}{2}°$.
3. (i) 8/33; (ii) 40/99. **4.** 764 ft; 176 ft/sec at 45° (approx.) to horizontal.
5. (i) 5 sec; (ii) 1386 ft; (iii) 49° 6'.
6. $\tan^{-1}(\frac{16}{33}) \doteqdot 26°$; $10\sqrt{1345} \doteqdot 367$ ft/sec.
7. (i) 78 ft/sec; (ii) $\sqrt{6532} \doteqdot 80·8$ ft/sec at $\tan^{-1}\left(\dfrac{4\sqrt{7}}{39}\right) \doteqdot 15°$ to horizontal.
8. (i) 2 sec; (ii) 216 ft; (iii) 114 ft/sec.
9. (i) 56 ft/sec; (ii) 196 yd; (iii) ± 13° 24'.
10. 3960 ft. **11.** No. **12.** 71 ft/sec. **14.** $(V^2 \sin 2\alpha)/g$.
15. $u\sin\alpha - gt$, $u\cos\alpha$; $(u^2 \sin^2\alpha)/2g$, $(u^2 \sin 2\alpha)/g$; 45°.
17. $32(\sqrt{3}+1) \doteqdot 87·4$; $32(3+2\sqrt{3}) \doteqdot 207$ ft.
20. $V^2t^2 - gVt^3 \sin\alpha + \frac{1}{4}g^2t^4$. **24.** 70 ft/sec.
25. (i) 5 miles; (ii) $3\frac{3}{4}$ miles.
26. $h = l\tan\alpha - (gl^2 \sec^2\alpha)/2\,V^2$; $\dfrac{V^2}{2g} - \dfrac{gl^2}{2V^2}$.

27. 44° 46'.   **29.** $\sqrt{(OA \cdot g \operatorname{cosec} 2\alpha)}$.
31. $\sqrt{(2gb)}$, $a\sqrt{(2g/b)}$. **32.** $a(\sqrt{3}-1)$ from nearer wall.
34. 1600 ft/sec.
35. $\sqrt{\{a^2 - 2uat\cos\alpha + 2u^2t^2(1 - \sin\alpha)\}}$; $t = a\cos\alpha/\{2u(1 - \sin\alpha)\}$.

EXERCISES 5.2. (p. 117)

1. (a) 49° E. of N.; (b) 31° W. of S. **2.** 84 m.p.h.
3. 43° 19' E. of N. and 16° 41' E. of N.
4. (i) 11° 20' N. of E.; (ii) 25·5 min; (iii) 17 min.
5. (i) 1 ft/sec; (ii) $1\frac{1}{3}$ ft/sec; 107 sec.
6. 1 hr 48 min. **7.** 40·7 knots 24° 40' W. of S.
8. 21·2 m.p.h.; W. 15° 6' S. **9.** 75 sec.
10. 20 knots from the SE.
11. $21\frac{1}{4}$ knots from 19° 47' W. of S.
12. $V\sqrt{2}$ from SW.; from $\tan^{-1}(\frac{1}{2}) \doteqdot 26° 34'$ S. of E.
13. 198 m.p.h., N. 7° 11' W.; (i) 9·45 a.m.; (ii) 42·2 m.p.h.
14. 8° 41' to the N.; 14·04 m.p.h.
15. 21·2 m.p.h.; W. 15° 6' N.

EXERCISES 5.3. (p. 127)

1. $13\frac{1}{2}°$ E. of N.; 8·7 min.   **2.** N. 61° 53' W.; 12·11·8 p.m.
3. 16·5 m.p.h., S. 75° 58' W. **4.** 12·12 p.m., 0·7 sea-miles; 24 min.
5. After 7·6 min.   **6.** 32·9 hr.
7. $5/\sqrt{7} \doteqdot 1·89$ miles; 3/14 hr.
8. N. 25° 26' E.; 9·15 a.m. **9.** 31° 22' W. of N.; 5·43 p.m.

MISCELLANEOUS EXERCISES. V (p. 128)

1. 18 m.p.h. from 56° 19' E. of N.
2. $\frac{1}{2}\sqrt{10} \doteqdot 1·58$ miles; $\tan^{-1}(\frac{1}{3}) \doteqdot 18° 26'$ W. of N.; $2\tan^{-1}(\frac{1}{3}) \doteqdot 36° 52'$ N. of E.
4. 15·4 miles; 43° N. of E. **5.** (i) 34 min; (ii) 58 min.

6. gt at 2θ with the vertical; $\ddot{g}$ at 2θ with the vertical.

7. $10\,\sqrt{2} \doteqdot 14\cdot4$ miles; $12\cdot11\cdot9$ p.m.

8. (i) 50 m.p.h., $\tan^{-1}(\tfrac{3}{4}) \doteqdot 36°\ 52'$ N. of E.; (ii) 150 yd; (iii) A, 90 yd; B, 120 yd.

11. $\sin^{-1}(u/2\,V)$.

12. $\sin^{-1}(\tfrac{4}{5}) \doteqdot 53°\ 8'$, 20 min; $\sqrt{11/10} \doteqdot 0\cdot332$ miles.

13. u from 2θ E. of N.   **14.** N. $57.6°$ E.; $7\cdot00$ a.m.; 1 hr 48 min.

15. $\{\sqrt{(u^2 - v^2)}\}/v$.   **16.** 60 m.p.h. from S. $53°\ 8'$ W.

18. (i) $15\,\sqrt{3} \doteqdot 26$ m.p.h.; $60°$ to the vertical; (ii) $\sin^{-1}(1/4\,\sqrt{2}) \doteqdot 10°\ 11'$ W. of N.

19. $20\sin(Vt/2a)$; $a\pi/v$ sec.   **20.** Approx. 16 miles.

22. Approx. 19 m.p.h.

24. (i) g at $2\angle BAC$ to AB; (ii) $2AC\cdot BC/AB$; (iii) the line joining the midpoints of AC and BC.

26. Two; 20 knots from $\tan^{-1}(\tfrac{3}{5}) \doteqdot 36°\ 52'$ S. of E. or $5\tfrac{3}{5}$ knots from $\tan^{-1}(\tfrac{3}{4}) \doteqdot 36°\ 52'$ N. of E.

EXERCISES 6.1. (p. 138)

1. X, 166 lb wt.; Y, 140 lb wt.

2. $M = 60$, $R = 36$.   **3.** 3 ft; $16\tfrac{2}{3}$ lb wt.

4. $x = 10$, $y = 30$.   **5.** $T_A = 39$ lb wt., $T_B = 31$ lb wt.

6. 2 ft; 20 lb.   **7.** $5\tfrac{1}{2}$ ft.

8. $R_C = W\,\{(2n + 1)\,l - (n + 1)\,b - nx\}\,/(2l - a - b)$, $R_D = W\,\{nx + l - (n + 1)a\}/(2l - a - b)$.

9. (i) A, $26\tfrac{2}{3}$ lb wt.; C, $8\tfrac{1}{3}$ lb wt.; (ii) 5 ft nearer A.

10. $7W/12$.   **11.** $\sqrt{(42)} \doteqdot 6\cdot5$ lb wt.

12. 10 lb wt; within 1 ft (on either side) of the centre of the beam.

13. $5\tfrac{9}{19}$ ft or 5 ft $5\tfrac{3}{4}$ in.

14. (a) $30/11 \leq x \leq 6$, 12 lb wt., 0 lb wt.; (b) $4 < x \leq 6$, 12 lb wt., 7 lb wt.

15. $AC = 2$ ft, $DB = 1$ ft.

16. With OF vertical (F above or below O).

18. 160 gm; $20\tfrac{5}{8}$ cm from A.

20. $R_A = (8a - x - 2y)\,W/2a$, $R_B = (x + 2y + 6a)\,W/(2a)$.

EXERCISES 6.2. (p. 149)

1. -15 lb wt., 8 in.   **2.** 5 lb wt., 24 in.

3. -2 lb wt., -16 in.   **4.** 5 lb wt., 6 in.

5. 6 lb wt., 66 in.   **6.** -10 lb wt., 12 in.

7. Couple, moment 48 in. lb wt.

8. -10 lb wt., $12\tfrac{4}{5}$ in.   **9.** Couple, moment 8 in. lb wt.

10. Equilibrium.   **11.** Couple, moment $-8Pa$.

12. Couple, moment $-a$ ft lb wt.   **14.** $7Pa\,\sqrt{3}$.

15. $Pa\,\{(1 + b)\cos\theta + \sin\theta\}$.

16. 3 ft from mid-point and towards B.

17. $Wa\sin\theta$; W vertically upwards.

18. $Wr\,\{\cos(\theta - \alpha) - \cos\alpha\}$; $\tfrac{1}{2}\theta$; 0.

24*

EXERCISES 6.3. (p. 153)

1. 7 lb wt.; 24 ft.　**2.** 80 lb wt.; 1 ft 4 in.
3. (i) $33\frac{1}{3}$ lb wt.; (ii) 28·5 lb wt. at 20° 33′ to the horizontal.
4. $8/\sqrt{3}$ lb wt.; $\sqrt{19}/3$ lb wt. at $\tan^{-1}(\sqrt{3}/4)$ to the horizontal.
5. 25 lb wt. at floor, $5\sqrt{3}$ lb wt. at wall; 10 lb. wt.
6. (i) 1·82 cwt at 61° 9′ to the horizontal; (ii) 2·56 cwt.
7. $W/6$; $W/6$.　　　**8.** Vertical $41\,W/40$; horizontal $\sqrt{7}\,W/40$.
9. 2/5 ft from B.　**10.** $30\sqrt{3}$ lb. wt.

MISCELLANEOUS EXERCISES. VI (p. 156)

1. 4 ft.　**2.** 175 lb wt.; 172 lb wt. at 11° 46′ above horizontal; 30.
3. $\frac{1}{2}(\sqrt{3}-1)$; $\tan\theta = (6+\sqrt{3})/11$, and $\tan\theta > 1/\sqrt{3}$.
4. (i) $-10x$; (ii) $-10\,l$, (iii) $15x - 30\,l$.
5. C, 220 lb wt.; D, 160 lb wt.; 40 lb wt. at A.
6. 25 lb wt.　**7.** 20 lb, 6 ft.
8. $8/\sqrt{3}$ lb wt.; $\sqrt{19}/3$ lb wt. at $\tan^{-1}(\frac{1}{4}\sqrt{3})$ to horizontal.
9. 18 lb and 12 lb; $\pm 4·8$ in.
10. $\frac{1}{2}W$; $\frac{1}{2}W\sqrt{5}$ at $\tan^{-1}\frac{1}{2}$ to downward vertical.
11. $P = 3\sqrt{2}$ lb wt.; $Q = \sqrt{2}$ lb wt.; 12 ft lb wt.
12. (i) 53° 8′; (ii) 4·8 lb wt.; 8·6 lb wt.; (iii) 9·85 lb wt.
13. $\tan^{-1}(\frac{1}{2}) \doteq 26\frac{1}{2}°$.　**15.** 30°.
16. $Wl\sqrt{3}/4$; $\sin^{-1}(\sqrt{3}/4) \doteq 25° 40′$ to vertical.
20. $3Wa/\{2(W - W_1)\}$.　**21.** $\tan^{-1}\frac{1}{2} \doteq 26\frac{1}{2}°$.
22. $\tan\alpha = \dfrac{Ma + ma - mb}{ma + 2Mb + 2mb}$, $\tan\beta = Ma/\{(m+2M)b\}$.
23. At P where $AP = W(8 - 5\sqrt{2})a/(2W_1)$.
24. Pressure $wa/(x\sqrt{2})$; $wa/(2x)$ horizontally, $w(2x - a)/(2x)$ vertically; $x = a$.
26. $\{12(w_1 + w_2)w_1\}/\sqrt{(16w_1^2 + 9w_2^2)}$.
27. $W/\sqrt{3}$ horizontally; $2W/\sqrt{3}$ along bisector of $\angle BAC$.

EXERCISES 7.2. (p. 164)

1. 3·85 ft.　　**2.** $\frac{27}{40}$ ft, $\frac{1}{2}$ ft.
3. $\dfrac{\sqrt{3}}{5}$ ft on same side as C, $\dfrac{1}{10}$ ft on same side as B.
4. $4\frac{4}{5}$ in., $\frac{5}{6}$ in.
5. $\dfrac{a}{10}$ on same side as C, $\dfrac{2a}{15}$ on same side as B.
6. $\dfrac{11a}{6}$.　　**7.** $\dfrac{6b}{5}$, $\dfrac{6a}{5}$.　**8.** $\dfrac{r\sqrt{3}}{12}$, 150°.
9. $(1+k)m$.　**11.** $\dfrac{bc\sqrt{2}}{a+b+c}$.　**12.** $x = 6\frac{1}{2}m$, $y = \frac{1}{2}m$.

EXERCISES 7.4. (p. 173)

1. $8\dfrac{5}{14}$ in.　**2.** 26 in.　**3.** $\dfrac{4(\sqrt{3}-1)}{3} \doteq 0·98$ in.
4. $17\frac{1}{3}$ in., $5\frac{1}{3}$ in.　**6.** $\dfrac{3a}{7}$, $\dfrac{10a}{21}$.

9. $\dfrac{r(4\pi - 3\sqrt{3})}{4\pi + 6\sqrt{3}}$ from O on AO produced. **10.** $\dfrac{a}{12}$.

11. $\dfrac{4a\sqrt{2}}{9\pi}$ from centre and on axis of symmetry.

EXERCISES 7.5. (p. 176)

1. $1\frac{4}{5}$ ft from AD and $2\frac{3}{5}$ ft from AB; $55°$.
2. 1 ft, $1\frac{1}{2}$ ft.   **3.** 2 in.; $\tan^{-1}(\frac{1}{2}) \doteqdot 26\frac{1}{2}°$. **4.** $3\frac{4}{5}$ in.;
$\tan^{-1}\left(\dfrac{19}{15}\right) \doteqdot 51\frac{3}{4}°$. **5.** $\dfrac{\pi}{4} - \tan^{-1}\left(\dfrac{9}{10}\right) = \tan^{-1}\left(\dfrac{1}{19}\right) \doteqdot 3°$.
6. $3\frac{13}{22}$ in.; $2\frac{48}{55}$ in.   **7.** $3\frac{1}{4}$ in. from A where $AC = 5$ in.
8. $60° - \tan^{-1}\left(\dfrac{13}{8\sqrt{3}}\right) = \tan^{-1}\left(\dfrac{11}{21\sqrt{3}}\right) \doteqdot 17°$. **9.** $a\sqrt{2}$.
11. $\frac{1}{10}$. **12.** $\frac{1}{3}M$.   **13.** $\frac{1}{2}W$.

EXERCISES 7.6. (p. 182)

1. 6 lb.; $3\frac{1}{3}$; $1\frac{1}{3}$ lb. **5.** $\bar{x} = \dfrac{104 + 25k}{4 + 2k}$ cm; $\dfrac{8}{5}$.
6. $\dfrac{3h(n^4 - 1)}{4n(n^3 - 1)}$. **8.** $a/\sqrt{2}$. **9.** $4h/9$.

MISCELLANEOUS EXERCISES. VII (p. 188)

1. 3 ft, 2 ft; $34°$; $P = 80$; 234 lb wt. at $20°$ (below) horizontal.
2. 8 in.; 2 in.; $\tan^{-1}(\frac{4}{5}) \doteqdot 39°$. **3.** (i) $2\frac{2}{7}$ cm; (ii) 3 lb.
4. $3\frac{4}{7}$ ft. **5.** $12\frac{7}{9}$ in., $7\frac{7}{9}$ in.
6. On median of triangle ABC through A at distance $\dfrac{38a\sqrt{3}}{63}$ from A, where $AB = 2a$.
8. $3\frac{13}{21}$ ft, $2\frac{5}{7}$ ft; $m = 16\frac{2}{3}$.   **9.** $\sin^{-1}(\frac{1}{3}) \doteqdot 19\frac{1}{2}°$.
11. $\left(\dfrac{a}{26}, \dfrac{11a}{26}\right)$.   **13.** $\dfrac{14a\sqrt{3}}{17}$. **14.** $\dfrac{h(4l - 3h)}{4(3l - 2h)}$ away from point.
19. $2 \cdot 2a$.   **20.** $\frac{1}{6}$. **21.** (i) $a = 12$, $b = -24$; (ii) 19 in.
25. $a/\{4(2\pi - 1)\}$, $29a/\{12(2\pi - 1)\}$.
26. $\dfrac{a(1 - \cos\theta)}{6}$, $\dfrac{a\sin\theta}{6}$. **27.** $\dfrac{3}{2\pi}$.
28. $\left(\dfrac{m_1 x_1 + m_2 x_2}{m_1 + m_2}, \dfrac{m_1 y_1 + m_2 y_2}{m_1 + m_2}\right)$; 4 cm; $\dfrac{\sqrt{105} - 5}{2} \doteqdot 2 \cdot 6$ cm.
29. $175 - 25\sqrt{3} \doteqdot 131 \cdot 7$ lb wt. **30.** $(a, 7a/5)$; $2w$.
31. $76°$, $(\tan^{-1}4)$. **38.** $9W/32$. **39.** $2a/3$, $16a/15\pi$.
40. $62°$.

EXERCISES 8.1. (p. 199)

1. (i) $0 \cdot 071$ pdl; (ii) $0 \cdot 9993$ gmf.
2. (a) 77 lb wt.; (b) 282 lb wt. **3.** 25 ft/sec^2; $(7\sqrt{3})/2$ lb wt.
4. 9 ft/sec^2; $2\frac{10}{13}$ lb wt.; $1 \cdot 5$ sec. **6.** $17\frac{1}{2}$ lb wt.; 10 sec.
7. 9405 lb wt. **8.** Lighter body 500 ft, heavier body 8 ft; $\frac{5328}{5333}$ sec.

9. (a) $148\frac{3}{4}$ cm; (b) 140. **10.** 4. **11.** $3\cdot3$ ft/sec².

13. (i) $72\frac{1}{2}$ cm; (ii) $69\frac{1}{2}$ cm. **14.** $\dfrac{m(s_1 - s_n)}{g(n-1)}$ lb wt.

EXERCISES 8.2. (p. 208)

1. (i) 4 ft/sec²; (ii) $7\frac{7}{8}$ lb wt.; (iii) $15\frac{3}{4}$ lb wt.

2. $T(AB) = 2\frac{1}{4}$ lb wt. $T(BC) = 2\frac{5}{8}$ lb wt.

3. $1\cdot62$ lb wt.; $14\cdot5$ ft/sec². **4.** $m = 4$; $T = 1\frac{1}{3}$ lb wt.

5. (i) $g/11$ ft/sec²; $5\frac{5}{11}$ lb wt.

7. (i) $1\frac{1}{4}$ lb wt., $3\frac{3}{4}$ lb wt.; 4 ft/sec.

9. (i) $3\cdot2$ ft/sec²; (ii) $7\cdot2$ lb wt.; (iii) $10\cdot4$ lb wt.

10. $(m - m')(g - \alpha)/(m + m')$; $\alpha = (m - m')g/2m$, 2α.

11. $\dfrac{g}{49}$ ft/sec²; $\dfrac{1}{5}m$.

12. (i) 2 oz wt.; (ii) $1\frac{5}{7}$ oz wt.; (iii) $1\frac{1}{3}$ oz wt.

EXERCISES 8.3. (p. 214)

1. (a) $m\{\sqrt{(2gh_1)} + \sqrt{(2gh_2)}\}$ pdl sec; (b) $m\{\sqrt{(2h_1)} + \sqrt{(2h_2)}\}/\sqrt{g}$ lb wt. sec.

2. $46\frac{7}{8}$ lb wt. **3.** $132{,}300{,}000$ dyn; $135{,}000$ gm wt.

4. $m\sqrt{(2gh)}\sec\alpha$ lb ft/sec.

5. $13\cdot8$ lb wt. **6.** Both $\sqrt{(3/7)}$ sec.

7. $\frac{1}{2}a$. **8.** $a\omega(2 - \cos\omega t_1)$.

9. 5 lb ft/sec; $2\frac{1}{2}$ ft/sec.

10. $10\frac{2}{3}$ gm wt. sec; $1046\cdot4$ cm/sec.

11. $m\{\varphi(t_1) - \varphi(0)\}$. **12.** 12 gm cm/sec.

13. $\sqrt{(v^2 + I^2/m^2)}$ cm/sec in a direction $\tan^{-1}\left(\dfrac{I}{mv}\right)$ N. of W.

14. $8/\sqrt{3}$ lb ft/sec. **15.** $32\sqrt{2}$ lb ft/sec.

16. $I/\sqrt{2}$ lb ft/sec.

EXERCISES 8.4. (p. 225)

1. If P is overtaking Q, after 12 sec, 72 ft from initial position of P; $9\frac{2}{3}$ ft/sec; If Q is overtaking P, after 4 sec, 8 ft from the initial position of P; $4\frac{1}{3}$ ft/sec.

2. 8 ft/sec²; $3\frac{3}{4}$ lb wt.; $10\frac{2}{3}$ ft/sec². **3.** 15 ft/sec; $2\frac{11}{32}$ tons wt. **4.** $\frac{17}{60}$ sec; 6 ft/sec.

5. 8 ft/sec²; (i) 1 sec; (ii) 6 ft/sec.

6. (i) $(MU - mu)/(M + m)$; (ii) $(MU - nmu)/(M + nm)$.

7. (i) $4\frac{1}{2}$ ft/sec; (ii) 12 ft/sec²; (iii) $6\frac{1}{2}$ ft/sec.

8. $\dfrac{8\sqrt{10}}{5}$ ft/sec. **10.** $2\frac{1}{4}$ sec.

11. (i) $8\sqrt{2}$ ft/sec; (ii) $1/\sqrt{2}$ sec; (iii) $8\sqrt{3}$ ft/sec.

12. $32m/3$ lb ft/sec, $2\frac{2}{3}$ ft/sec; $\frac{1}{2}$ sec, $5\frac{1}{3}$ ft/sec.

13. $\{\sqrt{(m^2u^2 + m'^2v^2 + 2mm'uv\cos\alpha)}\}/(m + m')$; $\tan^{-1}\{(m'v\sin\alpha)/(mu + m'v\cos\alpha)\}$.

14. $mu/\{2(M + m)\}$; $M(2M + 3m)u^2/\{3(M + m)^2g\}$.

EXERCISES 8.5. (p. 233)

1. 720 dyn; $5 \cdot 08 \times 10^6$ ergs.
2. (i) $231 \cdot 5$ ft pdl; (ii) $4 \cdot 92 \times 10^6$ dyn/cm².
3. $266\frac{2}{3}$ ft; $1333\frac{1}{3}$ ft lb wt.   4. 10 ft lb wt.; 2 lb wt.
5. $137\frac{1}{2}$ yd.   6. (i) 31,250 ft ton wt.; 2000 ft/sec; (ii) $0 \cdot 2$ ft/sec.
7. $mu^2/(2c)$; speed $\frac{1}{2}u$, time c/u.   8. 32 ft/sec; 132 lb wt.
9. 6 ft lb wt.; 5 lb wt.
10. Momentum 360 lb ft/sec, kinetic energy 540 ft pdl; 45 lb wt.
11. 1125 lb wt; 750 ft lb wt.; $29\frac{1}{3}$ ft/sec.
12. 220 lb wt.   14. $\frac{1}{2}n^2 W(a-t)$.
16. $\dfrac{11\,h\,W}{28} - \dfrac{45\,a\,h\,W}{28\,\gamma(a^2+4\,h^2)}$ where W is the weight of the frustum.
17. 28 ft pdl.   18. $\frac{1}{3}$ ft pdl.
19. $45\,k/4$ ft pdl.   20. $9\,k/2$ ft pdl.

MISCELLANEOUS EXERCISES. VIII (p. 235)

1. 4 ft/sec²; $4\frac{1}{2}\cos 30° = 9\sqrt{3}/4$ pdl.
2. 2 ft/sec in same direction; $65\frac{5}{8}$ ft lb wt.
3. 240 gm wt.   4. $6 \cdot 4$ ft/sec²; $3\frac{1}{2}$ in.
5. $3131\frac{1}{4}$ ft lb wt.   6. 6 ft/sec; 11,340 ft lb wt.
7. $(2n-3)/(2n-1)$ ft.   8. 320 ft; $3\sqrt{\frac{5}{2}} \doteq 4 \cdot 74$ sec.
9. (i) $6\dfrac{6}{13}$ lb wt., $\dfrac{\sqrt{39}}{4} \doteq 1.56$ sec; (ii) $7\dfrac{7}{26}$ lb wt., $\sqrt{\left(\dfrac{13}{6}\right)} \doteq 1.47$ sec.
10. 4 ft/sec; 5/32 ft tons wt.; $\frac{1}{2}$ ton wt.
11. Heavier truck 2 ft/sec, lighter truck 5 ft/sec; 1050 ft lb wt.   12. 8 ft/sec; $0 \cdot 31$ sec.   13. 5 ft/sec; $563\frac{43}{64}$ ft tons wt. $\frac{3}{4}$ ton wt.
14. 1970 gm cm/sec; 30 gm cm wt.
15. $11\frac{4}{9}$ ft/sec.   16. $5\frac{1}{8}$ lb wt.; $27\frac{3}{11}$ per cent.
17. (i) $4 \cdot 6$ and $3 \cdot 6$ ft/sec; $0 \cdot 75$ ft ton wt.; $32 \cdot 4$ ft.
18. 16 ft tons wt.; $18\frac{1}{4}$ tons wt.   19. 510 ft/sec.
20. (a) $9\frac{3}{8}$ ft lb wt.; (b) $13 \cdot 86$ ft/sec.   21. $\frac{3}{4}$.
23. $T = \dfrac{2g}{\dfrac{4}{M}+\dfrac{1}{m_1}+\dfrac{1}{m_2}}$; block $\dfrac{4g}{4+M\left(\dfrac{1}{m_1}+\dfrac{1}{m_2}\right)}$;

       particle (m_1) $\dfrac{\left(\dfrac{4}{M}-\dfrac{1}{m_1}+\dfrac{1}{m_2}\right)g}{\dfrac{4}{m}+\dfrac{1}{m_1}+\dfrac{1}{m_2}}$.

24. 5 ft/sec; $9\frac{3}{8}$ ft tons wt.; 140 sec, 350 ft.
25. $mu/(2M)$ ft/sec; $m(3M-m)u^2/(8M)$ ft pdl; $mu^2/4$ pdl.
27. $\frac{3}{8}$ ft/sec; $1\frac{1}{4}$ sec.   28. $16g/51$.
29. $\frac{11}{96}$, 264 ft; $\frac{35}{288}$, 264 ft.
30. $\{(M+m)g\sin\alpha\}/(M+m\sin^2\alpha)$.
32. gFt/m ft/sec.   33. $v+u$, $v-u$.
34. 5 tons wt.; $3\frac{1}{2}$ ft.   35. 120°.
36. $\dfrac{24\,m}{29}\,\gamma(2g\,h)$, $\dfrac{12\,m}{29}\,\gamma(2g\,h)$.

MISCELLANEOUS EXERCISES. IX (p. 259)

1. 50. **2.** At wall $6\sqrt{3} \doteqdot 10 \cdot 4$ lb wt. horizontally; at plane $6\sqrt{39} \doteqdot 37 \cdot 5$ lb wt.
at $\tan^{-1}\left(\dfrac{\sqrt{3}}{6}\right) \doteqdot 16°$ with vertical (on wall side of vertical).

3. 13. **4.** 240 lb wt. **5.** $40\sqrt{2} \doteqdot 56\frac{1}{2}$.
6. $\tan^{-1}(\frac{4}{3}) \doteqdot 53°$. **7.** 1·24. **8.** 1·6 ft/sec²; 22·3 ft.
9. $5\frac{1}{3}$ ft/sec². **10.** 8 ft/sec²; $1\frac{1}{2}$ lb wt., $1\frac{1}{8}$ lb wt.; $\frac{1}{6}$.
11. $\frac{3}{8}$; (i) 39·76 lb wt.; (ii) 44·76 lb wt.
13. $mg(\sin\alpha + \mu\cos\alpha)$, where m is mass of body.
15. $W/\{4(\mu+1)\}$.
16. $g(4 - 3\sin\alpha)/6$; $\dfrac{2}{3}mg(2 + 3\sin\alpha)\cos\left(\dfrac{\pi}{4} - \dfrac{\alpha}{2}\right)$ along bisector of HPK,
i.e. making angle $\dfrac{\pi}{4} - \dfrac{\alpha}{2}$ with downward vertical.

19. $\frac{1}{3}W$. **22.** 162·5; 37° 34′.
29. (i) 20·76 ft/sec; (ii) 0·964 sec; 0·21 ft lb wt.
32. Acceleration $(m_1 - \mu m - m_2)g/(m_1 + m + m_2)$;

$$T_{AB} = m_1(m + \mu m + 2m_2)g/(m_1 + m + m_2),$$
$$T_{BC} = m_2(2m_1 + m - \mu m)g/(m_1 + m + m_2).$$

33. 23/22.
34. $W(2 + \tan\theta)/\{2(1 + \tan\theta)\}$; tilts when $P = W/\{2(\cos\theta + \sin\theta)\}$.
35. $\frac{2}{3}$; $7a/2$. **38.** (i) slides; (ii) tilts about an edge.
39. (i) At A, $\frac{1}{2}W\tan\theta$ (horizontally); at B, W (vertically); (iii) 11/30.
40. Force of friction, $\frac{2}{3}P + \frac{1}{2}W\tan\theta$ (towards wall); at A, $\frac{1}{2}W\tan\theta - \frac{1}{3}P$ (horizontally).
41. $3a$; equilibrium is possible if $3a \leqq AX \leqq 6a$.
42. (i) $0 \leqq \alpha \leqq \tan^{-1}\frac{1}{2} \doteqdot 26\frac{1}{2}°$; (ii) $\tan^{-1}\frac{1}{2} < \alpha \leqq 90°$.
43. $7\frac{1}{2}°$. **45.** 3 : 1. **46.** (i) 1/4 sec; (ii) 2 sec.
49. $4\frac{1}{2}$ lb wt.; 45°.
50. The block on the sloping face whose inclination increases.
51. $(M + m)g(\mu\cos\alpha + \sin\alpha)/(\cos\alpha - \mu\sin\alpha)$.

MISCELLANEOUS EXERCISES. X (p. 276)

1. $\sqrt{(gx)}$. **2.** $8\sqrt{(\frac{2}{7})} \doteqdot 4 \cdot 28$ ft/sec. **3.** $g/11$ upwards.
4. $\sqrt{\{gh(1 - 1/\sqrt{3})\}}$. **5.** $\sqrt{\{2ga(4\sqrt{2} - 5)\}}$.
7. (i) $\sqrt{(ga/3)}$; (ii) $\sqrt{(ga)}$. **8.** $2l$.
9. $4\sqrt{2} \doteqdot 5 \cdot 66$ ft/sec. **10.** $\left(\dfrac{M-m}{M}\right)^2 l$.
11. 0·43 ft. **13.** 2·0 ft approx.
16. (i) $1\frac{1}{3}$ ft/sec; (ii) 2 ft 4·92 in., 2 ft 1·82 in.
17. Ring $\sqrt{(gl/3)}$, particle $2\sqrt{(gl/3)}$.
19. (i) $\sqrt{(ga)}$; (ii) $\sqrt{\{ga(8\sqrt{3} - 13)\}}$.

EXERCISES 11.1. (p. 284)

1. The 4 lb sphere $5\frac{1}{9}$ ft/sec, the other $5\frac{7}{9}$ ft/sec, both along original direction.
2. The 2 lb sphere 4 ft/sec, the other 1 ft/sec, both velocities being reversed.
3. 31/10. **4.** $\frac{1}{4}$. **5.** $2v$. **6.** 16/25.

7. $2 \cdot 1$ ergs.   **8.** $1\frac{1}{3}$ ft/sec, 3 ft/sec; 5/12 ft lb wt.

10. $\frac{1}{3}m(1 - e^2)u^2$.   **11.** 53/68.   **12.** $(4 - 2e)u/3$, $(4 + e)u/3$; 9 : 1.

14. $\frac{1}{2}$; 3/8.   **15.** 2/9.   **16.** B, $V/16$; C, $3V/16$ both in direction of original motion of A.

17. m, $\dfrac{m - em'}{m + m'}\,\sqrt{(2gl)}$; m', $\dfrac{m(1 + e)}{m + m'}\,\sqrt{(2gl)}$ both in direction of original motion of m'.

18. $16l/25$.   **19.** $3(1 + e)^2\,V/16$.   **20.** 7/8.

21. $\frac{1}{2}(1 \pm e^2)u$; $2\pi a/(eu)$.   **22.** $\{7\sqrt{(gh)}\}/4$.

EXERCISES 11.3. (p. 293)

1. $\left(\dfrac{1 + e}{1 - e}\right)\sqrt{\left(\dfrac{2h}{g}\right)}$.   **2.** $V = 10/\sqrt{3}$ ft/sec; $\beta = 60°$.

3. $u = 80/\sqrt{13}$ ft/sec; $\beta = \tan^{-1}(2\sqrt{3})$.   **4.** $e = 1/\sqrt{3}$.

5. $1/k$.   **6.** $e = \frac{1}{3}$.   **9.** $12a/(5V)$.

10. $\frac{1}{4}V$, $\frac{3}{4}V$; $3m\,V^2/16$; $\frac{1}{3}$.   **12.** $2ev/g$.   **13.** $e = \tan^2\theta$.

15. $\dfrac{2\,U^2(1 - e^2)\sqrt{2}}{g}$.

EXERCISES 11.4. (p. 298)

1. $u_1 = \sqrt{10}$ ft/sec, $\alpha_1 = 180° - \tan^{-1}2$, $v_1 = \frac{1}{2}\sqrt{10}$ ft/sec, $\beta_1 = \tan^{-1}2$.

2. $u_1 = (u\sqrt{34})/8$, $\alpha_1 = \tan^{-1}4$, $v_1 = (3u\sqrt{2})/8$, $\beta_1 = 0°$.

3. $u_1 = 5V/4$, $\alpha_1 = 180° - \tan^{-1}(4/3)$, $v_1 = V/4$, $\beta_1 = 180°$.

4. $u_1 = (V\sqrt{111})/9$, $\alpha_1 = 180° - \tan^{-1}\{(3\sqrt{3})/11\}$, $v_1 = (V\sqrt{21})/9$, $\beta = \tan^{-1}(3\sqrt{3})$.

5. $e = 1/n$, $u_1 = (V\sqrt{3})/2$, $v_1 = V/(2n)$, $\beta_1 = 0$.

6. $\tan^{-1}8$.   **7.** $\tan^{-1}\left\{\dfrac{(1 + e)\tan\alpha}{2\tan^2\alpha + 1 - e}\right\}$.   **8.** $e = \dfrac{1}{3}$.

9. $45°$.   **10.** $\tan^{-1}(\sqrt{e})$.

MISCELLANEOUS EXERCISES. XI (p. 299)

1. $e = 1/6$; 5/9.   **3.** 1250 lb wt.; 7 in.

4. $2ae$.   **6.** $V_1 = \frac{1}{3}(1 + e)V$; $k = 2(1 + e)^2/\{3(1 + 2e)\}$.

7. $\frac{1}{4}(1 + e)^2 a$, $\frac{1}{4}(1 - e)^2 a$.   **9.** $\frac{1}{2}$.   **10.** $7mu/4$.

11. $\frac{1}{2}(1 + e)v + \frac{1}{2}(1 - e)u$; $\frac{1}{4}m(1 - e^2)(v - u)^2$.   **13.** $(1 + e)^{n-1}u/2^{n-1}$.

14. A, $V/12$ in sense opposite to original direction of motion of B; B, $V/8$; C, $13V/72$ both in sense of original direction of motion of B.

19. $4V/9$.

20. First impact, ring $(1 + e)u/(n + 1)$, particle $(1 - ne)u/(n + 1)$; second impact, ring $(1 - e^2)u/(n + 1)$, particle $(1 + ne^2)u/(n + 1)$.

21. $M(1 - e^2)V/(M + m)$.

22. $\frac{1}{2}(1 + e)V \sin\alpha \cos\alpha$, $\frac{1}{2}\{2 - (1 + e)\sin^2\alpha\}V$.

27. $\tan^{-1}\{(1 + e)\tan\alpha/(\tan^2\alpha - e)\}$.

29. $\{V(1 + e)\cos\alpha\}/(1 + \cos^2\alpha)$ along plane, $V(\cos^2\alpha - e)/(1 + \cos^2\alpha)$ along line of centres.

31. $\frac{1}{3}(2 + e^2)V$; $\{2(1 + e)l\}/(3e)$.

EXERCISES 12.1. (p. 306)

1. $56/225 \doteqdot 0.25$. **2.** 6.6×10^7. **3.** $3\frac{73}{125} = 3.5804$.
4. £6. 17s. 9·2d. **5.** 0. **6.** 5.2×10^3 ergs/sec.

MISCELLANEOUS EXERCISES. XII (p. 313)

1. $\sin^{-1}(2/25)$. **2.** $31\frac{1}{4}$ m.p.h. **3.** 5/28 ft/sec².
4. 3/56 ft/sec². **5.** (a) 30 m.p.h.; (b) (i) 1710 ft lb wt., (ii) 270 ft lb wt.
6. 7·7 ft/sec; 30 h.p.
7. 22·4 h.p.; $93\frac{1}{3}$ lb wt.
8. (i) 80 ft/sec; (ii) 1250 lb; (iii) $45\frac{5}{11}$ h.p.
9. $16\frac{1}{4}$ lb wt.; 0·13 h.p.
10. (i) 2275 lb wt.; (ii) 34.6 m.p.h.
11. 337,040 lb wt.; 12·3 h.p.
12. 45 m.p.h.; 3/28 ft/sec². **13.** 20 lb/wt./ton; 23·15 m.p.h.
14. 57 h.p. **15.** 1·7 ft/sec²; 50 m.p.h. **16.** 20 m.p.h.
17. 70·31 m.p.h., 80 lb wt.; 113 lb wt.
18. $\frac{8}{25}$ h.p.; (i) 18 m.p.h.; (ii) $\frac{2}{5}$ ft/sec².
19. $\frac{1}{60}$; 50 m.p.h. **20.** 250 lb wt.; 0·56 ft/sec².
21. $(9\sqrt{13})/2 \doteqdot 10.58$ m.p.h. **22.** $3\frac{1}{3}$ tons wt.; $\frac{2}{5}$ ft/sec².
23. (i) $14\frac{3}{4}$ h.p. **24.** (i) 2200 ft lb wt.; (ii) 4 h.p.
25. $105\frac{7}{8}$ lb wt.; 12·235 h.p. **26.** $V = 70$; $358\frac{2}{5}$ h.p.
27. $V = 550H/\{m(\sin\alpha + \mu\cos\alpha)\}$. **29.** 50 m.p.h.
30. (a) 3·45 m.p.h.; (b) 4·07 m.p.h.
32. $a = 45,240/17$, $b = 8/85$. **33.** 462 h.p.
34. 15·6 h.p.
35. $2t(60 - t)/105$ ft/sec² for $0 \leqq t \leqq 30$; 349 h.p.
36. 8125 lb wt.; 25/64 ft/sec².
37. (a) $\int_0^a F \, ds$; $t(100 - t)/10$ cm/sec: $t = 50(3 - \sqrt{3})/3 \doteqdot 21.1$.
38. $2v\sqrt{V}/(v + V)$ m.p.h.
39. Tractive force = 7450 lb wt., resistance = 3250 lb wt.; 200 h.p.
40. Approx. 31 h.p.
41. $6\frac{2}{5}$ h.p.; 1408 ft lb wt./sec.

EXERCISES 13.3. (p. 322)

1. 6 kgm wt. **2.** 16 lb wt. **3.** 77 lb wt.
4. 7·4 lb wt.; 29 ft/sec.
5. Tension in string = $6\pi^2$ pdl $\doteqdot 1.85$ lb wt.;
Force exerted on table = $2 - \pi^2/8 \doteqdot 0.77$ lb wt. vertically downwards.
6. $\sqrt{\{Mg/(4\pi^2 ml)\}}$.
7. $T_{OA} = 3m\omega^2 l/g$, $T_{AB} = 2m\omega^2 l/g$.
8. 1·42 ft/sec at 84° approx. with AB; 2 ft/sec² at 45° with AB (and towards AB).

EXERCISES 13.4. (p. 331)

1. Tension 900 gm wt.   **4.** $2\pi \sqrt{(10a/3g)}$.   **6.** 12.
8. $m(g \cos \alpha + l\omega^2 \sin^2\alpha)$.   **10.** $3/\sqrt{17} \doteqdot 0.73$ tons wt.
11. $l_1/l_2 = m_2/m_1$.   **12.** 8 oz wt.; $\frac{1}{4}\pi\sqrt{3} \doteqdot 1.36$ sec.
13. $81 : 8$; $60\sqrt{(7/11)} \doteqdot 48$ m.p.h.
14. $5\pi^2/6 \doteqdot 8.22$ lb wt.
16. 14 lb wt. approx. down the track (exerted on the car).
17. $43° 58'$.   **19.** $\sqrt{(g/3a)}$.
20. $f = g R^2/x^2$; 16,600 m.p.h., 102 min.

EXERCISES 13.6. (p. 344)

1. (i) 15 oz wt.; (ii) 6 oz wt. **2.** 55.3 lb wt.
3. (i) 3 ft; (ii) 1/24 oz wt. **7.** 25.6 m.p.h.; 2205 lb wt.
8. $\cos^{-1}(\frac{2}{3})$, $\sqrt{(2ga/3)}$; $\frac{1}{2}\sqrt{(ga)}$.
12. $\sqrt{(2ga/3)}$; horizontal $\dfrac{2}{3}\sqrt{\left(\dfrac{2ga}{3}\right)}$, vertical $\dfrac{10}{3}\sqrt{\left(\dfrac{ga}{3}\right)}$.
13. $120°$. **16.** Speed $= \sqrt{\{V^2 - 2gl(1 - \cos\theta)\}}$,
    Tension $= m\{V^2 + gl(3 \cos\theta - 2)\}/l$; (i) $\sqrt{(2gl)}$; (ii) $\sqrt{(5gl)}$; $3l/5$.
17. $\cos^{-1}(-\frac{1}{3}) \doteqdot 109\frac{1}{2}°$. **18.** 15 oz wt. **19.** $\frac{1}{4}mg(17 + 12 \cos\theta)$.

MISCELLANEOUS EXERCISES. XIII (p. 346)

3. a/h. **4.** 4 rad/sec.
8. 528 lb wt. **9.** 58. **13.** $2g$.
17. (i) $T_{OP} = 10\,mg$, $T_{PQ} = 6\,mg$; (iii) $\pi\sqrt{\{a/(2g)\}}$.
18. v^2/g; mv equal and opposite to the direction of motion; arrives with speed v.
19. $T_{AB} = 10\,mg$; speed of $B = \sqrt{(2g/3)}$.
21. $2a$; velocity $2\sqrt{(ga)}$ at $45°$ below horizontal.
22. $R = ma\omega^2 - mg \cos\theta$, $F = mg \sin\theta$; $\cot\alpha$.
23. (i) $mgl \cos\theta$; (ii) $3mg \cos\theta$.
24. $\sqrt{\{ga(2 + 2 \cos\alpha + \sec\alpha)\}}$.
25. (i) 94 min; (ii) $\{\sqrt{2gR(n - 1)/n}\}$.
26. $\frac{1}{2}mg(1 - \sin\alpha)$.
27. $mg\{(M + 3m) \sin\theta - 2M\theta\}/(M + m)$; $m/M = (2\pi - 3)/9$; speed $= \sqrt{(ga)}$.
29. $mg(3 \cos\theta + 2)$. **31.** $\sqrt{(ga^2/r)}$: $mg a^2\left(\dfrac{1}{a} - \dfrac{1}{2r}\right)$.
32. $\omega^2 \geqq (2g \cos\beta)/(a \cos 2\beta)$.

INDEX

367